ACOUSTIC COAGULATION AND PRECIPITATION OF AEROSOLS

AKUSTICHESKAYA KOAGULYATSIYA I OSAZHDENIE AEROZOLEI

АКУСТИЧЕСКАЯ КОАГУЛЯЦИЯ И ОСАЖДЕНИЕ АЭРОЗОЛЕЙ

ACOUSTIC COAGULATION
AND
PRECIPITATION
OF
AEROSOLS

by

Evgenii Pavlovich Mednikov

Authorized translation from the Russian by
Chas V. Larrick, B. S., Dr. Eng.

Springer Science+Business Media, LLC
1965

The Russian text was published by the USSR Academy of Sciences Press
in Moscow in 1963 for the Institute of Combustible Minerals.

**Акустическая коагуляция
и осаждение аэрозолей**

Евгений Павлович Медников

Library of Congress Catalog Card Number 64-23251

ISBN 978-1-4899-4931-8   ISBN 978-1-4899-4929-5 (eBook)
DOI 10.1007/978-1-4899-4929-5

PREFACE

Almost all the natural and artificial gases with which man comes in contact in the course of his every-day life contain a certain amount of suspended solid or liquid matter as an impurity and they are thus aerodisperse systems, or, briefly, aerosols. The atmospheric air that we breath usually contains an insignificant amount (by weight) of suspended impurities, but in thick fogs and clouds, and at the working faces of mine shafts and ore deposits, the amount of impurities sometimes reaches several grams or more per cubic meter of air. In the natural hydrocarbon gases of petroleum, gas, and gas condensation deposits, the amount of suspended material is often measured in kilograms per cubic meter of gas. A considerable amount of suspended impurity is also contained in artificial gases, primarily in the gases used in fuel technology. These include such fuels as coke gas, domestic gas, generator gas, etc., as well as the smoke in the gases from industrial burners and furnaces, the exhaust gases from lamp black and other factories, and the ventilating air from mining establishments and from the fuel refining industry. Of other gases containing suspended impurities, we can mention various acid fogs, radioactive aerosols, smoke screens, etc.

Having suspended impurities in most of the above gases is an undesirable thing, and at some stage it becomes necessary to precipitate and extract a certain amount of the disperse phase, or, in some cases, modify it qualitatively, or, finally, destroy it completely or in part.

One of the ways of solving the first two problems is that of artificial coagulation of the aerosols, i.e., aggregation (flocculation or coalescence) of the aerosol particles by various physical methods. The most promising of these methods is that of using high-intensity sonic and ultrasonic vibrations, which have shown remarkable possibilities for application in many branches of science and engineering.

The increase in size of the suspended particles which occurs during acoustic coagulation of aerosols produces a substantial change in the physical properties of the aerosol. On the one hand, as a result of the reduction in the total external surface of the disperse phase, there is a reduction in light scattering, so that a large increase occurs in the translucency of the system, extending to total transparency. On the other hand, as a result of the increase in mass and size of the particles, they are more likely to settle out of the gas under their own weight, or when acted upon artificially by inertial, electrostatic, or other forces.

This is of exceedingly great interest in dust and drop collecting technology, which occupies an important place in present day industry. Modern dust and drop collecting equipment, such as settling chambers, cyclones, scrubbers, electrical filters, etc., are distinguished by the fact that the effeciency of precipitation of the suspended particles is largely dependent on the degree of dispersion. The more highly dispersed the particles are, the lower the precipitation efficiency. The precipitation of very fine particles, several microns or less in size, which occur to some extent or other in the majority of industrial smokes, dusts, and fogs, is particularly poor.

Preliminary acoustic coagulation of such particles makes precipitation by dust and drop collecting equipment substantially more efficient.

This idea first came to life at the end of the forties, after powerful acoustic sources, known as sonic sirens, had been built.

Unfortunately, the first, quite promising results achieved in this new and original area proved of little service in the development of acoustic methods for improving the purification of gases. Instead of starting with a detailed study of the mechanism of the new process and its possibilities and developing sound generators, attempts, often ill-advised, were immediately made to apply the method to specific industries where improved gas purification methods were required.

A great many advertising type articles appeared in a number of engineering and particularly popular science magazines during these years, exalting the acoustic method of aerosol coagulation as the panacea for all the ills associated with atmospheric contamination.

However this may be, the acoustic method of coagulating aerosols is by no means universal (as is, of course, true of the other physical methods used in dust and drop collecting technology).

The method is a specialized one. The fields of application are comparatively narrow, but in these particular fields no other one method can do quite the same things. This has become more and more obvious in recent years.

At the same time it became clear that sound waves not only made the suspended particles easier to coagulate, but could be applied directly to the precipitation process, which is sometimes a more efficient and economical way of getting better gas purification.

This is particularly true of the recently discovered method of sonic filtration of aerosols, which, judging from the first papers published, makes it possible to reduce the residual particle concentration to fractions of a milligram per cubic meter of gas with only very moderate specific energy consumption required by the sonic treatment and pumping of the gas. If these quite exceptional results are confirmed in the future, there will be a great many more applications of sound waves to dust and drop collecting problems.

If we consider how aerosols are coagulated and precipitated in a sonic field, we cannot help seeing that there are accompanying physical and physical-chemical processes. It has been found that sonic treatment of fogs tends to speed up evaporation, condensation, and degasification of the drops, while sonic treatment of moist smokes and dusts, as well as the precipitate formed makes the solid disperse phase dry out faster. This all has a definite effect on the coagulation and precipitation kinetics of aerosols, and in coarsely disperse systems the above processes become more important than coagulation and precipitation and in fact become the dominant effects. The side effects are of great practical interest in making a successful solution of such important problems as dispersing natural fogs, separating the condensate from natural gases, extracting the gases found in crude petroleum, improving the burning of pulverized liquid and solid fuel, drying pulverized materials that are sensitive to heat, etc.

At the present time, a large amount of theoretical and experimental material has been accumulated in the field of acoustic coagulation of aerosols and related processes, but it is notorious for its extremely fragmentary character, and the contradictions existing between the facts presented. This comes, to a large extent, from the exceedingly specialized nature of the new method, which requires knowledge of scientific fields as widely separated as hydrodynamics, acoustics, aerosol mechanics, physical chemistry, and chemical engineering (all in their least familiar aspects). Another reason is the extreme difficulty of making experiments in the field, due, on the one hand, to the lack of the necessary acoustic apparatus, and on the other, to the unusually high mobility of aerosol particles in a sonic field which makes it difficult to observe the elementary acts directly.

It is therefore not surprising that under these conditions many investigators have been unable to avoid erroneous conclusions as to the mechanism of the processes under study, how profitable they are in use, the fields of application, etc. The present monograph makes an attempt to systematize and generalize the material accumulated in the field of acoustic coagulation and precipitation of aerosols. Attention has been given both to the physical content of the processes and to the practical industrial applications in question. In addition, a short discussion has been given of the evaporation, condensation, burning, and degasification of a liquid disperse phase, as well as drying of precipitated solid materials in a sonic field.

The author recognizes his pleasant duty of expressing his graditude to Doctor of Chemical Sciences B. B. Kudryavtsev, Doctors of Physical and Mathematical Sciences, V. F. Nozdrev and S. N. Rzhevkin, and Candidate in Chemical Sciences I. F. Bogdanov for their interest in the work being done by the author and for valuable pieces of advice. The author is very grateful to Doctor of Chemical Sciences, L. V. Radushkevich, who took upon himself the task of reading and editing the manuscript.

The author also expresses his gratitude to Z. V. Grigor'eva and A. M. Timoshenko for their aid in preparing the material in the figures.

CONTENTS

CHAPTER I

INTRODUCTION

§1. Specific Features of a High-Intensity Sound Field

Neither the coagulating effect of sound on aerosols, nor the other physical and biological effects produced by sonic treatment in gases are observed except at very high sound intensitites, where the level greatly exceeds the threshold of painful sensation to the human ear. Such high-intensity sound vibrations have a number of specific features which distinguish them from sound vibrations at the ordinary level.

By sound vibrations, or simply sound, in physics, we mean, as we know, a mechanical back and forth motion of an elastic medium (in our case, a gas) which is propagated as a wave from the sound source. The sound source is usually a vibrating or pulsating solid, liquid, or gas set in motion by aerohydromechanical or electromechanical means. The vibrations or pulsations of the body produce alternating compression and rarefaction in the adjacent gas layer, and this results in a back and forth motion of the neighboring gas particles. The motion produces pressure changes of alternating sign in the gas layer, and this leads to vibratory motion of the particles in the next layer of gas, so that, from layer to layer, the vibrations are propagated farther and farther from the source of sound at a velocity known as the velocity of sound.

If, as the origin of the time axis ($t = 0$), we take the instant at which the medium has come to equilibrium at a given point in space, and the particles at the point are beginning to move along the wave, then, for sinusoidal vibrations of the sound source, the displacement a_g of the particles in the medium, the velocity u_g of the particles and the sound, i.e. excess, pressure p_g vary with time in the following way

$$a_g = A_g \sin \omega t, \tag{1.1}$$

$$u_g = U_g \cos \omega t, \tag{1.2}$$

$$p_g = P_g \cos \omega t, \tag{1.3}$$

where A_g, U_g, and P_g are the amplitudes respectively of the displacement and velocity of the particles, and of the sound pressure, and ω is the angular velocity equal to $2\pi f$ (f is the frequency of the vibrations in cps*).

The particle velocity and the sound pressure are thus displaced in time with respect to the displacement by 1/4 of the period T of the vibration.

If an obstacle is encountered in the path of the wave with dimensions quite large in comparison with the wavelength λ, the sound wave is reflected from the obstacle according to the laws of geometrical optics, and interacts with the direct wave. As a result of the interference, reinforcement occurs at some points, while at other points cancellation occurs in the amplitude of the particle motion. If the obstacle is a plane surface, located perpendicular to the direction of propagation of the sound wave at a distance from the source which is a multiple of $\lambda/2$, the results of interference between the direct and the reflected wave will be to form a so-called standing wave (Fig. 1). In this case the change in the values of a_g, u_g, and p_g are given by the equations:

$$a_g = 2A_g \sin kx \; \sin \omega t, \tag{1.4}$$

$$u_g = 2U_g \sin kx \; \cos \omega t, \tag{1.5}$$

$$p_g = 2P_g \cos kx \; \sin \omega t, \tag{1.6}$$

*1 cps = 1 cycle per second; 1000 cps = 1 kilocycle per second (kcps).

where k is the wave number, equal to $k = \omega/c_g = 2\pi/\lambda$, and x is the distance from the source or the nearest vibration node (VN), i.e., the point where the displacement and the velocity of the particles in the medium are always equal to zero (the point where these quantities reach a maximum is called a vibration loop (VL)).

Unlike the traveling wave described previously, the particle displacement, the particle velocity, and the sound pressure are here functions of both time and space.

At high sound intensities, the picture of sound wave propagation just given is enlarged by a number of new phenomena, the so-called second-order effects [133, 7, 10, 46, 72, 205].

These effects come from the fact that the sound pressure, and with it, the velocity and displacement of the particles in the medium, reach unusually high values, at which new physical laws come into play, which are not included in the equations of classical acoustics (small-amplitude acoustics).

The majority of the questions involved in the radiation and propagation of sound are solved in classical acoustics by means of an equation for the vibratory motion of the medium known as the wave equation, which, for a plane wave, is of the form [7, 62, 105].

$$\frac{\partial^2 u_g}{\partial t^2} = c_g^2 \frac{\partial^2 u_g}{\partial x^2}, \tag{1.7}$$

where c_g is the velocity of sound, given for gases by the familiar expression:

$$c_g = \sqrt{\frac{P_{st}}{\rho_g} \gamma} \tag{1.8}$$

(P_{st} is the static pressure in the medium, ρ_g is the density of the gas, γ is the ratio of the specific heats, C_p/C_v) and is equal to 331.5 m/sec for air at 0°C.

The wave equation is derived from the equation for the motion of an ideal liquid together with the equation of continuity of the medium and the equation of state of the gas, with all the equations "linearized," i.e., only the first order terms are used in the calculation, while the higher order terms are dropped [105]. This is permissible if the sound pressure is negligibly small in comparison with the static pressure in the medium, which makes it possible to neglect the difference in density of the medium in the regions of compression and rarefaction. This condition is equivalent to saying that the particle velocity is negligibly small in comparison with the velocity of sound (which makes it possible to neglect the difference between the velocities of propagation of the perturbations in the regions of compression and rarefaction), or that the particle displacement is negligibly small in comparison with the wavelength (this makes it possible to assume that the displacement is directly proportional to the sound pressure, as given by Hooke's law).

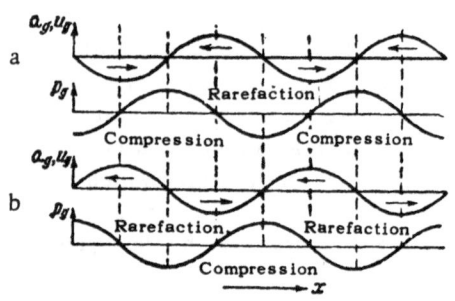

Fig. 1. Distribution of sound pressure, particle velocity, and particle displacement in a standing sound wave. a) At time t; b) at time $t + \frac{1}{2} T$.

Figure 2 gives values for the amplitude of the particle velocity U_g and the corresponding values for the amplitude of the sound pressure P_g at high sound intensities J* in various gases which differ greatly in their acoustic resistance $\rho_g c_g$, namely, hydrogen, air, and compressed methane (the principal component of natural gas).

The amplitudes U_g of the particle velocity are calcu-

*By the intensity or strength of the sound J, we mean the flux of acoustic energy passing through 1 cm² of the sound wave front per second. The unit of sound intensity in the CGS system is 1 erg/cm²·sec, and in the practical system 1 W/cm², equal to 10^7 ergs/cm²·sec.

lated from the familiar formula for a plane wave [7]:

$$U_g = \sqrt{\frac{2J}{\rho_g c_g}}, \tag{1.9}$$

while the sound pressure amplitudes are calculated from the formula*

$$P_g = \rho_g c_g U_g. \tag{1.10}$$

The effective values of the particle velocity u_g and the sound pressure p_g are found by dividing U_g and P_g by $\sqrt{2}$.

It may be seen from Fig. 2 that for the range of sound energy $J = 0.1-1.0$ W/cm^2, in which rapid coagulation of aerosols is observed, the amplitude U_g of the particle velocity reaches 2.2–7.0 m/sec in air, which is from 0.65 to 2.1% of the velocity of sound, while the sound pressure amplitude P_g reaches 9000–29,000 bar, which is from 0.9 to 3.0% of atmospheric pressure.

Unusually high values are reached at this sound intensity by the amplitude A_g of the particle displacement as shown by Fig. 3. In calculating A_g, use is made of the familiar relation [7]

$$A_g = \frac{U_g}{\omega} = \frac{1}{2\pi f} \sqrt{\frac{2J}{\rho_g c_g}}. \tag{1.11}$$

In the range 1000–5000 cps, most often used in acoustic coagulation of aerosols, the amplitude A_g of the particle displacement for values of $J = 0.1-1.0$ W/cm^2 lies in the range 700–1100μ, which is much greater than the dimensions of the aerosol particles, and is a quantity of the same order of magnitude as the mean distance between the particles (see § 9).

At the values of sound pressure, particle velocity, and particle displacement given above, it is impossible to neglect the higher-order terms in the fundamental equations, and the fact that they are there makes itself felt as a large increase in magnitude of some previously known acoustic effects and the appearance of a number of new ones.

Such effects include:

1. A large amount of inhomogeneity in the sound field, giving high gradients in the sound pressure and the particle velocity, particularly near the source of the sound,

2. Distortion of the shape of the sound wave as it is being propagated, with the results that harmoics appear,

3. Increased sound absorption by the medium,

4. Increase in the radiation pressure of the sound to perceptible levels,

5. Formation in the medium of a strong translational flux (or series of closed vortices), called acoustic ("sound") wind or streaming,

6. Turbulence in the medium.

Inhomogeneity of the Sound Field. In solving many acoustic problems, the sound field is idealized, and, in particular, the wave front is assumed to be absolutely plane. This assumption facilitates the solution of the problem, but it does not fit the facts in the majority of cases.

---

*The sound pressure is measured in acoustic bars (1 bar = 1 dyne/cm^2). The sound pressure is related to the sound intensity by the equation $J = P_g^2/\rho_g c_g$, where p_g is the effective sound pressure found, for example, from experimental measurements of the sound field made with acoustic probes (the subscript g on p and P will be omitted in the remainder of the text).

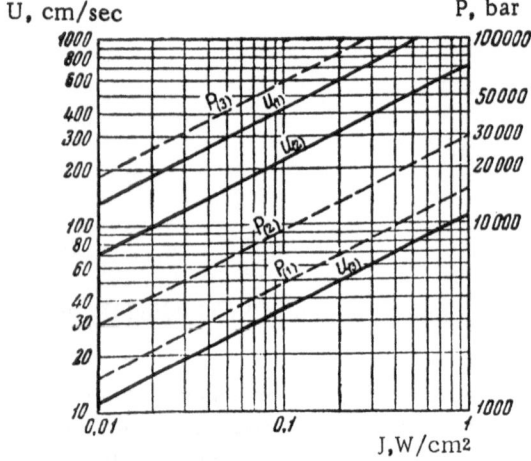

Fig. 2. Amplitudes of the particle velocity and sound pressure for several gases at high sound intensity. 1) Hydrogen at 760 mm Hg and 20° C ($\rho_g c_g$ = 11.5 g $\cdot$ sec$^{-1} \cdot$ cm^{-2}); 2) air at 760 mm Hg and 20° C ($\rho_g c_g$ = 41.3 g $\cdot$ sec$^{-1} \cdot$ cm^{-2}); 3) methane at 50 atmospheres absolute and 20° C ($\rho_g c_g$ = 1550 g $\cdot$ sec$^{-1} \cdot$ cm^{-2}).

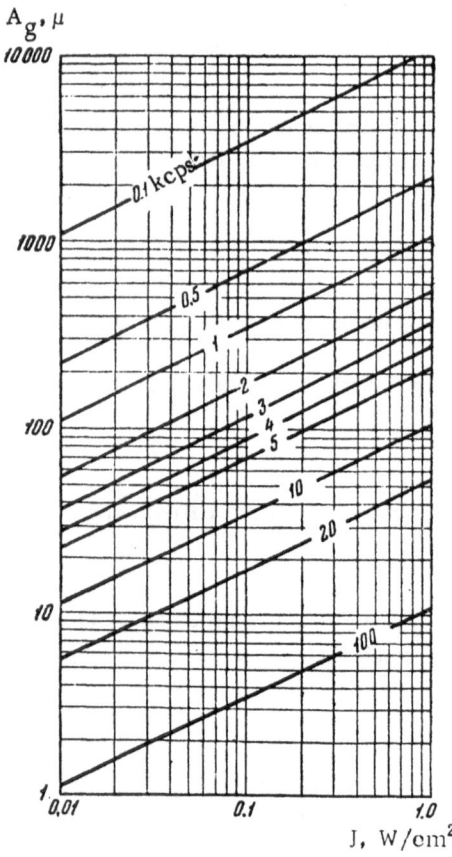

Fig. 3. Amplitudes of the vibrations of air particles at high sound intensities.

It has been found in [72, 105] that the field even in the immediate vicinity of ideal plane radiators is extremely irregular, having no features in common with a plane wave. As an illustration, Fig. 4, shows the distribution of sound pressure around a piston radiator, as calculated by Stenzel by making a summation at each point in space of the spherical waves emitted, on Huygen's principle, by each point on the surface of the piston. It may be seen that the local sound field is inhomogeneous in both the transverse and the longitudinal direction, the inhomogeneity increasing with increase in frequency of the sound. It is true that the mean pressure in the transverse direction, as has been shown by S. N. Rzhevkin [105], is approximately the same over any of the cross sections, which explains why it is possible to form a standing wave. The distance that determines the boundary of the immediate field is: $L \approx D^2/4\lambda$.

As we get farther from the source, the sound wave front gradually straightens out, but it is still irregular enough that it can only be regarded as plane over a small "nickel's worth" in the center. As an illustration, Fig. 5 gives the so-called directivity diagrams of pistion sound radiators, which show the distribution of the sound pressure for radiation into free space.

It may be seen from Fig. 5 that as the frequency is increased (for the same radiator diameter D), the sound beam becomes narrower, but the irregularity over the sound wave front is by no means decreased.

The sound wave front is even more irregular when it is being propagated through a bounded space, such as a tub. Here, a plane sound wave can only occur in the rare cases where the tube diameter D is small in comparison with the wavelength λ. Otherwise transverse vibrational modes occur.

The criterion for the occurrence of transverse vibrations in a tube is given by the following inequality [105]:

$$f_0 > \frac{1.84}{\pi} \frac{c_g}{D}. \tag{1.12}$$

Figure 6 shows the distribution of the sound pressure over the cross section of a coagulation chamber of diameter D = 20 cm [85]. We see that there is a clearly defined peak in the sound pressure at the center of the chamber, which becomes somewhat weaker on going farther from the sound source. Because of the reflection of oblique sound rays from the walls of the tube, the interference between the rays, and the flexural oscillations of the walls, the pressure decreases along the tube, rising and falling periodically [97, 126, 304].

All the things described above occur at any sound intensity, but at high sound intensities, the gradients in the sound

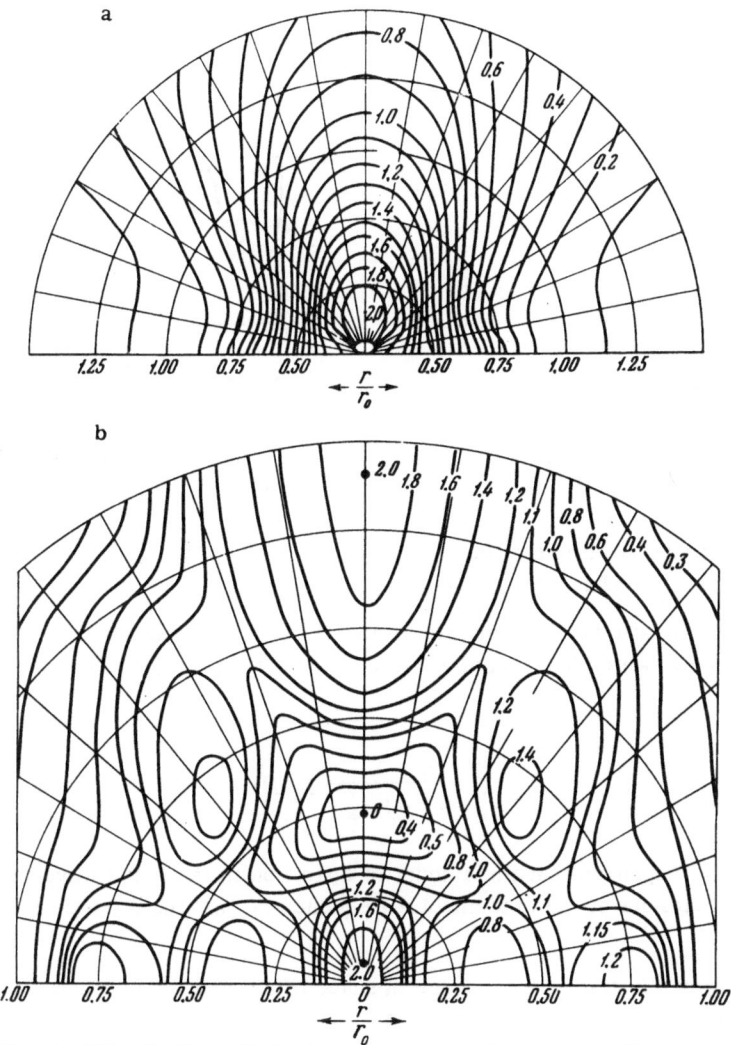

Fig. 4. Distribution of sound pressure around a piston radiator (according to Stenzel). a) $D/\lambda = 4/\pi$; b) $D/\lambda = 10/\pi$.

pressure, and hence in the particle velocity, take on enormous values, which cannot fail to effect the hydrodynamic stability of the sound field as a whole.

Distortion in the Shape of the Sound Wave. As the sound wave excited by a sinusoidally vibrating sound source is being propagated, it gradually changes from a sinusoidal to a sawtooth "shock" wave (Fig. 7a). This is due to the fact that different parts of the wave move with different velocities at high sound pressure amplitudes. The parts that are at high pressure (compressions), where the particles in the medium are moving in the direction of propagation of the wave, move at a higher velocity, and conversely, the parts where the pressure is low (rarefactions) and the particles are moving in the opposite direction, move at a lower velocity. As a result the profile of the wave becomes steeper and steeper between maximum compression and maximum rarefaction. Finally, the wave begins to "double up" and a discontinuity is formed [46, 124, 133]. The instant at which this occurs is held up somewhat by the inevitable attenuation of the particle velocity in the medium.

A nonsinusoidal saw toothed wave may be represented by Fourier analysis [11] as a group of waves consisting of a sinusoidal wave at the fundamental frequency ω_0 (first harmonic) and harmonic components at the frequencies $2\omega_0$, $3\omega_0$, etc. As an illustration, Fig. 7b is a graph of the expansion of a wave distorted so as to form a second harmonic [6].

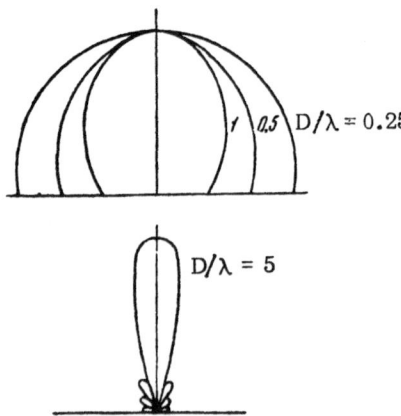

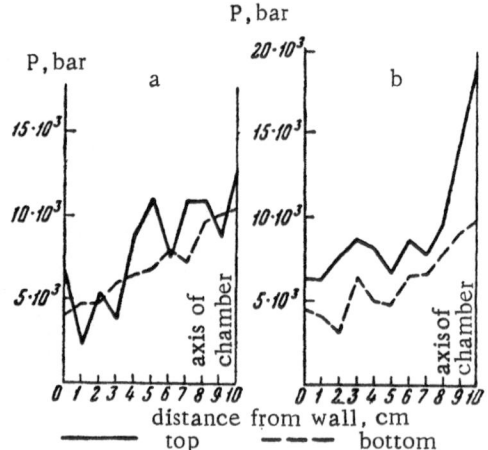

Fig. 5. Directivity of piston sound generators for different values of the ratio D/λ.

Fig. 6. Distribution of the sound pressure in a coagulation chamber. a) Frequency 3.6 kcps; b) frequency 6.0 kcps.

Thus, it may be seen that distorting the shape of a sound wave means, for practical purposes, that harmonic components are formed, and that they are very large.

On Riemann's theory, the ratio P_2/P_1 of the amplitude of the second harmonic of the pressure to the amplitude of the first harmonic, which is a measure of the amount of distortion in the sound wave, is given by the expression [46, 124, 6].

$$\frac{P_2}{P_1} = \frac{\gamma + 1}{2\sqrt{2}\, \rho_g c_g^3}\, \omega_0\, P_1 x. \qquad (1.13)$$

It may be concluded from this equation that the amount of distortion in the sound wave increases linearly with the frequency ω_0, the sound pressure at the fundamental frequency P_1 and the distance x over which the wave has passed.

Fig. 8 gives oscillograms illustrating the change in shape of a sound wave at a frequency $f_0 = 15$ kcps in air as the sound level is increased for a constant distance from the source (a), and as the distance is increased for a constant radiator level of 156 db* (b) (time scanning) [205].

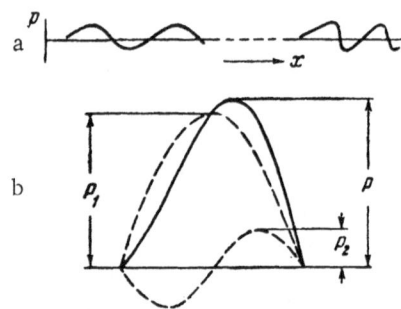

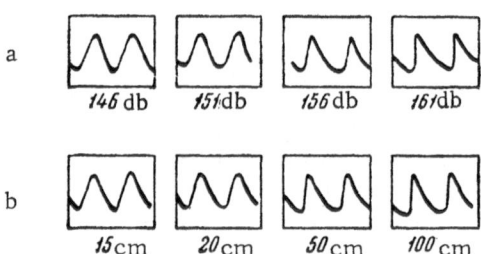

Fig. 7. Distortion of a sound wave during propagation. a) Over-all wave form; b) expansion of the distorted wave into two harmonics.

Fig. 8. Change in form of a sound wave ($f_0 = 15$ kcps). a) With increase in sound source level at a constant distance of 50 cm from the source; b) moving away from a source at a sound level of 156 db.

---

*The sound level, expressed in decibels (db), is related to the sound intensity J by the equation $L = 10 \log_{10} J/J_0$, where J_0 is a standard sound intensity of 10^{-16} W/cm².

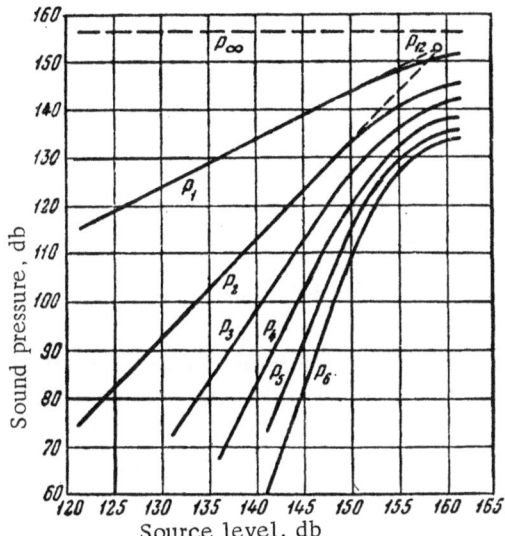

Fig. 9. Sound pressure level of the first six harmonics as a function of source level (f_0 = 15 kcps).

Fig. 9 gives a graph showing the sound pressure level of the first six harmonics of a sound wave of frequency f_0 = 15 kcps as a function of the source level [205]. With this graph, we can, by using Eq. (1.13), find the sound pressure level of any of the first six harmonics for any value of sound pressure, frequency, and distance from the source.

The criterion for the existence of a discontinuity in air, according to Z. A. Gol'dberg [25], is given by the inequality $P_{bar} \geq 2\pi f_{0kcps}$, which is always satisfied in gases. The distance to the place where the discontinuity occurs is given in this case by the following expression [25, 88]:

$$x_{cr} \leqslant \frac{2\rho_g c_g^3}{(\gamma + 1)\omega_0 P_x}. \tag{1.14}$$

In a standing sound wave, the distortion of the wave changes with time [133], so that the sound pressure at a loop takes on some finite value. The number, giving how many times this value is less than in a node, is called the standing wave ratio.

Increased Sound Absorption in the Medium. If the initial amplitude A_{g0}, of the vibrations or the initial amplitude P_0, of the pressure, in a sound wave is small, it is shown by experiment that as the wave is propagated along the x axis the amplitude will decrease according to the exponential law [7, 72]:

$$A_g = A_{g0}e^{-\alpha_g x},$$
$$P = P_0 e^{-\alpha_g x}, \tag{1.15}$$

where α_g is the so-called sound absorption coefficient in the gas, expressed in cm^{-1} (if the absorption coefficient is to be expressed in db, the value of α_g in cm^{-1} must be multiplying by 868.6).

The sound intensity decreases with distance according to the law

$$J = J_0 e^{-\alpha'_g x}. \tag{1.15'}$$

This law is arrived at on the assumption that the fraction of the energy being transmitted that is lost in a layer of the medium is proportional to the thickness of the layer, i.e., $dJ/J = \alpha'_g dx$. The sound absorption coefficient α'_g is the fraction of the acoustic energy lost in passing through a distance $\alpha'x = 1$. Obviously, $\alpha'_g = 2\alpha_g$.

The absorption of acoustic energy by a gas at small amplitudes is due primarily to the internal friction or viscosity and the thermal conductivity of the medium (since heat exchange occurs between the compressed and rarefied parts of the medium). With this in mind, the theory of sound gives the following expressions [7, 46, 233] for the absorption coefficient in a medium undergoing compression:

$$\alpha_{g0} = \alpha_g^\eta + \alpha_g^\lambda + \alpha_g^{\eta'} = \frac{b\omega^2}{2\rho_g c_g^3}, \tag{1.16}$$

7

where

$$b = \frac{4}{3}\eta + \frac{\gamma - 1}{C_{p_g}}\lambda_q + \eta' \tag{1.17}$$

(η is the dynamic viscosity, λ_q is the coefficient of heat conduction, and η' is the bulk viscosity). For air, the second term in (1.17) is equal to 0.554η, so that we have approximately $b \approx 2\eta + \eta'$. For practical calculations in air, we may assume $b \approx 2.5\eta$ [233].

From Eq. (1.16), the absorption coefficient of dry air under normal conditions is negligibly small. Thus, in the range from 3 to 10 kcps, $\alpha_{g_0} = 10^{-3} - 10^{-2}$ db/m.

Measurements under atmospheric conditions give a much larger value. This is due to the presence of water vapor in the air [6, 7, 46, 267]. Knudsen verified this at frequencies of 1, 5, 3, 6, and 10 kcps, and determined that the sound absorption coefficient has its smallest value in dry air, then rises rapidly, reaching a maximum at relative humidities of 12−20%, and then drops off again. In the range from 3 to 10 kcps, the maximum value of the sound absorption coefficient reaches $\alpha_{g_0}^e = 0.17 - 0.56$ db/m.

Having walls present produces additional viscous and heat losses of acoustic energy.

For a tube of radius R, the additional absorption coefficient as given by Kirchhoff [6, 7], is:

$$\alpha_{\text{wall}} = \frac{1.1}{c_g R}\sqrt{f}. \tag{1.18}$$

Thus we see that the sound absorption increases rapidly as the dimension of the opening is decreased.

In a high-intensity sound field, the absorption coefficient is several orders of magnitude greater than the values of α_{g_0} given above. This is due mainly to the formation of the harmonic components which, as shown by (1.16), are much more strongly absorbed than the fundamental.

According to the theory developed by Z. A. Gol'dberg [25], the local absorption coefficient for a saw-tooth sound wave is given by the following formula:

$$\alpha_g = \alpha_{g_0}\frac{\gamma + 1}{\pi}\frac{P_x}{b\omega_0}, \tag{1.19}$$

where P_x is the sound pressure amplitude at the point x. Thus, the absorption coefficient at high sound intensity is directly proportional to the frequency [if we use (1.16)], and the local sound pressure.

In air, Eq. (1.19) takes the form

$$\alpha_g = 3.6 \cdot 10^{-8} f P_x \text{ db/m} \tag{1.19'}$$

which, for frequency range $f = 1-10$ kcps, gives:

$$\text{for} \quad J = 0.1 \text{ w/cm}^2 \qquad \alpha_g = 0.23 - 2.3 \text{ db/m}$$
$$\text{»} \quad J = 1.0 \text{ w/cm}^2 \qquad \alpha_g = 0.73 - 7.3 \quad \text{»} \quad .$$

That there is a linear relation between α_g and p has been confirmed experimentally in [97], the results of which are illustrated in Fig. 10 (f = 13 kcps, R = 6 cm). These results give the linear equation.

$$\alpha_g^3 = \alpha_{g_0}^3 + mp_x, \tag{1.20}$$

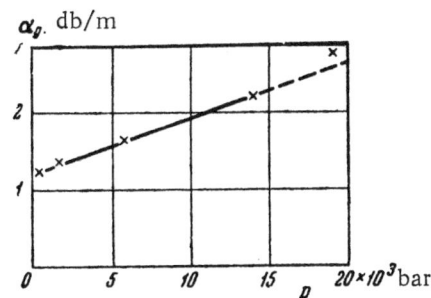

Fig. 10. Attenuation coefficient as a function of sound pressure (f = 13 kcps).

where α_{g0}^e is the sound absorption coefficient determined experimentally at zero sound pressure, including the losses in the walls of the vessel in addition to the energy loss in the gas, and m is a proportionality constant.

The absolute value of mp_x is, however, much less (by a factor of 6 to 7) than the theoretical values of α_g given by Eq. (1.19), which is not surprising, since (1.19) is for a sawtooth wave, i.e., one having the maximum amount of distortion.

In view of the relation that exists between the sound absorption coefficient and the magnitude of the sound pressure, the attenuation of the sound with distance does not follow an exponential law, but is given by the following formula [98]:

$$p = p_0 \frac{\alpha_{g0}}{\alpha_{g0}\, e^{\alpha_{g0}x} - mp_0\, (1 - e^{\alpha_{g0}x})} \ , \qquad (1.21)$$

which only holds for a plane sound wave.

Note in conclusion that in free space the attenuation of sound with distance from the source is due both to absorption of acoustic energy by the medium and to purely geometric factors, namely, expansion of the sound beam (see Fig. 5), in which the sound intensity decreases in accordance with the increase in cross-sectional area of the beam.

Radiation Pressure of Sound. Sound waves exert a definite force when they encounter an obstacle. In a traveling wave, the radiation pressure is exerted in the direction of propagation of the wave, but in a standing wave the pressure is exerted in the direction from a node to a vibration loop (where the sound pressure approaches zero).

It is difficult to give a clear explanation of this phenomenon.

V. A. Krasil'nikov in his popular book "Sonic and Ultrasonic Waves" [46] gives the following explanation:

"In the parts where compression occurs, the velocity of the gas particles is in the direction of motion of the wave, and is in the opposite direction in the rarefied parts. It is thus easily seen that the resistance to motion of the particles will be less when the particles move from a compressed region to a rarefied region, than when the particles are moving from a rarefied to a compressed region. Since the pressure is determined by the product of the velocity of the particles by the specific resistance of the medium [see Eq. (1.10)], the pressure in the direction of propagation of the wave will be somewhat greater than in the opposite direction. Thus, a constant sound pressure exists in the direction of propagation of the wave."

Solving the wave equation, including the quadratic terms (second approximation), shows that at an obstacle, the sound pressure does not vary exactly according to a sinusoidal law, so that the value averaged over the time does not become equal to zero, as is assumed in small amplitude acoustics (the proof of this fact is well presented in [72, 205]).

The radiation pressure is the time average of the pressure developed by the sound wave at the obstacle, calculated including the interaction between the sound field and the unperturbed medium.

The value of the radiation pressure at a wall is easily obtained by following the arguments given by Pol' in [100], where he writes:

"Let two straight lines designate the parallel boundaries of a beam of waves. The air particles vibrate back and forth sinusoidally in the beam in the direction of the double arrows, at the maximum velocity U_g [the notation here and below is ours—E. M.]. As a result, the static pressure P_{st} inside the beam decreases, according to Bernoulli's equation, by the amount $\frac{1}{2}\rho_g U_g^2$. Thus outside air flows into the wave. The beam is incident on a wall at the right. Then the velocity becomes equal to zero, and the pressure increases by the amount $p_R = \frac{1}{2} \rho_g U_g^2$. This is the radiation pressure. The quantity $\frac{1}{2} \rho_g U_g^2$ is at the same time equal to the fraction:

$$\frac{\text{Kinetic energy in the volume V of the sound field}}{\text{Volume V of the sound field}}$$

i.e., it is equal to the sound energy density $\overline{E}$. For this reason, the sound pressure p_R is equal to the density $\overline{E}$ of the radiation energy in space":

$$p_R = \overline{E} = \frac{J}{c_g} . \qquad (1.22)$$

This is the value of the radiation pressure at a completely absorbing obstacle the dimensions of which are much greater than the wavelength. For complete reflection of the sound, the radiation pressure is twice this value:

$$p_R = 2\overline{E} = \frac{2J}{c_g} . \qquad (1.22')$$

In the general case, where the obstacle has the reflection coefficient β, the radiation pressure is given by the equation

$$p_R = (1 + \beta^2)\overline{E} = (1 + \beta^2)\frac{J}{c_g} . \qquad (1.23)$$

The magnitude of the radiation pressure force exerted on small obstacle ($L < \lambda$) depends, on the one hand, on the kinetic energy density of the vibratory motion, averaged over the time, and, on the other, on the shape, the dimensions and reflecting power of the obstacle.

In a high-intensity sound field where the energy density is very large (for $J = 0.1 - 1.0$ W/cm^2 in air $E = 30 - 300$ ergs/cm^3) the radiation pressure force on not too small objects reaches very perceptible levels. Evidence for this is provided by the "levitation" of glass balls, coins, and similar objects, observed in a high-intensity standing sound wave field [137, 179].

The Acoustic Wind. At high sound intensities, the vibratory motion is accompanied by translational (aperiodic) acoustic streaming in the medium.

In a traveling wave, the gas flows away from the source at the center of the sound beam, and in the opposite direction at the periphery, as shown in Fig. 11a. In a standing wave bounded by longitudinal walls we observe a series of closed (in a cylinder, toroidally closed) vortices, running from the loops to the nodes of the vibrations at the walls, as shown in Fig. 11b.

According to the opinions commonly accepted at the present time, the acoustic wind is due to the radiation pressure gradient set up by absorption of the sound waves in the medium.

It is not without interest to note that the acoustic wind phenomenon was first detected with aerosol particles while observing Kundt dust figures (Dvorzhak, 1887). Attention was soon turned to the phenomenon by Rayleigh, who, taking account of the viscosity of the medium, derived the following equations for the components of the aperiodic velocity in a standing wave [107]: for the velocity parallel to a plane surface (x axis),

$$u_2 = -\frac{3U_g^2 \sin 2kx}{16c_g}\left[1 - \frac{3(y_1 - y)^2}{y_1^2}\right] ; \qquad (1.24)$$

for the velocity perpendicular to a plane surface,

$$v_2 = - \frac{3U_g^2 2k \cos 2kx}{16c_g} \left[y_1 - y - \frac{(y_1 - y)^3}{y_1^2} \right], \tag{1.25}$$

where x and y are the distances from a loop in the vibrations along the surface and perpendicular to the surface respectively, and y_1 is the distance from the wall to the plane of symmetry.

The flow lines in an acoustic vortex may be found by means of the following flow function [73]:

$$\psi = \sin 2kx - \frac{1}{y^3 - 3y_1 y^2 + 2y_1^2 y}. \tag{1.26}$$

Velocity curves and flow lines for acoustic vortices, found from Eqs. (1.24), (1.25), and (1.26) may be found in [73]. Note, however, that considerable difference is observed between experiment and theory at high sound intensity. The experimental flow lines show less "angularity," i.e., they are smoother and more rounded in form, the amount of rounding being greater, the higher the sound intensity [140].

The velocity of the forward acoustic streaming in a wave traveling, along the axis of a cylindrical vessel is given by Eckart (187) as:

$$(u_2)_{max} = \frac{\omega^2 J_0 R^2}{\rho_g c_g^4} \left(2 + \frac{\eta'}{\eta} \right) \Phi(R_{br}), \tag{1.27}$$

where J_0 is the sound intensity in the immediate vicinity of the radiator, and $\Phi(R_{br})$ is a coefficient determined by the ratio of the radius R of the sound beam to the radius R_0 of the tube, along the axis of which the sound is being propagated

$$\Phi(R_{br}) = \frac{1}{2} \left(\frac{R^2}{R_0^2} - 1 \right) - \log \frac{R}{R_0}.$$

Eckart's equation, like Rayleigh's equations, only holds for extremely small sound absorptions, where the sound absorption coefficient is independent of the sound intensity. The equation is also inapplicable at low sound frequencies, since it was derived under the assumption that the wavelength is much less than the dimensions of the vessel.

In this connection, new theoretical studies have been made in recent years on the acoustic wind, among which the paper by Westervelt [287] deserves special mention.

Recently, A. I. Ivanovskii [36] made a detailed theoretical study of the problem of acoustic streaming, and found a general solution of the problem which gives a value for the velocity for any values of the sound absorption coefficient α_g and vessel length L, with an accuracy up to the coefficient $\Phi(R_{br})$.

For $\alpha_g L \ll 1$, the velocity of the acoustic wind is given by

$$u_2 = \frac{2\alpha_g J_0}{c_g \eta} R^2 \Phi(R_{br}). \tag{1.28}$$

This expression is identical with Eckart's formula (1.27), if the value of α_{g0} from (1.16) is substituted in it, taking account of (1.17), in which $b \approx 2\eta + \eta'$.

11

For $\alpha_gL \approx 1$, the velocity of the acoustic wind is equal to

$$u_2 = \frac{2J_0}{c_g\eta} \cdot \frac{1 - e^{-\alpha_gL}}{L} R^2\Phi(R_{br}). \qquad (1.29)$$

For $\alpha_gL \gg 1$, i.e., when the sound is completely absorbed in the vessel, the velocity of the acoustic wind is equal to

$$u_2 = \frac{2J_0}{c_g\eta} \frac{1}{L} R^2\Phi(R_{br}). \qquad (1.30)$$

It follows from these equations that the velocity of the acoustic wind is proportional to the fraction of the sound energy that remains in the vessel as a result of absorption in the medium (in aerosols it is also necessary to take account of the absorption of acoustic energy by the aerosol particles, as discussed later on in §8).

No experimental check has yet been made of the above formulas as applied to gases. Furthermore, there is almost no concrete information at all on the values of the acoustic wind velocity in gases. Something of an exception is provided by the work in [233], which, unfortunately, was done at a very high frequency (f = 185 kcps), and further no absolute measurements were made of the sound intensity.

It is known, however, that the acoustic wind velocity is considerably higher in gases than in liquids, and reaches several meters per second in very strong sound fields [137].

Acoustic Turbulence. Visual observation of the behavior of aerosols under intense sound treatment leads to the conclusion that the gaseous medium is in a turbulent state. This shows up with particular clarity if a thin stream or cloud of smoke is introduced into the gas being treated. Once the smoke is caught up in the regular acoustic streaming, it is rapidly spread sideways at the same time.

Turbulent acoustic flow may be thought of as the result of superimposing a continuous spectrum of pulsations of different magnitudes and directions on the back and forth motion of the medium.

Acoustic turbulence is related to the description given above of the unusual amount of inhomogeneity found in the sound field near the radiator [10, 46], which, at high sound intensity, leads to the formation of vortices, all carried along by the acoustic wind. In a traveling wave, this has added to it the interaction between the foreward and backward streams [36], on the boundaries of which, as shown by Kwiek [219], rotational motion occurs. In a standing wave, the same thing is favored by the circulating motion occurring in the regions between the nodes and loops, as well as by the aerodynamic motion observed by Mickelson and Baldwin [236].

All the above effects are maintained by the energy of the vibratory motion in the medium. For this reason, the Reynolds number, characteristic of sound propagation in a gaseous medium, as was pointed out by V. A. Krasil'nikov [46], may be written in the form

$$\mathrm{Re}^{ac} = \frac{u_g\lambda}{b/\rho_g}. \qquad (1.31)$$

The role of the mean flow velocity is played here by the effective particle velocity u_g, the role of the scale of the motion is played by the wavelength λ, and the role of the kinetic viscosity is played by the constant b [see (1.17)] divided by the density ρ_g of the medium.

Using the relation $\lambda = c_g/f$, and Eq. (1.11), the expression for Re^{ac} may be written in the following form:

$$\mathrm{Re}^{ac} = \pi\sqrt{2}\,\frac{\rho_gc_g}{b}A_g, \qquad (1.31')$$

from which it follows that the Reynolds number is directly proportional to the acoustic resistance and the amplitude of the vibrations in the medium, and inversely proportional to the viscosity of the medium.

If A_g is expressed in terms of the parameters J and f, the expression (1.31) may be written as:

$$\mathrm{Re}^{ac} = \frac{(\rho_g c_g)^{1/2}}{b} \frac{J^{1/2}}{f}. \tag{1.31''}$$

There are no experimental data on the critical Reynolds number Re_{cr}^{ac} at which the acoustic streaming loses its hydrodynamic stability and becomes turbulent. The only work done along this line, that of Kastner and Shih [209], is for low frequencies (up to 30 cps), and provides no means of determining how Re_{cr}^{ac} changes with increase in frequency.

V. A. Krasil'nikov [46], based on his experience with sonic treatment of liquids, suggests that Re_{cr}^{ac} is approximately an order of magnitude lower than for flow in tubes (in which $\mathrm{Re}_{cr} = 2300$).

There is likewise absolutely no information on the internal structure of the acoustic turbulence, without a knowledge of which it is impossible to evaluate the role played by this phenomenon in the physicochemical processes that are being intensified by the sound.

It seems to us, as stated in [83], that if the acoustic turbulence is sufficiently developed, information on the microstructure far from the sound source and boundary surfaces may be obtained from the theory of isotropic turbulence developed by A. N. Kolmogorov.

According to this theory, the energy of the primary large scale vortices is gradually transformed into small scale vortex energy (following a "two thirds" law). Then, after reaching the so-called "internal" scale l_0, in which viscosity forces predominate ($\mathrm{Re} < 1$), the energy is dissipated (going into heat). On this scale, interaction between the pulsations stops, so that all the properties of the medium become isotropic, i.e., independent of the direction of flow. In particular, the frequency of the pulsations becomes independent of the scale of the motion, and is constant, and has its highest value.

Since the theory of isotropic turbulence does not specify the mechanism by which the vortices are formed and transformed, the deductions from the theory may be extended to acoustic turbulence, if the comprehensibility of the medium is included as given by Eq. (1.17).

A. N. Kolmogorov has postulated in [44] that the properties of the turbulent motion in regions small in comparison with the internal scale l_0 are determined by two quantities: the energy dissipation ε, and the viscosity of the medium ν (the role of which in an acoustic field is played by the quantity ν/ρ_g).

From dimensionality theory [62] we may write for the energy dissipation:

$$\varepsilon \sim \frac{u_g^3}{\lambda} \sim \frac{J^{3/2} f}{\rho_g^{3/2} c_g^{5/2}} \left[\frac{\mathrm{erg}}{\mathrm{g \cdot sec}} \right]. \tag{1.32}$$

On the other hand, the energy dissipation may be calculated from information on sound absorption in the gas, using the simple formula:

$$\varepsilon = \frac{\alpha_g' J}{\rho_g}, \tag{1.33}$$

where α_g' is the sound absorption coefficient less the molecular absorption, which "bypasses" the turbulence.

Substituting in this equation the expression found by Z. A. Gol'dberg for the sound absorption coefficient at finite vibration amplitudes (1.19) and making use of (1.16) and (1.17), we obtain the maximum value of the energy dissipation:

$$\varepsilon = 2\sqrt{2}\,(\gamma + 1)\,\frac{u_g^3}{\lambda} = 2\sqrt{2}\,(\gamma + 1)\,\frac{J_x^{3/2}f}{\rho_g^{3/2}c_g^{5/2}}. \qquad (1.34)$$

As we can see, this equation is identical with the relation (1.32). This shows that the fundamental characteristics of the acoustic turbulence have been correctly chosen and that the method of dimensionality applies, if, in front of the equation derived in (1.32), we write the coefficient ξ, which takes account of the distortion in the sound wave. For a sine wave, ξ is of the order of 1, and for maximum (sawtooth) distortion, $\xi = 2\sqrt{2}(\gamma + 1)$, or about 6.8 in air.

The experimental values of the energy dissipation, found with the aid of (1.33) from [85] and [97], the results of which are illustrated in Figs. 6 and 10 respectively, as well as from [304], fall well within the above limits.

However, for our subsequent calculations, the purpose of which is only to show the order of magnitude of the local values of the acoustic turbulence, none of this is too important, the more so, since the quantity ξ enters into the subsequent equations to a fractional power, so that the effect of the value of the coefficient ξ is greatly masked.

Eq. (1.32) gives the following values for the energy dissipation in the frequency range $f = 1-10$ kcps:

for the sound intensity $J = 0.1$ W/cm^2, $\varepsilon = 1.1 \cdot 10^5 - 1.1 \cdot 10^6$;
for the sound intensity $J = 1.0$ W/cm^2, $\varepsilon = 3.4 \cdot 10^6 - 3.4 \cdot 10^7$;

It may accordingly be concluded that the acoustic turbulence is not distinguished by particularly high intensity. It is equivalent to the usual turbulence occurring in a tube with a diameter D equal to λ/ξ, when the flow rate is equal to the particle velocity in the gas ($w_g = u_g$).

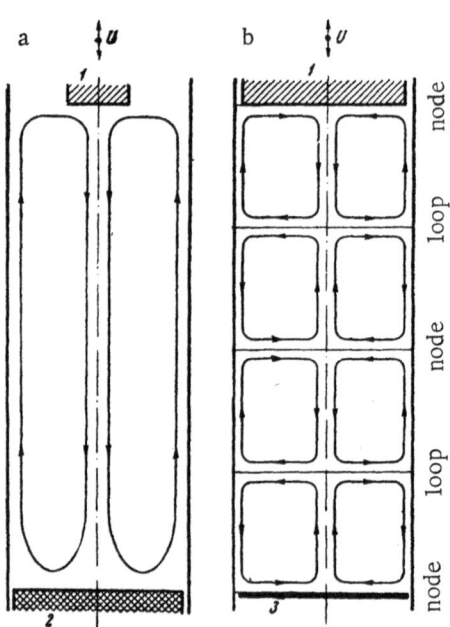

Fig. 11. Acoustic streaming (sound wind) set up in a sound field. a) In a traveling wave; b) in a standing wave. 1) Sound radiator; 2) sound absorbing material; 3) sound reflector. The distance between a node and a loop is $\lambda/4$.

In accordance with dimensionality theory [62], we obtain the following expression for the internal scale of the acoustic turbulence:

$$l_0 \sim \left[\frac{(b/\rho_g)^3}{\varepsilon}\right]^{1/4} \sim \frac{b^{3/4}c_g^{5/8}}{\xi^{1/4}\rho_g^{3/8}}\,J^{-\frac{3}{8}}f^{-\frac{1}{4}}. \qquad (1.35)$$

It may be seen from this equation that the dependence of l_0 on the sound intensity J and particularly on the frequency f is very weak. In the range $f = 1-10$ kcps, we have, for $J = 0.1$ W/cm^2, $l_0 \approx 260-150\mu$, while for $J = 1.0$ W/cm^2, we have $l_0 \approx 110-65\mu$.

The relative pulsational velocity of gas particles, separated from one another by a distance f not exceeding the internal scale of the turbulence ($l < l_0$), is given by

$$v_l = \sigma_1 \left(\frac{\varepsilon}{b/\rho_g}\right)^{1/2} l \approx \frac{1}{4}\frac{\xi^{1/2}J^{3/4}f^{1/2}}{b^{1/2}\rho_g^{1/4}c_g^{5/4}}\,l, \qquad (1.36)$$

while beyond the limits of the internal scale ($l > l_0$) we have:

$$v_l = \sigma_2\,(\varepsilon l)^{1/3} = \frac{\xi^{1/3}J^{1/2}f^{1/3}}{\rho_g^{1/2}c_g^{5/6}}\,l^{1/3}, \qquad (1.37)$$

where σ_1 and σ_2 are proportionality constants usually taken to be $1/\sqrt{15} \approx 1/4$ and 1 respectively.

The magnitude of the relative pulsational velocity of the particles is independent of the fact that flow is undulatory in nature, since it is assumed that $l \ll \lambda$, so that the two particles in the medium are in practically the same phase of the vibratory motion.

The maximum velocity of the pulsations within the scale range $l < l_0$, found for pulsations with $l = l_0$ at $J = 0.1$ W/cm^2 and $f = 1-10$ kcps lies in the range $v_{l_0} = 3.6-6.4$ cm/sec which is $2.3-4.1\%$ of the particle velocity in the gas.

The lower limit of frequency of the turbulent pulsations developed inside the acoustic stream is given by the relation:

$$\omega_\lambda \sim \frac{u_g}{\lambda} \sim \frac{J^{1/2} f}{\rho_g^{1/2} c_g^{3/2}},$$ (1.38)

The order of magnitude of the upper limit of the frequency spectrum of turbulent pulsations lying within the scale range l_0 is:

$$\omega_{l_0} \sim \frac{v_{l_0}}{l_0} \approx \sigma_1 \left(\frac{\varepsilon}{b/\rho_g} \right)^{1/2} \approx \frac{1}{4} \frac{\xi^{1/2} J^{3/4} f^{1/2}}{b^{1/2} \rho_g^{1/4} c_g^{5/4}}.$$ (1.39)

At normal sound intensity, $J = 0.1$ W/cm^2, the frequency spectrum of the turbulent pulsations is:

at the frequency $f = 1$ kcps, $f_l = 0.7-20$ cps,
at the frequency $f = 10$ kcps, $f_l = 7-70$ cps.

At higher sound intensity, $J = 1$ W/cm^2, the frequency spectrum lies somewhat higher:

at the frequency $f = 1$ kcps, $f_l = 2.5-120$ cps,
at the frequency $f = 10$ kcps, $f_l = 25-380$ cps.

Thus, it may be concluded that the frequency spectrum of the turbulent pulsations is comparatively narrow and is always in a low frequency range lying much below the fundamental frequency of the vibrations.

In conclusion, we give some information on the motion in the boundary layer adjacent to large obstacles and walls.

The thickness of the boundary for vibration of a medium under the condition $A_g \ll L$ (where L is the length of the surface) is equal to the "depth of penetration" of the vibration as given by the expression [62].

$$\delta \sim \sqrt{\frac{2\nu}{\omega}} \approx \sqrt{\frac{\nu}{\pi f}}.$$ (1.40)

In the frequency range $f_0 = 1-10$ kcps, $\delta = 70-22\mu$.

The energy dissipation in this layer is several orders of magnitude higher than in the rest of the volume, and from [62], may be calculated from the formula

$$\varepsilon \text{ bound} = \frac{1}{4} \omega U_g^2.$$ (1.41)

However, unlike the acoustic turbulence, which is present throughout the volume of the sound field, the effect in the boundary layer is limited to vortex motion. Isotropic pulsations cannot occur, since the thickness of the boundary layer is of the same order of magnitude as the internal scale of the turbulence as given by Eq. (1.35) for $\varepsilon = \varepsilon_{\text{bound}}$.

TABLE 1

Effect	Sound intensity J required, in W/cm²	Corresponding sound level L, in db
Threshold of painful sensation to the human ear [110]	0,00001 — 0,001	110 — 130
Start of coagulating effect of sound on aerosols (slow coagulation) [156]	0,003 — 0,01	135 — 140
Point at which the effect of sound begins to improve the drying of fibers, friable, and powdered materials [8]	0,01 — 0,03	140 — 145
Rapid coagulation of aerosols [184], accelerated drying of fibers and powdered materials [8], destruction of foams [157], filtration of aerosols [313].	0,1 — 1,0	150 — 160
Slow heating of sound absorbing materials (wadding, cotton, cloth, etc.) [137, 253]	1,0	160
Burning sensation between the fingers when held close together. Kills insects (wasps, bumble bees, spiders), and rodents (rats, white mice) [137, 252, 253]	1 — 3	160 — 165
Strong acoustic wind (several m/sec) [137]	3 — 10	165 — 170
Glass balls, coins, and other objects floating in a standing wave field from the effects of sound pressure [137, 179]	3 — 30*	165 — 175
Rapid ignition of sound absorbing materials (several seconds) [137]	10 — 30	170 — 175
Maximum sound intensity found by calculation to be reached at the mouth of a siren producing sound [208]	300 — 1000	185 — 190

*In a standing sound wave field, the concept of "sound intensity" loses its meaning, since there is no acoustic energy flux. In this case, it is more correct to operate with the sound pressure, but in practice use is often made (provisionally) of the units of sound intensity.

The specific features of high-intensity acoustic vibrations just discussed have turned out to be the source of a whole list of physical and biological effects observed in gases carrying sound waves. The most important of these effects are given in Table 1.

§ 2. High-Intensity Sound Sources

Special sound sources are used to produce high-intensity sound waves in gases. Siren-type pneumatic sound generators have been employed on an industrial scale. In the laboratory, various types of whistles, electrodynamic, and sometimes magnetostriction sound radiators are also used.

There are two types of sirens: dynamic (rotating) and static (whistle types).

Until recently, most of the industrial generators were dynamic sirens. They give uniform coverage of a wide frequency range, and high acoustic efficiency in converting the energy of compressed air (gas or vapor) into sound waves with practically no limit on the power radiated.

A dynamic siren consists of a stator (housing with openings around the circumference, and a moving toothed rotor in the form of a perforated disc or cylinder. A special compressor feeds compressed air (vapor or gas) to the stator housing. As the rotor moves, the teeth periodically shut off the compressed air stream coming out of the openings in the stator, thus producing pulsations in air pressure, which impart a vibrational motion to the gas.

Dynamic sirens are constructed in two forms, axial and radial.

In sirens of the first type (Fig. 12a), the openings through which the pulsating air stream flows are arranged axially, and the sound is directed toward the object through a special, usually exponential horn. In sirens of the second type (Fig. 12b) the openings are located radially, and the sound is directed toward the object by a special, usually parabolic reflector.

Axial sirens are more easily constructed in small sizes, and radial sirens in large sizes.

The fundamental frequency of the radiated sound is given by

$$f_0 = \frac{z n_c}{60} , \tag{2.1}$$

where z is the number of teeth on the rotor, and n_c is the rpm of the rotor. In addition to the fundamental frequency (unless special measures are taken), dynamic sirens radiate rather strong harmonics, and the method by which they may be calculated is given in the paper of Inoue [37].

The acoustic power generated by a dynamic siren is found in the following way:

$$W_{ac} = \alpha_c (1 + \delta) \frac{Q_m L_{ad}}{102} \eta_{ac} \quad kW \tag{2.2}$$

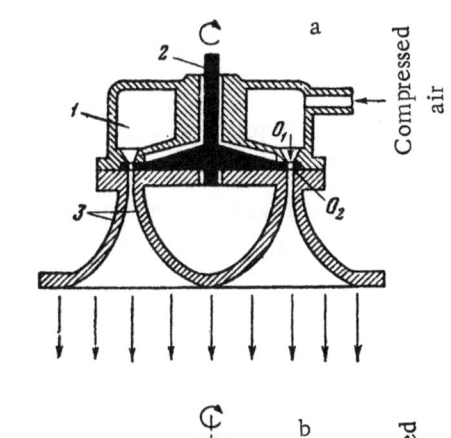

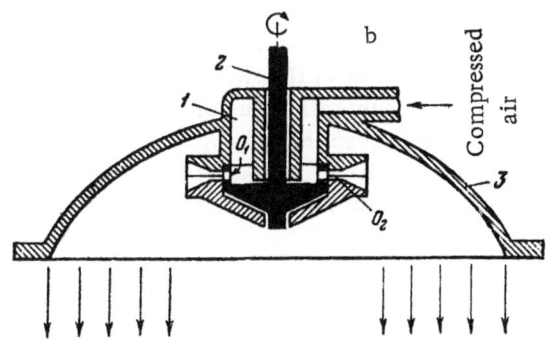

where Q_m is the theoretical compressed air flow through the openings in the siren, in m^3/sec, α_c is the constriction coefficient in the air stream cut off by a tooth, δ is a coefficient giving the fraction of the air escaping through the gap between the stator and the rotor, with the product $\alpha_c(1 + \delta)$ lying in the range $0.7-1.4$ [247], L_{ad} is the theoretical work done in the adiabatic expansion of $1\ m^3$ of compressed air (in kgm/m^3), and η_{ac} is the acoustic efficiency of the siren.

The values of Q_m and L_{ad} are given by the formulas

$$Q_m = (\varepsilon_0 S_0) w \frac{\gamma_к}{\gamma_c} , \tag{2.3}$$

$$L_{ad} = \frac{\gamma_c}{2g} w^2, \tag{2.4}$$

where S_0 is the total cross-sectional area of the openings in the siren (in m^2), ε_0 is a coefficient giving the extent to which the openings are blocked off by the teeth (approximately 0.5), γ_k is the density of air at the pressure p_k (in kg/m^2), and w is the air flow velocity, given by the equation [112]:

$$w = \sqrt{2g \frac{\gamma}{\gamma - 1} \frac{p_c}{\gamma_c} \left[1 - \left(\frac{p_к}{p_c} \right)^{\frac{\gamma - 1}{\gamma}} \right]} \quad m/sec \tag{2.5}$$

Fig. 12. Diagrams of dynamic sound sirens. a) Axial type (1) stator with openings O_1; 2) rotor with openings O_2; 3) horn); b) radial type (1) stator with openings and funnels O_2; 2) rotor with openings O_1; 3) reflector).

[p_c is the absolute pressure of the compressed air in the housing of the siren (in kg/m^2), p_k is the absolute pressure in the medium being irradiated (in kg/m^2), γ_c is the density of the compressed air (in kg/m^3), γ is the adiabatic exponent, C_p/C_v, which is equal to 1.4 for air, and 1.3 for natural gas and water vapor].

If the difference $\Delta p = p_c - p_k$ is small in comparison with p_k, the velocity is $w \approx [2g(\Delta p/\gamma_c)]^{1/2}$ and $L_{ad} \approx \Delta p$.

The acoustic efficiency η_{ac} of the siren depends on the geometric shape and the ratio between the dimensions of the openings in the stator and the teeth on the rotor, which determine the shape of the radiated pressure pulses, as well as on the compressed air pressure, the frequency of the vibrations, whether or not a horn is present and what shape it is, and the engineering features of the siren (gap between the rotor and the stator at the points where the openings are closed off, wobbling of the rotor, etc.).

A method of calculating the acoustic efficiency of sirens provided with horns is given in the paper by Jones [208], using an electromechanical analogy method. This method is presented briefly in the book by Hueter and Bolt [205].

For the rectangular pressure pulses obtained when the openings in the teeth are rectangular and the width of the teeth is much greater than the width of the openings, the acoustic efficiency of the siren is approximately equal to [208, 105]:

$$\eta_{ac} \approx \varphi(y) = \frac{(1+2y)^{1/2} - 1}{y} , \tag{2.6}$$

where y is a parameter that is approximately equal to $4\Delta p/\gamma p_k$. Another formula is given in [205]:

$$\eta_{ac} \approx \frac{\varphi(y)}{1 + 0.5(ka)^2 + 0.42\beta a} \tag{2.6'}$$

(where k is the wave number $2\pi/\lambda$, a is the width of the opening, and β is the expansion factor of the exponential horn on the siren). This formula gives better agreement with experiment.

Values of the function $\varphi(y)$ are given in Table 2. This table gives a clear idea of the approximate value of the acoustic efficiency of sirens giving rectangular compressed air pulses. It may be seen that highly economical sirens ($\eta_{ac} \geq 75\%$) are only found at low air pressures ($p_c \leq 0.3$ atmospheres gage), but an exception is provided by sirens made with openings shaped like Laval nozzles [17].

The acoustic efficiency of sirens drops as the frequency of the emitted sound is increased, as follows from Eq. (2.6'). Here, the fundamental frequency contains no more than 81% of the radiated power.

For the sinusoidal pressure pulses produced approximately (up to 96%) by round openings and rectangular teeth when the openings are of the same width as the teeth, the acoustic efficiency of the siren is only half the value given by Eqs. (2.6) and (2.6') shown in Table 2. Accordingly, the maximum efficiency of sirens with sinusoidal pressure modulation does not exceed, 50% while the value attainable practically is $\eta_{ac} = 35\text{-}40\%$, since the use of pressures below 0.2-0.3 atm gage involves constructional difficulties. The most widely used sirens are those having round holes in both the rotor and the stator. If the holes are all the same size, about 82% of the acoustic energy is radiated at the fundamental frequency.

It should be remembered that all the values of the acoustic efficiency given above are for dynamic sirens provided with an exponential horn (conical horns are not practical), i.e., a horn, the cross-sectional area of which increases according to the law [124]

$$S_x = S_0 e^{\beta x}, \tag{2.7}$$

TABLE 2

Δp	y	$\varphi(y)$	Δp	y	$\varphi(y)$
0.00	0	1.000	0.90	2.570	0.577
0.10	0.286	0.888	1.00	2.860	**0.556**
0.20	0.572	0.813	1.25	3.570	0.518
0.30	0.858	0.758	1.50	4.285	0.488
0.40	1.144	0.712	1.75	5.000	0.463
0.50	1.430	0.675	2.00	5.720	0.442
0.60	1.714	0.642	3.00	8.575	0.380
0.70	2.000	0.618	4.00	11.420	0.340
0.80	2.288	0.595	5.00	14.300	0.309

where S_0 is the cross-sectional area at the input to the horn, x is the distance between the plane in question and the input plane, and β is the expansion coefficient of the horn.

If there is no exponential horn, the acoustic efficiency of sirens drops rapidly, in particular at low frequencies [137]. The theory and calculation of the "hornless" sirens used in signaling are given in the papers by M. I. Karnovskii [41, 42]. The acoustic efficiency of these sirens does not exceed 1-2%, due to the mismatch between the sound source and the medium receiving the sound.

Every exponential horn has a critical frequency below which no sound is transmitted. The value of the critical frequency depends on the expansion coefficient of the horn [124], thus:

$$f_{cr} = \frac{\beta c_g}{4\pi}.$$ (2.8)

This fact may be made use of when it is desired to cut off the sound without stopping the compressed air flow to the siren. It is only necessary to drop the n_c of the siren below n_{cr}.

The rotors of dynamic sirens are driven by a commutator type electric motor or a pneumatic turbine. The drive power required is small, about 100-400 W for experimental sirens, and 1-2 kW for industrial sirens (the lower values are for the lower frequencies, while the higher values are for the higher frequencies). This amount of power is insignificant in comparison with the power required to compress the air for the siren.

So far, industrial models of dynamic sirens have only been put out by Ultrasonic Corporation (USA). From the data in the literature [6, 7, 47, 184, 240, 254, 272, 291], models U-1, U-2, U-3, U-4, et al. give acoustic efficiencies up to 50—70%, which, in our opinion, is obviously too high a value.

The literature [1, 6, 7, 92, 137, 227, 229, 246, 252, 253, 259, 274, 291, 317] also describes other ways of building dynamic sirens as used on a laboratory and experimental industrial scale in foreign countries.

A number of designs for dynamic sirens have been produced in the Soviet Union. The first operating models were those of the LIOT and Moscow Power Institute [73, 74, 75]. Sirens were later built at Mining Institute of the Academy of Sciences, USSR [60, 75], the All-Union Scientific Engineering and Technical Institute [17, 18, 302], the State Institute of Nonferrous Metals [126], Promenergo [308], the Institute of Applied Geophysics of the Academy of Sciences, USSR, [20] and the Scientific Research Institute of Mechanical Engineering [35].

In recent years, investigators have been attracted to static sirens, which are extremely simple and have no rotating parts or special drives. A static siren consists of a set of whistles arranged radially in a single ring-shaped resonating chamber, provided at the output with an exponential horn (when it is possible to limit the design to a single whistel, a parabolic reflector is used in place of the ring-shaped chamber).

Five types of whistles are known which are suitable for use in combination to produce high acoustic power (Fig. 13):[*]

a) The Hartmann shock-jet whistle [199,7], in which the sound vibrations are generated by the impact of a gas jet moving at ultrasonic velocity onto a cylindrical resonator, thus producing normal shock waves in the jet,

b) The Kurkin shock-jet whistle [53, 55, 56, 304], which differs from the preceding model in having a conical pin in the path of the gas, thus, in the opinion of the inventor, producing an oblique shock wave,

c) The rod-jet whistle [221], which differs from the Hartmann whistle in having a concentric rod to eliminate the low-efficiency central zone in the gas jet,

d) The vibrojet whistle [190], in which the sound vibrations are generated by directing a plane gas jet onto a knife edge in the wall of a cylindrical (or toroidal) resonator, where, as a result of the reaction on the gas jet of the characteristic vibrations of the resonator cavity the jet vibrates, if it is quite thin,

e) The vortex whistle [282, 47], in which the sound vibrations are generated by a moving vortex spiral producing rarefaction in the center of the chamber, which is periodically broken down by the gas flowing back in, with the result that an obliquely pulsating gas jet is formed at the output.

The acoustic and geometric constants of Hartmann shock-jet whistles, actuated by compressed air, are given by the following eight empirical formulas (d_n is the diameter of the nozzle in cm, and p_n is the excess pressure in atmospheres).

I. Maximum attainable frequency

$$f_0^{max} = \frac{5860}{d_n} \text{ cps.} \qquad (2.9)$$

II. Relative range of frequency variation

$$R = \frac{f_0^{max} - f_0^{min}}{f_0^{max}} 100 = 8.85\,(p_n - 0.93)\% . \qquad (2.10)$$

III. Distance from the nozzle to the start of the first region of instability (in which the resonator is placed)

$$a_1 = [1 + 0.04\,(p_n - 0.93)^2]\,d_n \text{ cm.} \qquad (2.11)$$

IV. Length of the first region of instability

$$a_2 - a_1 = 0.43\,d_n \sqrt{p_n - 1.86} \text{ cm.} \qquad (2.12)$$

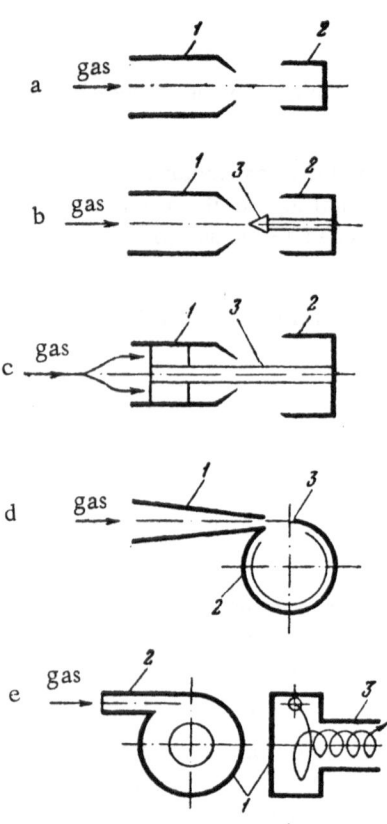

Fig. 13. Diagrams of gas jet sound radiators (whistles) a) Hartmann shock-jett whistle, 1) nozzle, 2) resonator; b) Kurkin shock-jet whistle, 1) nozzle, 2) resonator, 3) cone; c) rod-jet whistle, 1) nozzle, 2) resonator, 3) rod; d) vibrojet whistle, 1) slit-type nozzle, 2) cylindrical (or toroidal) resonator with 3) knife edge; e) vortex whistle 1) cylindrical chamber, 2) tangential input, 3) output cylinder.

---

[*]The terminology given below differs from the terminology used in the literature, which is partly based on undistinctive features. For example, the Hartmann shock-jet whistle is given the name "gas-jet" sound radiator, but this is also applicable to the vibrojet whistle, which is called a "police" or "lip" whistle in foreign countries [190].

TABLE 3

d_c, mm	p_c, atm gage	λ, mm	f, kcps	W_e, W	W_{ack}, W	η_{ac}, %
2	2.61	11.7	28.2	335	13.4	3.99
3	2.61	18.2	16.3	694	38.2	5.40
4	2.74	24.6	13.4	1380	73.1	5.29
5	3.44	32.7	10.0	2920	103.0	3.52
6	3.16	37.0	8.9	3570	145.0	4.00

V. Total acoustic power (including the harmonic components):

$$W_{ac} = (295 \sqrt{p_n - 0.93}\, d_c^2 \quad \text{W.} \tag{2.13}$$

VI. Power required to maintain the air stream

$$W_e = 5250\,(p_n + 1.033)\,[(p_n + 1.033)^{0.291} - 1.01]\,d_n^2 \quad \text{W.} \tag{2.14}$$

VII. Efficiency of a single whistle

$$\eta_{ac} = \frac{W_{ac}}{W_e}\,100\ \%. \tag{2.15}$$

VIII. Air volume consumed by the whistle

$$Q = 0.852\,(p_n + 1.033)\,d_n^2 \quad \text{m}^3/\text{min}. \tag{2.16}$$

Table 3 gives experimental data on shock-jet whistles of various dimensions with $d_r = d_n = h_r$ (h_r is the depth of the resonator).

It may be concluded from Table 3 that the acoustic efficiency of shock-jet whistles is not high (4-5%) and that the acoustic power radiated is comparatively small, in particular at high frequencies (which does not come from raising the frequency, but from decreasing the cross section of the jet, and thus reducing the air flow). For these reasons, using whistles with no resonating chamber or horn, i.e., "outside the siren," is limited mainly to labortaory scale setups.

Note, that because of the expansion of the gas jet as it leaves the nozzle, it is now recommended to make the resonator diameder d_r somewhat greater than the nozzle diameter d_n, so that $d_r = (1.25-1.33)d_n$ [1.58, 173]. Further, to avoid rapid wear on the resonator lips it is recommended that d_r be raised 1.65 d_n. The efficiency of the whistle is increased by a factor of three or more in the process [311].

Figure 14 shows a static siren designed by the State Scientific Research Institute for Sanitary and Industrial gas Purification, (NIIOGAZ), fitted out with Hartmann whistles. It differs from a similar siren built by Boucher [148, 149, 150, 151, 158, 173, 315] in having a movable (threaded), end, which makes it possible to adjust the depth and volume of the resonating chamber, and an anular slot for taking off the air [52]. The acoustic efficiency of this siren is about 10% at a frequency of 4.5 kcps.

Information on the V. P. Kurkin shock-jet whistles which are more ecnomical than the Hartmann whistle, is still very scarce. Unlike the Hartmann whistles, these whistles work at comparatively small excess pressures, of the order of 1 atm and below. The diameter of the resonator is equal to or greater than the diameter of the nozzle. The frequency emitted by the V. P. Kurkin whistles is appreciably lower than in Hartmann whistles of the same diameter. The whistle is mounted at the input to a special horn having an elliptical or circular cross section, and expanding exponentially toward the output.

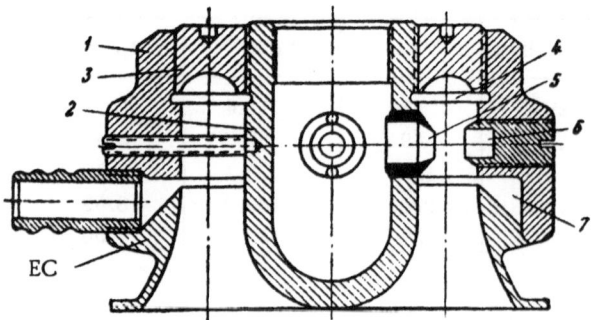

Fig. 14. NIIOGAZ static siren with vacuum collector.
1) Housing and external horn cavity EC; 2) internal
horn cavity and input nipple- 3) movable end; 4) annular resonating chamber; 5) nozzle and 6) resonator
(several sets); 7) annular slot for removing the air.

As in the NIIOGAZ static siren, a vacuum collector is provided in this siren to take the air out after
the kinetic energy has been transformed into sound vibrations. The results obtained from a shock-jet
whistle as designed by V. P. Kurkin with a nozzle diameter of 10 mm are given in Table 4.

Rod-jet whistles were first tried out by Sevor
[47] but have not been widely used as high-intensity
sound sources until recently, as a result of studies
made by the Demister Company (Sweden) [221]. These
whistles operate efficiently at low gas pressure right
down to 0.3-0.5 atm gage, so that the velocity at
which the gas jet flows out lies below the velocity of
sound. The diameter of the resonator is made much
greater than the diameter of the nozzle, with $d_r = 2.5$
d_n. The effective frequency range is 6-15 kcps. At
low frequencies, the air flow is about a third of that
in Hartmann whistles. The whistles are simple to make as well as tune (since they are less sensitive to getting
the proper distance between the nozzle and the resonator).

TABLE 4

Rod aperture angle 2β, deg	Pressure p, atm gage	Air flow Q, m³/hour	Sound frequency f, kcps	Acoustic power W_{ac}, kW	Acoustic efficiency η_{ac}, %
0 (no rod)	3.8	255	5.3	1.410	10.4
20	1.0	177	3.5	1.380	38.9
40	1.0	177	3.4	0.473	13.3
44	1.0	177	3.5	1.005	28.2
44.5	1.0	177	4.0	0.670	18.8
47.0	1.0	177	4.0	0.734	20.7
51.0	1.0	177	4.0	0.667	18.7
80.6	1.0	177	3.8	0.915	25.7

Vibrojet whistles have been known for a long time (they are essentially a development of the idea of the
Galton whistle) but the theory has been worked out in recent years [190].

The fundamental frequency of a vibrojet whistle is given by the following equation derived by Rayleigh
[107] from the familiar Helmholtz formula for the characteristic frequency of a three dimensional resonator:

$$f_0 = \frac{c_g}{2\pi} \sqrt{\frac{Kb}{V}}, \qquad (2.17)$$

where b is the length of the opening in the resonator along the axis of the cylinder, K is a constant which is a
function of the width δ of the opening (for δ = 7.3 mm, K = 0.713), and V is the volume of the resonator. Since
V/b is the cross section of the resonator, the frequency of the whistle is determined by the cross-sectional area.

The acoustic efficiency of a vibrojet whistle is given, according to Gavreau [190], by the expression

$$\eta_{ac} = \frac{p_c^2}{\rho_g c_g} \frac{a^2 b^3 \delta}{q_0^3} \left[\cdot \frac{(V + 2q_0/\omega_0)^\gamma - V^\gamma}{(V + 2q_0/\omega_0)^\gamma + V^\gamma} \right]^2, \qquad (2.18)$$

where a is the width of the jet (in m), q_0 is the air flow per second (in 10^{-9} m^3/ sec), and p_n is the air pressure in kg/ m^2.

The principle of the vibrojet whistle has been used in constructing the multiple-whistle siren of Gavreau [190, 150], the toroidal siren of Levavasseur [244, 7], and the "end-window" siren of Jahn [206, 150, 151].

Vortex whistles have seen described by Vonnegut in [282]. As was pointed out by Gregush in [28, 196], to get efficient operating of a vortex whistle, the radius R_c of the chamber, the radius r_n of the nozzle, and the radius r_c of the cylinder should be related by the following equation

$$R_c = \frac{r_n^2 r_m}{r_c^2 z} + r_n, \tag{2.19}$$

where r_m is the inner radius of the quasi-solid cylinder produced by the rotational motion of the gas ($r_m \approx r_c - 0.07$ cm), and z is a constant which depends on the coefficient of friction of the gas passing over the wall of the cylinder, and on the kinematic viscosity of the gas ($z \simeq 0.1$).

The fundamental frequency of a vortex whistle is given by the formula [282, 235, 47]:

$$f_0 = \frac{\alpha_{fr} c_g}{\pi D} \left(\frac{p_n - p_\kappa}{p_n} \right)^{1/2}, \tag{2.20}$$

where α_{fr} is a constant taking account of the reduction in the velocity of rotation of the vortex produced by friction at the wall of the chamber. The directivity diagram of a vortex whistle, unlike all the sound sources previously discussed, is "two-lobed," and there is practically no radiation along the axis of the whistle.

Theoretically, the acoustic efficiency of static sirens gets as high as the values given above for dynamic sirens with sinusoidal pressure modulation, i.e., it is equal to half the values of the function $\varphi(y)$ given in Table 2. For sirens provided with Hartmann shock-jet whistles, which only operate stably at an air pressure of the order of 2.5-5.0 atm gage, the maximum attainable acoustic efficiency as given by Table 2 is $\eta_{ac} = 15$-20%. For sirens with Kurkin whistles, operating at a pressure of one atm gage or below, the maximum efficiency is above the values $\eta_{ac} = 28$-29%. The maximum acoustic efficiency of sirens based on the principle of vibrojet and vortex whistles, which also operate a low pressures, may reach 35-38%. Thus, it may be concluded that static sirens are about half or one third as good as the highly efficient dynamic sirens.

Other drawbacks of static sirens are: the need for adjustment, no means of regulating the frequency, and increased wear on the working elements. Thus, static sirens should be used with a gas or vapor having an excess pressure that would otherwise go to waste, or in small scale setups, etc.

Difficulties have been experienced from the air stream issuing from the dynamic and static sirens so far used (unless a special diaphragm is put up to block the stream, but this lowers the sound intentisy). However, it has recently been found possible to get rid of the trouble by pumping off the air as it comes out of the siren The method is covered in the patents of Schaufler [260] and Levavasseur [225]. In the Soviet Union, the same principle has been used to build the "two-chamber" dynamic siren of the All-Union Scientific Engineering and Technical Institute [18] and the static siren with vacuum collector of NIIOGAZ, shown in Fig. 14.

In the laboratory, in addition to sirens, powerful electrodynamic loud speakers and special electrodynamic resonant core radiators, as developed by St. Clair [178, 47] are used. The former give a small amount of power at low frequencies (less than 1-2 kcps), but the latter, only give high efficiency (20-30%) and more power at high frequencies (above 10 kcps). Both these sources differ from sirens in giving a purer and more stabile tone, which is sometimes extremely desirable in laboratory work.

So-called electropneumatic radiators have also been built [157], in which the sound is generated by an electrically modulated air stream. With an insignificant amount of electrical energy expended in modulating the air stream (20 W), the ER6786 electropneumatic radiator gives 2.5 kW of acoustic power at a frequency of 0.5 kcps, and 1 kW at a frequency of 1 kcps (for p_n = 1.75 atm gage, Q = $4.3 \cdot 10^{-9} m^3$/min).

A few words in conclusion as to the technique of making acoustic measurements. The fundamental frequency of the sound emitted by a dynamic siren is usually determined by measuring the rpm of the drive motor with a stationary or portable tachometer, and then converting the value of frequency by Eq. (2.1). The frequency of the sound emitted by a static siren is found by means of an acoustic analyzer (an AN-1-50 harmonic analyzer, or an AS-3 or ASChKh-1 spectrum analyzer [113]). This type of apparatus is also needed to find the harmonic content of the sound from dynamic sirens. Type ICh frequency meters are of little use for the purpose. An oscillograph (ÉO-7 et al.) may also be used to determine the sound spectrum by connecting the appropriate output frequency from a sound generator (type 3G-12 et al.) onto the input as a standard in addition to the frequencies being measured. The analysis is made from the Lissajous figures.

Sound pressure is measured with a calibrated microphone (detector) connected to a vacuum tube amplifier, and the sound intensity is found by means of the formula given in the note on page 3.

For sound levels above 130-140 db, it is convenient to use condensor microphones with a titanium membrane, and piezoelectric sound detectors. It is particularly convenient to use the miniature detectors made of barium titanate ceramic and consisting of small hollow cylinders or spheres [298]. It is often possible in this case to get along without an amplifier by feeding the electrical oscillations directly to the input of a tube millivoltmeter (type MVL-2 etc.). It must however be kept in mind that the sensitivity of these receivers is strongly dependent on the temperature of the medium. Accordingly, in measuring sound pressure in media at high temperature, a specially cooled or ventilated probe must be used. Recently, piezoelectric detectors have been made of a special ceramic (TsTS brand etc.) which are suitable for high temperatures of the order of 200°C and above. Calibrating the detector is simply a matter of finding the sensitivity (μW/bar) at different frequencies. The most reliable method is that described by N. N. Pisarevskii and T. V. Smyshlyaeva [91].

Piezoelectric detectors are only slightly frequency dependent, and are preferably used in place of condensor microphones or other detectors, since strong harmonic components are always present in a high intensity sound field, and can greatly distort the results of sound pressure measurements.

More detailed information on the technique of acoustic measurements may be found in the monograph by Beranek [6] and in a number of papers published in the Acoustical Journal of the Academy of Sciences of the USSR.

§3. Short Outline of the Development of the Problem of Acoustic Coagulation and Precipitation of Aerosols

In 1926-1927, the well-known physicist R. W. Wood and his wealthy patron Loomis, made a series of experiments in which they investigated the properties of high-power ultrasonic vibrations in liquid media and discovered a number of very interesting physical and biological effects [294], which aroused lively interest in the scientific world. These experiments provided the impetus for setting up similar experiments in gases, and Patterson and Cawood [249] soon discovered that when aerodisperse systems are subjected to ultrasonic irradiation, the suspended particles form aggregates and accumulate locally in the nodal points of the standing wave, in the same way as the dust figures in the familiar Kundt experiment [218]. This phenomenon, which was given the name of acoustic or sonic coagulation of aerosols, attracted the attention of investigators, and detailed studies were made in succeeding years in England, Germany, and the Soviet Union.

Andrade made an experimental study of the behavior of suspended particles in a sound field [141], and found that the smallest particles are actively engaged in the vibratory motion of the gaseous medium, while the medium tends to flow around the larger particles, which, if they are large enough, become centers of vortex motion in the medium, and in the process execute peculiar spiral and zig-zag motions in the coagulation vessel. At the same time, the aerosol particles take part in the circulation of the gas between the nodes and loops of the vibrations. Also, the particles are found to accumulate locally, both in the nodes at the walls of the vessel and in the loops, where the particles are concentrated in the form of peculiar discs [142]. Andrade came to the conclusion that the motive force in acoustic coagulation of aerosols is the hydrodynamic attraction between particles, once studied theoretically by Köning [215], and then mentioned by Rayleigh[107] as being one of the reasons why dust "ridges" are formed in a Kundt tube. Using Köning's equations for the attractive forces, derived on the assumption that a potential field is set up when spheres are surrounded by acoustic flux, together with the experimental study of the acoustic coagulation kinetics of a magnesium oxide aerosol at high ultrasonic frequencies made by Parker [248a], Andrade [141a] attempted to give a mathematical theory of acoustic coagulation of aerosols, but he made some serious fundamental errors, so that his theory was rejected as soon as it appeared [192 a].

The most detailed studies were those made by Brandt, Freund, and Hiedeman [1, 171, 163, 167, 168, 170, 200]. These authors made an experimental study of coagulation of aerosols (tobacco smoke, amonium chloride, paraffin oil fog) in the static and in the flowing state at different sound frequencies, and found that coagulation occurs with incomparably greater ease at audio frequencies than at the high ultrasonic frequencies which Andrade and Parker used in their experiments.

By taking motion pictures, the above authors were able to confirm the relation between the amplitude of the vibrations and the dimensions of the particles, and in addition gave a theoretical derivation of an approximate equation for the extent to which the particles are entrained in the vibrations of the medium, after having found by calculation that the gas flow around aerosol particles in a sound field is predominantly viscous in nature.

Since it was more easily grasped intuitively than Köning's equation [214], the new equation showed how the amplitude and phase shift of the particles varied with dimensions and density, as well as with the viscosity of the medium and the frequency. This made it possible to point out another effect which helps to coagulate aerosols in a sound field, namely, collisions between small actively vibrating particles and larger, but less mobile particles (the orthokinetic effect). It was felt that this was the leading effect in the process, and so the theory of orthokinetic coagulation of aerosols in a sound field was advanced [1, 167].

One of the above authors, Brandt, showed in his dissertation [161] that the acoustic coagulation rate of aerosols is a linear function of the particle count concentration, which was a weighty proof in favor of the orthokinetic theory.

The Soviet scientists S. V. Gorbachev and A. B. Severnyi [26, 195] made an ingenious study of the elementary process in hydrodynamic interaction between water droplets suspended on glass threads in a sound field. It was found that ponderomotive forces of attraction and repulsion are produced between the droplets by the sound, similar to the forces occurring in a stream. The ponderomotive effect of sound waves on large bodies in a liquid has also been studied experimentally, as we know, by P. N. Lebedev [64].

A. B. Severnyi [109] tried to make an approach to calculating the ponderomotive interaction between drops in a sound field, starting with Bjerkness' hydrodynamic theory [146], which includes virtual pulsations of the drops. However, not all the facts in the matter were taken in to account, so that the equation found for the time required for droplets in a fog to come together was of no theoretical or practical value.

After the studies carried out in the thirties, which made a definite contribution to the theory of acoustic coagulation of aerosols, by showing that the process was highly efficient, interest in theoretical studies dropped off, and investigators switched their attention over to finding concrete practical ways of using the phenomenon that had been discovered.

The first application — using the coagulating effect of sound to disperse natural water fogs — was made by Amy in 1931, and in 1934 he received a U.S. patent on his method [139]. In the next few years, there was a second application, protected by appropriate patents, that of using the coagulating action of sound to speed up the removal of industrial smokes, dusts, and fogs [164, 165, 166, 169, 177, 204].

In 1938, Gies (Lugri Company, Germany) made experiments on the purification of dust-laden industrial gases [193], using whistles and magnitostriction radiators as sound sources, but the results were of little comfort: the specific energy consumed in treating the aerosols with sound was tens and hundreds of times greater than the energy consumed in cleaning the gases by other known methods. The principal reason why the process was so unprofitable was that the sound sources used had extremely low acoustic efficiency (several percent).

During these years, St. Clair (U. S. Bureau of Mines) engaged in studies on acoustic coagulation of aerosols, principally ammonium chloride [179, 181], and developed a new type of electrodynamic sound generator (with a resonant core), which made it possible to get an acoustic efficiency of the order of 20-30% at high frequencies [178]. However, this sound generator was not very suitable for industrial purposes, since the efficiency dropped off sharply at the lower frequencies, and it had other defects which limited its use to laboratory-scale setups.

In the next few years, coincident with the second World War, vigorous efforts were made in the USA to produce high-power, highly efficient sound generators of siren type to meet the special needs of the U.S. military and naval forces, in particular acoustic dissipation of fogs at airports.

Jones [208], using an electromechanical analogy, developed a theory of dynamic sound sirens which indicated that there was a real possibility of attaining very high acoustic efficiencies. Unfortunately, this work did not receive the attention it deserved in other countries, with the result that in the years following, sound siren models were being produced head over heels without meeting any standard of economical performance.

Using Jones' theory and calculations as a basis, the Chrysler Corporation produced the "Victory" sound sirens, in which the acoustic power radiated reached 50 horsepower at an acoustic efficiency of 70-90% [208]. Using these sirens, Lamer and Sinclair [266, 156] made experiments in 1943 on acoustic dispersal of natural fog at the Lunken Airport (Cincinnati, Ohio, USA), which gave a positive result in calm weather after the runway had been irradiated for about one minute.

Previously, the same investigators had made a number of laboratory and larger-scale experiments on dispersing artificial water fogs, which gave both positive and negative results (negative, because of improper choice of sound frequency). The sound sources used were loud speakers and small sound sirens built by the Federal Electric Company.

In the same year, Lamer, Sinclair, and Breccia [156] made experiments on acoustic dissipation of sea fog (Sandberg, California) at high wind velocities (5-6 m/sec), but the acoustic power radiated by eight "Victory" sirens was insufficient to get the required visibility under these unfavorable conditions.

In the post-war years, Ultrasonic Corporation (USA) put out a number of commercial models of sound sirens with an acoustic efficiency of the order of 40-60%, and this made it possible to move toward experimental work on improving the purification of industrial gases. In 1947, this firm set up the first experimental equipment for trapping highly disperse gas black [254, 184, 272]. It consisted of a sound coagulation chamber, with two inertial precipitators, cyclones, mounted in series behind it. In what follows, we shall give the name sonic-inertial to combined dust-drop collecting equipment of this type.

The results of the experiments on the first sonic-inertial equipment were encouraging, and, in the next few years, experiments were laid out on trapping other industrial products, such as sulphuric acid fog, calcined soda, molybdenum sulfite, cement dust, open-hearth gas dust, fly ash, etc. [183, 184, 186, 216, 240, 241, 269, 273, 281].

In the course of this work, values were found for the acoustic constants, sound intensity, frequency, and treatment time, which determine the acoustic coagulation efficiency when applied to industrial aerosols.

In particular, it turned out that each aerosol has an optimum frequency at which the process goes most efficiently. It was found that the efficiency of sonic-inertial precipitation is strongly dependent on the physical properties of the aerosol — the degree of dispersion, the concentration of the particles by weight, etc. It was found that highly disperse aerosols have the best acoustic coagulation properties, but it requires high sound intensity to increase the size of the primary particles in a short time up to dimensions where they can be precipitated efficiently by precipitators. It was found that low concentration aerosols have poor acoustic coagulation properties, but the process is speeded up by squirting atomized water into the aerosol ("sprinkling"), although this, of course, can not always be done. Also, it was found that the residual particle concentration was quite large, etc.

The above facts greatly limited the range of application of sonic-inertial aerosol precipitation in industry, but no serious attempts were made to improve the process [203, 204, 264, 319]. This is to a considerable degree due to the fact that the work took on a narrowly practical tinge, to the complete neglect of theoretical studies, without which, as we know, it is impossible to make any systematic improvement in industrial processes. It is sufficient to say that in this period almost no work was being done in the USA on the theory of acoustic coagulation of aerosols An exception is provided by the work St Clair and co-workers on the drift of aerosol particles brought about by the radiation pressure of sound [179, 181]. Using King's equation for the radiation pressure on a sphere immersed in a nonviscous medium [212], St. Clair derived an equation for the motion of the sphere toward the nearest vibration loop. This led to the conclusion [179] that it is the radiation pressure of sound which is the decisive factor in producing rapid coagulation of aerosols in a sound field. However, elementary calculations do not support this point of view [73]. Further, the paper by Westervelt, which soon came out, on the aperiodic ("constant") forces acting on particles suspended on a sound field [286] threw doubt on St. Clair's equation itself. Westervelt showed that in addition to the radiation pressure, the suspended particles are acted upon by much larger viscous forces and particularly by forces coming from the inevitable distortion that occurs in the shape of sound waves of finite amplitude.

In view of the limited application of sonic-inertial aerosol precipitation revealed during the experimental work, the method was only used industrially in special cases (sulfuric acid fog, calcined soda ash, molybdenum sulfite). This greatly reduced any interest in undertaking experimental work among U.S. industrialists, and after 1951-1952, the work along this line was almost completely stopped.

However, in other countries, interest in the new method began to grow by leaps and bounds each year. Experimental work was done in the Soviet Union, Hungary, West Germany, Japan, Poland, Austria, France, and Czechoslovakia.

In the Soviet Union, the first work on sonic-inertial precipitation of industrial aerosols was done in 1950-1951 by P. A. Kouzov in the Leningrad Institute of Industrial Safety (LIOT). Experiments were made on the precipitation of aggregated fly ash, trapped in the electrical filters of power station boiler assemblies, which had been introduced into the air by mechanical dispersion. These experiments, like the others [193, 73], showed that aggregated aerosols obviously have only slight acoustic coagulation properties, so that studies of the coagulating effect of sound could only be made on unaggregated aerosols.

In the light of these facts it is impossible to give credence to the markedly negative conclusions of Schnitzler (Lurgi Company, West Germany) on the method [262], since they are based on experiments with sonic-inertial precipitation of aggregated magnesium oxide and aluminum oxide aerosols.

After the unsuccessful attempts at acoustic coagulation of carbon black made by the Baku Branch of the VNIIGAZ (Kh. Grigoryan [29]), the author of the present book set up experiments in the Moscow Power Institute (1953-1955) on sonic-inertial precipitation of an artificial oil fog, which gave very positive results [73, 74].

In Hungary, the coagulating effect of sound was tested for improving the gravitational precipitation of cement dust right in the gas duct (Tarnoczy and Greguss [275]). Extensive tests of the sonic-inertial method of precipitating industrial aerosols were made in 1950-1954 in Japan (Oyama, Inoue, Sawahata, and Okada [246, 38]). Experiments were set up on the sonic-inertial precipitation of zinc oxide, gas black, sulfuric acid, coke gas tar and cracking gas condensate, and high-quality results were obtained for the last two aerosols. As a result of the work, some empirical relations were established for the sonic-inertial aerosol precipitation process. In particular, it was found that there is an exponential relation between the residual particle concentration and the specific energy consumption and treatment time. The authors of this work helped to install an industrial sonic-inertial setup for the purification of cracking gas in Tokyo in 1952 [259].

Considerable interest has been aroused by the work on sonic-inertial precipitation of zinc oxide sublimates, done in these same years in Poland at the Metallurgical Factory in Szopienice (Maczewski-Rowinski et al. [227, 228, 229, 92]). The experiment showed that zinc oxide sublimates have good acoustic coagulation properties. Maczewski-Rowinski et al. later made extensive experiments at a nitrogen factory on sonic-gravitational precipitation of phthalic anhydride [88, 306, 325].

Experiments have been made in Austria on sonic-inertial precipitation of iron oxide, cobalt oxide, and other products (Jahn [206]), during which it was found necessary to maintain a certain critical velocity in the inertial precipitators, since above this velocity the dry particle aggregates formed begin to be rapidly destroyed.

Some experiments were made later on acoustic dissipation of artificial water fogs and on the sonic-inertial precipitation of smokes in France. In the experiments on sonic-inertial precipitation of the smoke from carbide furnaces (Boucher [150, 151]), it was shown that good results are found by treating the aerosols with a group of sound waves of different frequencies (produced by a static siren of "multiple whistle" type constructed by Boucher [148, 148, 150, 151, 315].

In Czechoslovakia, the sonic-inertial method of precipitation has been used on smoke gases, artificial water fog, etc. (Taraba, Brzica [274]).

The experimental work described above has extended our information on the acoustic coagulation properties of industrial aerosols, but at the same time has brought an even greater amount of uncertainty into the question of how profitable the process is, since the sound sirens used are not economical. Further, in the majority of cases, even this work was carried out along narrow practical lines. The mechanism of acoustic aerosol coagulation remained a mystery, as before, which prevented improvement to the process.

In the next few years, thanks principally to the work of Soviet scientists, definite progress was made in clearing up the mechanism of the process.

In 1954-1955, the author of this book made a critical analysis of the theoretical hypotheses relating to the mechanism of acoustic coagulation of aerosols, based on the materials in existence at that time, and came to the conclusion [73, 74] that no one of the hypotheses alone can give a satisfactory explanation of the phenomenon. The only tenable scheme for the coagulation was considered to be orthokinetic interaction in combination with the random motion observed in aerosol particles. This scheme has maintained itself up to the present time, in spite of the fact that many previous ideas of what governs the behavior of aerosol particles in a sound field have gone out of fashion.

S. V. Pshenai-Severin showed in [103] that in considering the interaction between aerosol particles in a sound field, we have to start with the pattern of viscous flow given by Oseen's hydrodynamic theory, which takes partial account of the inertial terms in the equation of motion of the medium. For this reason, the formulas of Bjerkness and Köning, formerly used for the hydrodynamic interaction forces between spheres, and derived on the assumption of potential flow, are unsuitable for calculating the forces of attraction between aerosol particles in a sound field. S. V. Pshenai-Severin found that in a sound field, longitudinal attraction occurs between the aerosol particles of the same size, similar to the hydrodynamic attraction between drops in a cloud [101, 102, 104, 250]. In the rest of the book, we shall give this type of interaction the name attractional interaction.

Recently, V. I. Timoshenko [116] found that attractional interaction is also a property of aerosol particles of different sizes, and that it occurs in this case for both Oseen and Stokes flow, and that it ends up by aggregation of the particles for a definite ratio between the dimensions of the particles of the frequency of the oscillations.

The author of this book, starting with Oseen's pattern of the flow around aerosol particles in a sound field, found [81] that hysteresis occurs in the flow around small obstacles, with the result that the particles in the vibrating medium execute a zigzag motion with respect to the particles the medium is flowing around. Here, a peculiar type of acoustic flow is set up around each of the aerosol particles in the medium. It was shown in another paper by the author [82] that self-centering of the particles takes place during orthokinetic interaction between aerosol particles in a sound field, with the result that the probability of their being captured by one another increases.

At the same time it was shown that a transverse hydrodynamic interaction exists between particles of different sizes, which we shall, from now on call parakinetic. The author showed recently in [305] that transverse interaction also occurs during attractional approach between particles of the same size but the effect is to deflect the particles away from one another.

High-speed motion pictures of the behavior of aerosol particles in a sound field, made recently in the Acoustics Institute of the Academy of Sciences of the USSR, by O. K. Éknadiosyants and L. I. Buravov [12], during which it was shown that particle aggregates are formed in space, give indirect evidence that hydrodynamic particle interaction is present.

There is some interest in the experimental study of acoustic coagulation of a highly disperse dioctyl-phthalate fog, made by B. F. Podoshevnikov [94]. He found that an exponential relation exists between the droplet count concentration and the product of the sound pressure by the length of time treated, which agrees with Inoue's conclusion [37], based on the experimental study of acoustic coagulation of tobacco smoke made by Brandt, Freund, and Hiedemann. A study was made of the change in dispersion of the droplets occurring during acoustic coagulation of a fog in [95]. Together with V. A. Gudemchuk and B. D. Tartakovskii, Podoshevnikov found in [30] that longitudinal partitions in the coagulation chamber have a negative effect on the acoustic coagulation rate of a fog (which is attributed by the authors to the reduction in turbulence of the medium observed in this case). This observation finally puts an end to P. N. Kubanskii's idea that it is well to have precipitation surfaces in coagulation chambers [48, 49], an idea which had previously been refuted theoretically in our papers [73]. However, in spite of the assertion of the author of [30, 93], his experiments do not throw any doubt on the idea that the leading role in acoustic coagulation of aerosols is played by ortho-kinetic interaction between the particles. In view of the difference in the phase shift angles of the particle vibrations with respect to the medium, the instantaneous velocities of the aerosol particles are appreciably different, even for an insignificant difference in the degree to which they are caught up in the vibrational motion of the medium. Since all the aerosols are more or less polydisperse, this means that orthokinetic and parakinetic interactions between particles in a sound field are the rule rather than the exception.

It follows from our other paper [83], in which a theory of acoustic turbulence was developed, that the turbulent pulsations occurring in a sound field are able to bring the aerosol particles together quickly to distances where the self-centering phenomenon, and then the orthokinetic effect come into play (the idea that Brownian motion is the leading factor in diffusion of the particles into the space where the aggregates are formed was also refuted by us in [76]).

To gain a more complete understanding of the behavior of aerosol particles in a sound field, some interest attaches to the paper by S. S. Dukhin [34], which gives the theory of the drift of aerosol particles into the nodal points of a standing wave, resulting from the asymmetry in the vibrations of the particles in the medium which occurs in this case. Approximately the same problem had already been solved by A. D. Bagrinovskii in [3], but he assumed without reason that the effect was the most important factor in acoustic coagulation of aerosols.

In addition to the papers of a theoretical sort mentioned above, a number of experiments have been made recently in the Soviet Union on acoustic coagulation and precipitation of industrial aerosols, in which several new schemes were tried out. One of the schemes was to combine acoustic coagulation with a cloth filter, which gave a low residual particle concentration, and increased the filtration rate of the gas. This scheme was first tried out on precipitating drilling dust by R. Sh. Shkol'nikova ("Gipronikel'," Leningrad) [130, 131, 132, 310], and was favorably received by industry.

V. P. Kurkin (State Scientific Research Institute for Sanitary and Industrial Gas Purification), working on acoustic coagulation of highly disperse injected carbon black, investigated a scheme consisting of an acoustic coagulator, two cyclones connected in series, and a glass cloth filter [54, 57, 304], and found that it worked better than the familiar "Canadian" scheme. During the investigation, Kurkin developed a new type of gas jet sound generator [53, 55, 56], with an acoustic efficiency much higher than that of previous generators of this type. At the present time one of the carbon black factories of the USSR is doing the final work on installing experimental industrial equipment designed on the above scheme. The scheme has already been tested on experimental industrial "Proménergo" equipment installed in a bronze and brass factory to remove zinc oxide sublimates [23, 308].

Experiments of the Leningrad Electrical Engineering Institute on sonic-inertial precipitation of zinc white at the Mendeleev factory in Leningrad have shown that when low frequencies are used, only small amounts of energy are required to give improved trapping of the fine dust fractions in the aggregated aerosols, but the health norms for dust-laden air cannot be met even in this case without the use of cloth filters [89,90].

It has now been suggested that acoustic coagulators should be used in a special class of dust collecting equipment, namely, that using turbulent, condensation, and electrical coagulators in addition [59].

There is a large amount of interest in the sound equipped gas separators used for low-temperature separation of natural gas condensates [79, 84], which are going through experimental tests. The sound is generated by using part of the excess pressure found in the natural gas, so that the question of economy is not of great importance here. The first support for the idea was obtained in one of the gas condensate deposits in the Volgograd regions [86].

The prospects for using the acoustic method in the gas industry are very good, but it will require serious efforts to overcome the difficulties standing in the way.

Interesting possibilities are opened up by the step-by-step method of carrying out acoustic coagulation of aerosols [77, 78]. In this method, the aerosol to be coagulated is passed through a number of coagulation chambers, in which it is subjected to sound waves of successively decreasing frequency, so as to give the best frequency at each stage of enlargement of the particles.

Another method, which we described in [76], is not devoid of interest. In this method, the aerosol is treated with sound in an electrical precipitation chambers, into which charged droplets of water or other liquid have previously been introduced, and these transport the dust deposited on them to the precipitating electrodes. Thus, this method, which we shall call the electroacoustic method of precipitating aerosols, succeeds in bringing the particle coagulation and precipitation zones together at the same point.

Originality is exhibited in the experiments on using the coagulating effect of sound to produce rain, made by the Él'brus Complex Mountain Climbing Expedition [32].

A number of other studies have also been made in the USSR on these problems [13, 14, 15, 301, 312].

Of foreign work in the field of acoustic coagulation of aerosols there are two proposals presenting definite practical interest: Smith's patent [268] on a method for catalytic pyrolysis of hydrocarbons in which the suspended catalysts are recovered by acoustic coagulation, and Slavik's idea [24] in which dangerous chemical gas contaminants are removed by adding chemical reagents to form suspended solid or liquid products with the contaminants, which are then precipitated by acoustic coagulation.

A large amount of practical interest attaches to the attempts made in recent years to use sound waves to improve in the actual precipitation process itself.

The first proposal along these lines is contained in Westervelt and Sieck's patent [290], which describes a method of aerosol separation using specially shaped sirens to distort the shape of the sound wave, so that the drift velocity of the particles becomes as large as possible.

Asklöf has proposed a sound-type drop catcher [313], in which the use of sound improves the filtration of a fog through a porous packing. This proposal turns over a new page in acoustic dust and drop collection, since the residual concentration of aerosol particles may be reduced to fractions of a mg/m^3 of gas with perfectly acceptable energy consumption.

Boucher [147, 157] has made a proposal for improving aerosol precipitation in existing dust and drop collecting equipment such as the Venturi scrubber and the cyclone.

Treatment with sound is also of help in bag filters. Abboud [135, 157] has proposed a method for cleaning the dust out of them with sound waves.

Interesting ideas have also appeared outside the country in the field of acoustic dissipation of natural fogs. Boucher proposed a new, so-called thermoacoustic method of dissipating airport fogs [152], consisting of a combination of sound treatment and thermal heating of the fog. He also proposed a sonic-chemical method of fog dissipation [156], consisting of a combination of sound treatment with atomization of hygroscopic materials into the fog. This method is going through tests in a whole list of countries (France, England, Sweden, USA, etc.).

Both methods provide examples of the use of sound to speed up evaporation of a liquid disperse phase. This possibility was pointed out as early as 1938-1942, and is based on the idea that the treatment causes sound and turbulent pulsations to flow around the aerosol particles.

With this idea in mind, Horsley and Danser in 1947 devised a method for spray drying wet materials (such as soap solution) in a sound field, which, as far as we know, has not yet found any industrial application.

However, on Greguss's initiative (1955), a method was developed for sonic drying of wet, powdered materials. Interesting experiments along these lines were made by Boucher [173, 153, 154, 155, 157], which are now being continued by the Acoustics Institute of the Academy of Sciences of the USSR [8, 9], and other scientific research institutions here and in foreign countries.

The distinctive feature of the new method is that drying is accomplished by a "cold" method, without raising the temperature of the material, which is extremely valuable when heat sensitive materials have to be dried.

Up to the present time, sonic drying has been tried on such difficulty driable materials as carboxylmethylcellulose, titanium dioxide, colloidal zirconium hydroxide, silica gel, heat sensitive enzymes and hormones, ethyl cellulose, etc. The high quality of the results attained in sonic drying of these materials make the method suitable for industrial use even now.

Greguss [28, 196] made some interesting experiments on speeding up burning of atomized liquid fuel in a metallurgical furnace used to extract malleable pig iron, making use, for the purpose, of a combination whistle-atomizer that he had constructed. Very good results were obtained.

Attempts have been made at improving other physical-chemical processes taking place between a disperse phase and a gas. Thus in 1947, Richardson [256] suggested using ultrasonic waves to speed up ammonia synthesis when using a suspended iron catalyst. Karlström [7] showed that it was possible to speed up hardening of the amalgams used in dentistry. Workers at the General Aniline Company (USA) [102] proposed a process for molding parts out of finely disperse carbonyl iron by thermal decomposition of iron pentacarbonyl in a sound field. However, as far as we know, these proposals have so far found no practical application.

Audio and ultrasonic sound waves have been used in experiments on fluidizing powdered materials (gypsum, etc.) [237, 217], as well as on producing aerosols [134, 207, 270]. However, these processes are based on completely different physical effects so we shall not stop to discuss them. For the same reason, we cannot consider examples of the application of sound treatment of aerosols to physical research practice. Sound treatment of aerosols has been used to determine the amplitude of the vibrations of a gas [226, 174, 140, 141, 143, 263], to determine the form of a sound wave [191], to investigate acoustic streaming [140] and the sound field at a sound absorbing surface [234], to find the dispersion spectrum of aerosols [175, 198], to find the concentration of aerosol particles, and for a number of other purposes.

CHAPTER II

MOTION OF AEROSOL PARTICLES IN AN ACOUSTIC FIELD

§4. Preliminary Information

Solid or liquid particles suspended in gaseous media are distinguished by high mobility. If the particles are quite small ($r < 1\,\mu$) they execute a rapid Brownian motion, and if they are not too small they settle to the bottom more or less rapidly under their own weight. If the temperature is irregularly distributed in the medium which is, generally speaking, inevitable in large volumes of gas, the suspended particles are also carried along with the convective flow in the medium. Further, in turbulent flow, the particles are also drawn into the turbulent pulsations of the medium. Special motion of the particles is observed in long cylindrical pipe lines, as well as motion of the particles toward the perphery [121].

In addition to the above types of motion, the particles in an acoustic field in a gas execute a number of motions of incomparably more complex and violent nature. This is due to the fact that the particles:

    1) take some part or other in the vibrations of the gas,

    2) execute a translational motion, or "drift" as a result of certain second order effects (radiation pressure, asymmetry in the sound waves, etc.)

    3) are carried along in the translational ("circulating") motion, or acoustic wind, in the vibrating medium, at the same time following the turbulent pulsations, and

    4) execute a complex type of migration due to hydrodynamic (parakinetic or attractional) interaction with neighboring particles.

Further, the suspended particles undoubtedly rotate, but we shall not take up the phenomenon here, since it is of no inherent importance to the problem under discussion. The remaining sections of this chapter deal successively with the laws governing the first three types of motion executed by aerosol particles in an acoustic field. The particle migration due to mutual interaction is taken up separately in §11 and 12 of the next chapter.

Thus, Chapter 2 only deals with types of motion of aerosol particles in an acoustic field which occur under conditions that are not restricted by the mutual presence of the particles, such as occur in practice only in "infinitely dilute," i.e., low-concentration aerosols.

Let us note the following before we get into a specific treatment of each of the types of motion of aerosol particles in an acoustic field. The final problem of the succeeding sections of the chapter is to derive and analyze the equations of motion of the aerosol particles, which describe how they move about in time and space as a function of the physical constants of the particle and the medium. The basis of the derivation in all cases is, as of hydrodynamics generally, the differential equation for Newton's second law

$$m_p \frac{d^2 x_p}{dt^2} = F' + F'', \tag{4.1}$$

where m_p, x_p and t are the mass and absolute displacement of the particle, and the time, F' is the "static" force on the particles, not directly related to the particle moving about, such as that due to the pressure gradient in the sound wave, the radiation pressure of sound, etc., while F'' is the "kinematic" force involved in relative motion between the medium and the particle, which inevitably determines whether the particles lag behind or get ahead of the motion of the medium. This force depends in an essential way on how the medium flows around the particle. The type of flow, as we know, determines the Reynolds number $Re = 2ru_{gp}/\nu$, which gives the ratio between the inertial forces (numerator) and the viscous forces (denominator)(see [100], p 209)

At small Reynolds number $(Re < 1)$, where the inertial forces are small in comparison with the viscous forces in the medium, the retarding effect of the surface of a solid in a gas stream extends a considerable distance into the medium. A peculiar envelope consisting of a retarded, "boundary" gas layer is formed around the solid, in which the thickness of the layer, as will be shown in §9, may be much greater than the dimensions of the aerosol particles. This is the physical picture which corresponds to so-called viscous flow around a solid.

As the Reynolds number increases, so that the inertial forces begin to outweigh the viscous forces in the medium, the above picture begins to change: the boundary layer of gas becomes thinner and thinner, and finally gets down to nothing. In this case, the viscous losses and their associated vortex effects may be neglected. A state of affairs sets in which is called potential flow around the solid. The difference between viscous and potential flow around spheres is well illustrated by Fig. 45 in the familiar monograph by N. A. Fuks [121].

Let us see what type of flow is set up around aerosol particles in a vibrating medium for the constants usually encountered in a sound field. The maximum possible rate of flow around aerosols in a sound field is given by the maximum value of the particle velocity in the medium. All other forms of motion are obviously of lower velocity, since they are produced by secondary effects "fed" by energy from the vibrations of the particles in the medium.

The amplitude, or maximum value of the particle velocity U for a "normal" sound intensity of the order of 0.1 W/cm^2, is 220 cm/sec. At this velocity, the maximum particle radius for which $Re = 1$ is, in air ($\gamma = 0.15$), $r \approx 3.5\mu$. The radii of the aerosol particles to be consolidated are usually less than $r = 3$-5μ, which means that $Re < 1$, for the greater part of the period of a vibration.

Accordingly, in dealing with the types of motion of aerosol particles in a sound field discussed below we can usually proceed on the assumption of viscous flow. Only in very high-intensity sound fields is it necessary to assume that approximately potential flow is occurring around large aerosol particles.

All the forms of motion of aerosol particles in a sound field discussed below are, generally speaking, nonuniform in nature. For this case, hydrodynamic theory gives the following general expression for the force F'', due to relative motion of a spherical particle in a viscous medium with an arbitrarily varying velocity u_{gp} ([160], p. 224; [61], p. 121; [111] p. 349; [121], p. 76; and [108]):

$$F'' = \frac{2}{3}\pi r^3 \rho_p \frac{du_{gp}}{dt} + 6\pi\eta r u_{gp} + 6\sqrt{\pi\rho_g}\, r^2 \int_{-\infty}^{t} \frac{du_{gp}}{dt_i}\frac{dt_i}{\sqrt{t - t_i}}\,. \qquad (4.2)$$

The first term in this equation gives the part of the force due to direct exchange of momentum between the particle and the medium, with no viscous forces involved, i.e., just as in an ideal medium. The magnitude of this term is one half the inertial force of the mass of medium replaced by the particle ([61], p. 52-53). Since the gas is of low density as compared with the particles, this term may almost always be neglected (an exception is provided by aerosols under very high pressure, like natural gas).

The second term in Eq. (4.2) is the force due to relative motion of the viscous medium at the velocity which it has at a given instant of time t. This is usually the principal component of the force F''. The third integral term of Eq. (4.2) gives the inertial part of the force F'', due to the nonuniform relative motion of the viscous medium. The value of this term depends in an essential way on the path that the particle has already moved through, and particularly on the accelerations received in the preceding instants of time t_i. If the velocity changes slowly, so that the acceleration du_{gp}/dt is small, the integral term may be neglected. In this case, the expression for the "kinematic" force acting on the particle takes the form

$$F'' = 6\pi\eta r u_{gp}, \qquad (4.3)$$

which is the familiar Stokes formula, derived assuming steady state flow of a viscous medium around a sphere. At high Reynolds numbers (Re > 1), this formula must have added to it Oseen's correction factor $(1 + \frac{3}{16} Re)$, which is, however, to be avoided if possible, since it means that the square of the velocity occurs in the differential equation of motion of the particle, and this makes it exceedingly difficult to solve.

By a "slow" change in the force acting we mean a change that lasts for a time T much greater than the relaxation time τ of the particle, as given by the expression:

$$\tau = \frac{2}{9} \frac{\rho_p}{\eta} r^2. \tag{4.4}$$

This parameter, which is widely used in aerosol mechanics, determines the rate at which the equilibrium state is restored in the "particle-medium" system, as well as the sensitivity of the particle to changes in the force acting on it, which is not surprising, since the above expression is the momentum $m_p u_{gp}$ acquired by the particle divided by the Stokes force $F_{St} = \pi \eta r u_{gp}$.

The relaxation time is very small for aerosols undergoing coagulation. For unit density ($\rho_p = 1$) in atmospheric air ($\eta = 1.85 \cdot 10^{-4}$), it takes on the following values:

$$\text{for } r = 0.1 \; \mu \quad \tau = 1.2 \cdot 10^{-7} \text{ sec};$$
$$\text{for } r = 1.0 \; \mu \quad \tau = 1.2 \cdot 10^{-5} \text{ sec};$$
$$\text{for } r = 10 \; \mu \quad \tau = 1.2 \cdot 10^{-3} \text{ sec}.$$

Hence, the smaller the relaxation time of the particle, the more rapidly the particle takes on a new velocity relative to the medium, corresponding to the instantaneous value of the force acting on the particle.

If the relaxation time is small in comparison with the length of time during which the velocity in the medium changes, this means that the particle moves almost without departing from the instantaneous velocities in the medium correspoing to the changes in the acting force with time. A motion of this type is called quasi-steady state in hydrodynamics.

A general solution of the integrodifferential equation for nonuniform motion of spherical particles in a nonuniformly moving medium [obtained after substituting the expressions for F' and F" in Eq. (4.1)] has been found comparatively recently by Chan [278, 122].

§5. Vibration of Aerosol Particles

If the particles suspended in a vibrating gas are quite small, they are carried along with the motion. The degree to which any particular particle is carried along [by which we mean the ratio of the amplitude (or velocity) of the vibrations in the medium], depends in an essential way on the physical constants of the particle in the medium. The exact theoretical solution of this problem was first given by Köning in [214]. Later, this question was touched upon briefly by Sewell in an appendix to [265]. The problem has also been discussed by S.M.Rytov, V. V. Vladimirskii, and M. D. Galanin in [108]. The problem as applied to actual aerosols undergoing coagulation in an acoustic field has been reviewed anew by Brandt, Freund, and Hiedemann in [167]. A throughgoing analysis of the problem of vibrations of aerosol particles in a sound field is given in the monograph by N. A. Fuks [121], some additions and corrections to which are to be found in the review [122] by the same author.

Let us set up the corresponding equation for the motion of an aerosol particle. The "static" force acting on the particle is, in this case, the force due to the pressure gradient present in the medium. It may easily be seen that the magnitude of the force is completely independent of the density of the particle itself. Let us assume that the density of the particle is exactly equal to the density of the medium. In this case, the particle will move as a unit with the medium, which has the velocity u_g. The force that is able to produce such a motion in the particle is equal to the product of the mass of the particle by its acceleration. The mass of our particle is equal to the mass m_g of the medium which it displaces, while the acceleration is equal to the acceleration du_g/dt in the medium, so that the "static" force that we are looking for turns out to be equal to

$$F' = m_g \frac{du_g}{dt} \tag{5.1}$$

For the "kinematic" force, which varies periodically at the frequency ω, we get, in place of the general equation (4.2), the following equation, derived by Stokes ([61], p. 811; [121], p. 85):

$$F'' = - m_g \left(\frac{1}{2} + \frac{9}{4} b \right) \left(\frac{du_p}{dt} - \frac{du_g}{dt} \right) - \frac{9}{4} m_g \omega b (1 + b)(u_p - u_g), \tag{5.2}$$

where

$$b = \frac{1}{r} \sqrt{\frac{2\nu}{\omega}} = \frac{\delta}{r} \; . $$

(in place of the absolute particle velocity occurring in [61] and [121], we have here only the relative velocity between the particle and the medium).

The equation of motion of the particle in the vibrating medium, using (5.1) and (5.2), is of the form

$$m_p \frac{du_p}{dt} = \frac{3}{2} m_g \frac{du_g}{dt} - \frac{1}{2} m_g \frac{du_p}{dt} - \frac{9}{4} m_g \omega b (1 + b)(u_p - u_g) - \frac{9}{4} m_g b \left(\frac{du_p}{t} - \frac{du_g}{dt} \right) . \tag{5.3}$$

We introduce the notation:

$$M = m_p + \frac{9}{4} m_g b \quad (M - \text{reduced mass})$$

$$\frac{1}{B} = \frac{9}{4} m_g \omega b (1 + b) = \frac{9}{4} m_g \omega b + 6 \pi \eta r \quad (B - \text{ reduced mobility}).$$

Substituting these values and neglecting the term $\frac{1}{2} mg \, du_p/dt$ (since $mg \ll m_p$), we obtain

$$M \frac{du_p}{dt} + \frac{u_p}{B} = \frac{9}{4} m_g \omega b (1 + b) u_g + \left(\frac{9}{4} m_g b + \frac{3}{2} m_g \right) \frac{du_g}{dt} . \tag{5.4}$$

If the vibrations in the medium are given by the equation

$$u_g = U_g \sin \omega t, \tag{5.5}$$

Eq. (5.4), after performing the necessary algebra, takes the form

$$M \frac{du_p}{dt} + \frac{u_p}{B} = \frac{3}{2} m_g \omega U_g \sqrt{1 + 3b + \frac{9}{2} b^2 + \frac{9}{2} b^3 + \frac{9}{4} b^4} \sin (\omega t + \theta), \tag{5.6}$$

where

$$\theta = \arctan \frac{2/3 + b}{b (1 + b)} \; . \tag{5.7}$$

The solution of this equation is as follows [39]:

$$u_p = U_g \sqrt{\frac{1 + 3b + \frac{9}{2}b^2 + \frac{9}{2}b^3 + \frac{9}{4}b^4}{a^2 + 3ab + \frac{9}{2}b^2 + \frac{9}{2}b^3 + \frac{9}{4}b^4}} \sin [\omega t - (\varphi - \theta)], \tag{5.8}$$

where

$$a = \frac{2}{3}\frac{m_p}{m_g} + \frac{1}{3} \approx \frac{2}{3}\frac{\rho_p}{\rho_g}.$$

For $\sin [\omega t - (\varphi - \theta)] = 1$ the particle reaches its maximum velocity $u_p = U_p$, from which it follows that the degree of entrainment of the particle is given by the equation

$$\mu_p = \frac{U_p}{U_g} = \sqrt{\frac{1 + 3b + \frac{9}{2}b^2 + \frac{9}{2}b^3 + \frac{9}{4}b^4}{a^2 + 3ab + \frac{9}{2}b^2 + \frac{9}{2}b^3 + \frac{9}{4}b^4}}. \tag{5.9}$$

The phase shift between the oscillations of the particle and those in the medium is

$$\tan (\varphi - \theta) = \frac{\frac{3}{2}(a - 1)(b + b^2)}{a\left(1 + \frac{3}{2}b\right) + \frac{3}{2}b + \frac{9}{2}b^2 + \frac{9}{2}b^3 + \frac{9}{4}b^4}. \tag{5.10}$$

Thus we see that the expressions obtained from an exact solution to the problem of the vibrations of aerosol particles are extremely unwieldy and not very easy to grasp, so that it is anything but clear how the degree of entrainment of the particles and the phase shift in the vibrations are related to the physical constants of the particle and the medium. It is accordingly very useful to have the approximate solution of the problem as given by Brandt, Freund, and Hiedemann, which, let us hasten to add, gives an accuracy that is perfectly good enough for practical purposes. In the approximate solution of the problem, when setting up the equation of motion of the aerosol particles, we limit ourselves to the viscous force as given by Stokes' equation (4.3):

$$m_p \frac{du_p}{dt} = 6\pi\eta r (u_g - u_p). \tag{5.11}$$

By using (5.5) and (4.4), we obtain the following equation:

$$\tau \frac{du_p}{dt} + u_p = U_g \sin \omega t. \tag{5.12}$$

The general solution of this equation is of the form [39]

$$u_p = \frac{U_g \sin (\omega t - \varphi)}{\sqrt{1 + \omega^2\tau^2}} + \frac{\omega\tau U_g}{1 + \omega^2\tau^2} e^{-\frac{t}{\tau}}, \tag{5.13}$$

37

while the phase shift angle φ is given by the equation

$$\tan \varphi = \omega \tau. \tag{5.14}$$

That there is a phase shift between the vibrations in the medium and those of the particle it is carrying along is accounted for physically by the fact that all particles have inertia, with the result that they are carried along in the motion of the medium with a certain amount of retardation, as measured by the angle φ. The second, aperiodic term in Eq. (5.13), corresponding to the initial transient stage of the vibrations, approaches zero rapidly, so that the vibrations of the particle follow the equation

$$u_p = \frac{U_g}{\sqrt{1 + \omega^2\tau^2}} \sin(\omega t - \varphi). \tag{5.15}$$

Hence it follows that the degree (or coefficient) of entrainment of the particle in the vibration of the medium is given by the expression[*]

$$\mu_p = \frac{U_p}{U_g} = \frac{A_p}{A_g} = \frac{1}{\sqrt{1 + \omega^2\tau^2}} . \tag{5.16}$$

The equation for the vibrations of the particle in this case is of the form

$$u_p = \mu_p U_g \sin(\omega t - \varphi). \tag{5.17}$$

Note that the factor μ_p is nothing but the cosine of the phase shift angle between the vibrations of the particle and those in the medium

$$\mu_p = \cos \varphi, \tag{5.18}$$

as may easily be seen from (5.14).

If we substitute the expression (4.4) in Eqs. (5.16) and (5.14), and bear in mind that $\omega = 2\pi f$, we obtain the following general equations:

$$\mu_p = \frac{1}{\sqrt{1 + \left(\frac{4\pi\rho_p r^2 f}{9\eta}\right)^2}} , \tag{5.19}$$

$$\tan \varphi = \frac{4\pi\rho_p r^2 f}{9\eta} . \tag{5.20}$$

_____

[*]It has been pointed out by the author that this equation, like (5.19), may also be found from Köning's formula (5.9) if some of the terms are neglected. Thus, as long as μ_p is nearly unity, all of the terms in the equation may be neglected in comparison with b^4. If μ_p becomes less than unity, the value of b^2 begins to approach the value of a in order of magnitude. Then, all the terms except a^2 and b^4 may be neglected in the first approximation. In this case the Köning formula takes the form (5.16) or (5.19). It continues to hold until μ_p becomes equal to about 0.5, at which neglecting the term $3ab$ leads to appreciable errors.

In the author's opinion, below this limit, some doubt is cast on the validity of the theoretical assumptions on which Köning's formula is based. From their observations, as soon as the particles coagulate to a size where the amplitude of the vibrations drops to several tenths of the amplitude of the vibrations in the gas, the particles suddenly stop vibrating altogether and move along irregular, often sharply bent paths (spherical particles exhibit zigzag trajectories, while the others have spiral trajectories).

If the particles are very small (r < 1μ), η/Cu must be used in these equations instead of η, Cu being the Cunningham correction factor for the discrete properties of the medium, defined as Cu = (1 + A l_m/r (where A is a coefficient, and l_m is the mean free path of the molecules in the gas [121]). For droplets with r = 1μ, Cu = 1.086, and for r = 0.1μ, Cu = 1.86 (Cunningham's formula does not hold for smaller values of r).

It follows from Eq. (5.19) as derived by Brandt, Freund, and Hiedemann [167] that if particles are suspended in a vibrating gas, they follow more closely after the vibrations in the medium, the smaller the radius and density of the particles, the higher the viscosity in the medium, and the lower the frequency of the vibrations.

For the same physical properties in the particle and the medium (ρ_p and η = const), the degree of entrainment of the particles is determined by the product $r^2 f$.

Figure 15 shows graphically how the degree of entrainment of particles of density ρ_p = 1 varies with radius in air at different frequencies. It may be clearly seen from the graph that for each frequency there are small particles which practically follow the vibrations of the medium completely ($\mu_p \approx 1$), and large particles which are scarcely carried along at all by the vibrating medium ($\mu_p \to 0$). Absolutely complete entrainment of the suspended particles by the vibration of the medium is, however, not possible, since the particles are carried along in the motion principally as a result of viscous forces which only show up when motion with respect to the medium occurs.

The difference between the degree of entrainment calculated from the simplified formula (5.19) and that obtained from the exact equation (5.9) is usually small. This is illustrated by Fig. 16, taken from N. A. Fuks' monograph [121], in which the solid line 1 shows the degree of entrainment μ_p as a function of the ratio τ/T, as found from the exact formula (5.9), while the dotted line is that obtained from the simplified formula (5.19). The same graph shows a curve of the amount of flow around the particle, μ_g (see below). At the bottom of the graph are shown the values of r $\sqrt{\omega}$ corresponding to the values of τ/T.

The maximum difference for a range of τ/T = 0.2-2, is not greater than 4% in either case.

Figure 17 gives a graphical representation of the phase shift (lag) angle between the vibrations of the particles and those in air, for the same frequencies. If the particles are completely carried along in the vibration of the medium, the phase shift is equal to zero, while if the particles are not carried along in the motion, the phase shift reaches π/2.

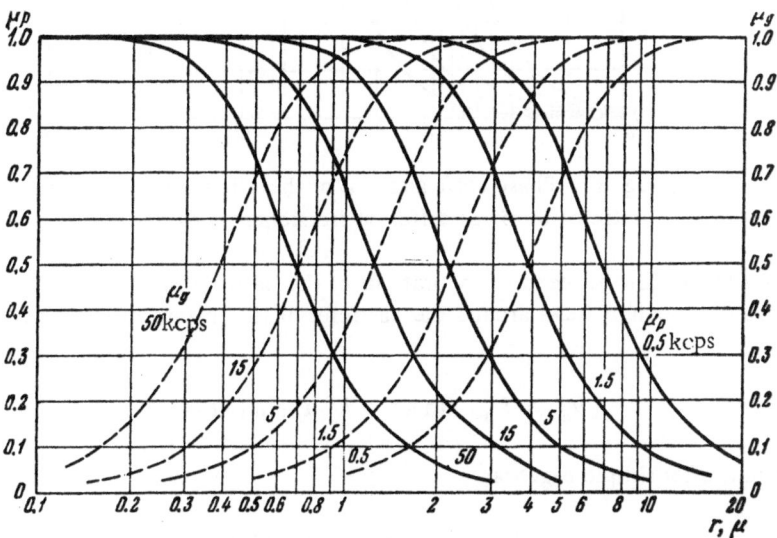

Fig. 15. μ_p, degree of entrainment, and μ_g, degree of flow around aerosol particles in air at different frequencies (ρ_p = 1 g/cm³).

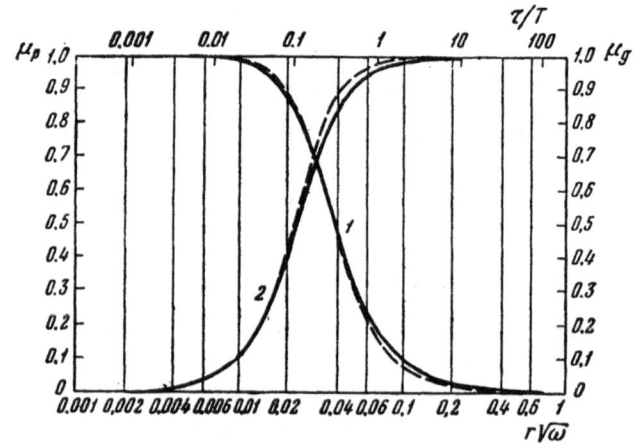

Fig. 16. Degree of entrainment and amount of flow around aerosol particles in air as a function of the ratio τ/T (ρ_p = 1 g/cm³). 1) Degree of entrainment of particles; 2) amount of flow around particles.

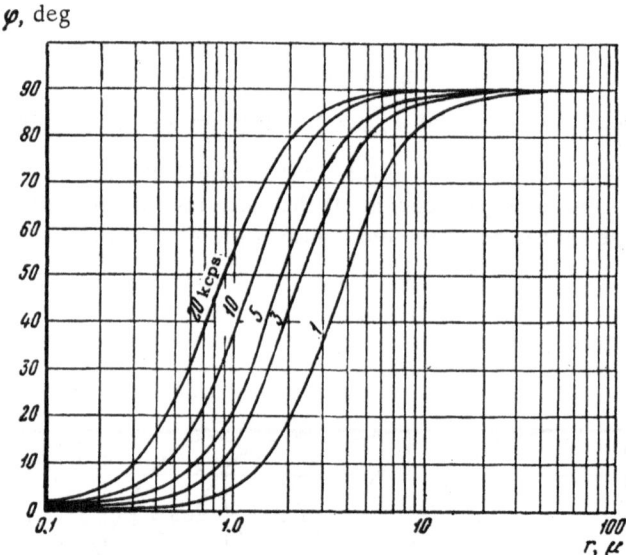

Fig. 17. Phase shift angle φ of the vibrations of aerosol particles in air at different frequencies (ρ_p = 1 g/cm³).

Since there is a phase shift between the vibrations of the particle and vibrations in the medium, the velocity u_{gp} at which the medium flows around the particles at the instant of t is given by the following equation:

$$u_{gp} = U_g \cdot \sin \omega t - U_g \mu_p \sin (\omega t - \varphi). \qquad (5.21)$$

From (5.18), we obtain, after simple algebra:

$$u_{gp} = \mu_g U_g \cos (\omega t - \varphi), \qquad (5.22)$$

where u_g is the flow-around factor of the medium around the particle, equal to

$$\mu_g = \sin \varphi = \frac{\omega\tau}{\sqrt{1+\omega^2\tau^2}}. \tag{5.23}$$

The maximum velocity of the medium flowing around the particle is

$$U_{gp} = \mu_g U_g. \tag{5.24}$$

Values for the flow-around factor of the particles at different frequencies are shown by the dotted line in Fig. 15. We are struck by the fact that the flow-around factor μ_g is of quite appreciable magnitude even for the finest particles where the degree of entrainment $\mu_p \to 1$. For $\omega\tau \ll 1$, the flow-around factor is equal to

$$\mu_g \approx \omega\tau. \tag{5.25}$$

It may be shown that large particles for which $\omega\tau \gg 1$, do not remain completely at rest, but are carried along in the vibration of the medium to the following extent:

$$\mu_p \approx (\omega\tau)^{-1}. \tag{5.26}$$

There is a simple relation between the entrainment factor μ_p and the flow-around factor μ_g of the particle, thus:

$$\mu_g = \omega\tau\mu_p, \tag{5.27}$$

$$\mu_p^2 + \mu_g^2 = 1. \tag{5.28}$$

All the above is illustrated for clarity of presentation in Fig. 18. The heavy curve represents the sinusoidal time variation of the velocity in the vibration of the air (which is the same as the motion of the finest particles with $\mu_p = 1$). The light curve is the vibratory motion of a suspended particle where the degree of entrainment is $\mu_p = 0.8$, which lags behind the vibration of the medium at a phase shift angle of $\varphi = \arccos \mu_p \approx 34.4°$. The dotted curve is the relative velocity of the medium flowing around the particle with the flow-around factor given in this case by $\mu_g = (1-\mu_p^2)^{1/2} = 0.6$. This velocity leads the motion of the particle by an angle of 90°, so that the phase shift with respect to the vibration of the medium is $\varphi - 90° = -53.13°$.

Equations (5.9) and (5.19) have been satisfactorily confirmed experimentally. Qualitative confirmation has been found repeatedly in many experiments. Figure 19 shows microphotographs from the paper Brandt, Freund, and Hiedemann [168, 171], made with an exposure considerably greater than the period of vibration of the gas. The picture shows droplets of a paraffin oil fog in a 10 kcps sound field. It may be seen that the largest particles remain at rest ($\mu_p = 0$) in the field, while the small particles ($r < 1\mu$), on the other hand, take an active part in the vibratory motion of the medium, as shown by the fact that they leave longitudinal traces ("tracks"), equal to twice the amplitude of the vibrations they are executing.

The first, relatively crude qualitative confirmation of Eqs. (5.9) and (5.19) for the degree to which aerosol particles are carried along in the vibratory motion of the medium was obtained by Wagenschein [283], who measured the amplitude of the vibrations of lycopodium spores ($r = 15.85\,\omega$, $\rho_p = 1.1$) at a frequency of 85 cps for vibrations with amplitudes of from 0.58 to 2.40 mm. The vibrations in the medium were set up by Zernov's method: a light air-tight vessel containing the aerosol was fastened to the vibrating prong of a tuning fork, excited electromagnetically. The amplitude of vibration of the vessel and together with it of the gas, and the amplitude of vibration of the particles were photographed through a microscope. The choice of lycopodium spores for use in the study was fortunate, because they have little ridges on the surface that cut down the mobility of the particles. For this reason, the experimental results at first differed as much as 25-30% from the theory, and it was only after correcting for the mobility of the particles from their rate of free fall that the difference came down to 5%.

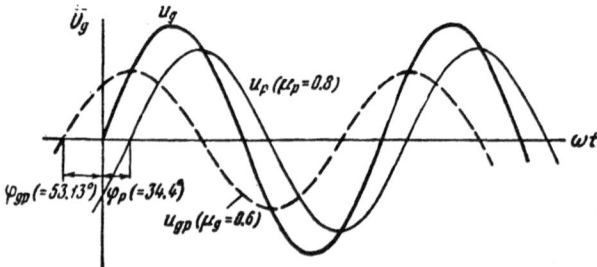

Fig. 18. Graph showing the phase difference between the absolute particle velocity in the medium (u_g), the absolute velocity of the aerosol particle (u_p) and the relative velocity (u_{gp}) between the particle and the medium.

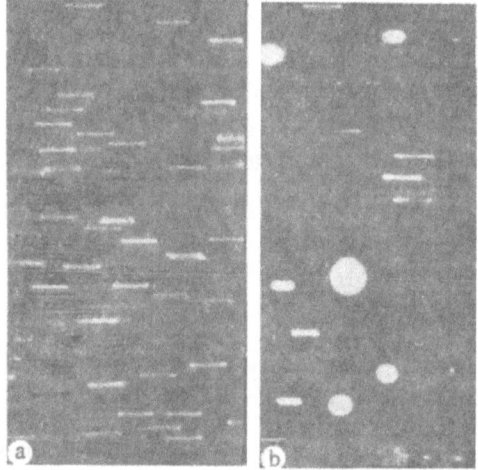

Fig. 19. Photographs illustrating the difference in the degree to which aerosol particles (paraffin oil fog droplets) are carried along in the vibration of the medium (f = 10 kcps, exposure time 1/250 sec, X 80). a) Particles of radii 0.3-0.6μ; b) particles of radii from 0.3-4.5μ. [Trans. Faraday Soc., 32 (184):1101-1110 (1936); Z. Physik, Nos. 7-8:511-533 (1937).]

Experiments have been set up in recent years to find the degree to which particles are entrained at higher frequencies approximating those used in acoustic coagulation of aerosols (the final goal of these experiments was to develop an acoustic method for finding the distribution in dispersion of aerosols). As such, we have the preliminary experiments of Cassel and Schultz [175] and the detailed experiments of Gucker and Doyle [198].

Figure 20 gives a comparison between the experimental results of Gucker and Doyle and the theoretical data. The results were obtained in experiments on dioctylphthalate (DOP and 39H "Fleksol" fog droplets) with radii of from 0.8 to 3.9ω, at a frequency of 4.85 kcps, the sound being produced by a St. Clair electrodynamic vibrator. The amplitude of the particle vibrations was measured microphotographically at a standing wave maximum. The particle dimensions were measured by observing the rate of fall microphotographically and then applying Stokes' formula with Cunningham's correction. It may be seen from Fig. 20 that the experiments are in good agreement with theory.

In conclusion, we shall stop briefly to consider the stability of aerosol particles in a vibrating gas. It is well known that behind some obstacles in a gas stream, in particular suspended rods and wedges, a vortex system is formed which pulls loose alternately from each side of the obstacle, and, under certain conditions, can lead to loss of stability and produce transverse vibrations in the body. A similar phenomenon, of an auto-oscillational nature [125], is also observed in spherical obstacles in a gas stream [114], in that a vortex state is formed behind them as might be expected.

It was pointed out in the footnote on page 38 that aerosol particles with a strong sound field flowing around them execute a certain type of random motion with a transverse component of velocity.

Now isn't this the result of the suspended particles becoming unstable in an acoustic stream?

The theory shows that in a stream moving forward with the Reynolds number Re, loss of stability occurs for the condition [111]

$$\mathrm{Re} > \frac{9}{2}\left(\frac{h}{r}\right)^2 \frac{1}{\sqrt{k_2(1-k_2)}}, \qquad (5.29)$$

where h is the width of the stream, and k_2 is a dimensionless factor which is not greater than unity.

It will be shown in §9 that the flow around aerosol particles in an acoustic field is of a quasi-steady state, from which it follows that the inequality (5.29) also holds for our purposes. It may be concluded from the

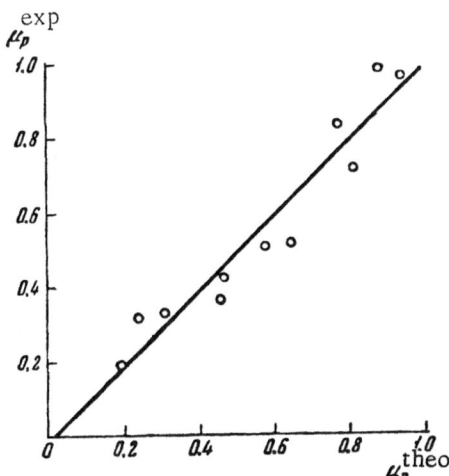

Fig. 20. Experimental values for the degree of entrainment of dioctylphthal-ate fog droplets (from Gucker and Doyle).

inequality that suspended particles only become unstable for $Re \gtrsim 10^7$, which is impossible in an acoustic field.

Hence, the reason for the random motion of aerosol particles in an acoustic field must be sought in other phenomena which we shall take up in their proper place.

§ 6. Drift of Aerosol Particles

During vibratory motion of particles suspended in a vibrating gas, the particles execute a certain translational motion, or "drift," with respect to the medium in the longitudinal direction.

There are at least five factors which tend to make aerosol particles drift in an acoustic field:

1. The radiation pressure exerted by the sound on the particles,
2. Periodic change in viscosity of the vibrating medium,
3. Difference in phase of the vibrations of particles in the medium in a sound wave,
4. Distortion of the sound wave, and
5. Asymmetry in the vibration of the medium in a standing sound wave.

In addition to the above factors, drift of aerosol particles in an acoustic field is also favored by the presence of other particles having a well developed boundary layer, which, however, is random in nature and so will not be considered here.

Drift Due to the Radiation Pressure of Sound on the Particles. This type of particle drift was the only one known for a long time, and it was evaluated quantitatively by means of King's equation for the radiation pressure exerted on a stationary spherical obstacle of arbitrary density, the radius of which is much less than the wavelength: $kr \ll 1$. From King [212], we have, in a traveling wave:

$$F_R = 4 (kr)^4 (\pi r^2) G (\rho_g/\rho_p) E, \tag{6.1}$$

and in a standing wave:

$$F_R = 2 (kr) (\pi r^2) G (\rho_g/\rho_p) E \sin 2kx_0, \tag{6.2}$$

where k is the wave number and $G(\rho_g/\rho_p)$ is the density factor given by the expression

$$G (\rho_g/\rho_p) = \left[1 + \frac{2}{3} (1 - \rho_g/\rho_p) \right] / (2 + \rho_g/\rho_p)$$

(for aerosol particles, in which $\rho_p \gg \rho_g$, $G(\rho_g/\rho_p) \simeq 5/6$); here x_0 is the distance to the nearest vibration node in the standing wave.

The method by which these equations were derived was to make an exact solution of the problem of flow around a spherical body in an acoustic field. The viscosity and heat conductivity of the medium were not taken into consideration.

The method used later on by Westervelt [286] as well as by L. D. Landau and E. M. Lifshits [62] is simpler and clearer. The essence of this method is as follows.

If a sound wave encounters some body in its path of propagation, it is reflected and scattered in all directions when it strikes the body. In this case, the scattered wave may be regarded simply as a wave radiated by the body. The momentum transferred to the body by the incident wave is greater than the momentum scattered by the body in the direction of propagation of the incident wave. Hence a certain excess force occurs which is related to the radiation pressure forces in an acoustic field.

An energy flux is scattered from the incident sound wave equal to $\Pi_s c_g E$, where Π_s is the so-called total effective cross section, by which we mean the ratio of the total scattering intensity to the energy density in the incident energy flux, for which, with particles carried along in the vibratory motion of the medium, we must substitute the quantity $E_{gp} = \frac{1}{2} \rho_g U_{gp}^2 = \mu_g^2 \overline{E}$ ($\overline{E}$ is absolute energy density equal to J/c_g).

The momentum flux in the incident sound wave is $\Pi_s E_{gp}$, and, in a scattered wave, within the solid angle $d\theta$, is $E_s r^2 d\theta = E_{gp} d\Pi_s$. If we project this latter quantity onto the direction of the propagation of the incident wave, we have:

$$F_R = E_{gp} \int_0^\pi (1 - \cos\theta)\, d\Pi_s \tag{6.3}$$

(θ is the angle between the direction of the incident wave and the direction of scattering).

The effective differential cross section, from [62], is

$$d\Pi_s = \frac{1}{9}\left(\frac{\omega}{c_g}\right)^4 r^6 \left(1 - \frac{3}{2}\cos\theta\right) d\theta.$$

Substituting this expression in (6.3) and integrating, we obtain the following value for the radiation drift force acting on a sphere in a traveling sound wave:[*]

$$F_R = \frac{11}{9}\pi\left(\frac{\omega}{c_g}\right)^4 r^6 \mu_g^2 \overline{E}. \tag{6.4}$$

Maidanek [230], and then L. P. Gor'kov [27] solved the problem in a more general form (including the compressibility of the sphere and the refraction of the incident wave at the surface) which leads to exactly the same expression in the case of aerosol particles.

If we compare the equation (6.4) just derived with Eq. (6.1), it is not difficult to see that they only differ by a numerical coefficient, which is a factor of approximately 2.7 greater in King's equation. The force F_R is in the same direction in both cases, namely, in the direction of propagation of the sound wave.

The radiation drift force is many orders of magnitude higher in a standing wave field. In calculating the force, account must be taken of the momentum in both the forward and the back wave, the values of which depend on where the sphere is located in the sound field. In the final count, we get the following equation for the radiation pressure force on a sphere in a standing-wave field:

$$F_R = \frac{8}{3}\pi\left(\frac{\omega}{c_g}\right) r^3 \mu_g^2 \overline{E} \sin 2kx_0. \tag{6.5}$$

---

[*]Westervelt in his paper [286] instead of the expression for the drift force F, gives in all the cases that he discusses, the expression for the reduced specific pressure $F/\pi r^2 \overline{E}$, which he designates with the subscript d, and calls the "resistance coefficient." This parameter is of some interest in getting comparative values of different types of drift, but it is not good enough for calculating them in practice, since it does not include a value for the amount of flow μ_g around the particles.

This expression (but without the factor μ_g) was first obtained by Westervelt in [286]. The problem was recently solved in more general form by L. P. Gor'kov [27] who, however, found a 25% higher value for the numerical coefficient ahead of the formula.

If we compare Eq. (6.5) with King's equation (6.2), it is easily seen that they are identical. The only difference is in the numerical coefficient, which is a factor of 1.6 greater in the first case than in the second, which is the case that received experimental confirmation in Rudik's work [258] on cork spheres of radius $r \sim 1$ mm, suspended on threads in a standing sound wave field at a frequency of 400-2800 cps.

It may be seen from (6.5) that the radiation pressure force on the aerosol particles in a standing sound wave is a function of the coordinates of the particles. The force F_R is equal to zero in the vibration nodes ($x_0 = 0$, $\lambda/2$, and λ) as well as in the loops ($x_0 = \lambda/4$ and $3\lambda/4$). However, the particles are in a stable position in a node, while they are in an unstable position in a loop. The maximum value of the force F_R occurs halfway between a node and a loop, i.e, for $x_0 = \lambda/8$, $3\lambda/8$, $5\lambda/8$, and $72/8$.

Let us find an expression for the radiation drift velocity of an aerosol particle. Since we are talking about translation motion of the particle, any changes in which require a length of time enormous in comparison with the relaxation time of the particle, it may be assumed that the radiation pressure force F_R, as given by Eqs. (6.4) or (6.5), is, at any instant of time, in equilibrium with the resistive force of the medium, as given by Stokes' equation $F_{St} = 6\pi\eta r V_R$. Hence, we obtain, for any traveling wave:

$$V_R = \frac{11}{54\eta} \left(\frac{\omega}{c_g}\right)^4 r^5 \mu_g^2 \overline{E} \qquad (6.6)$$

and, for a standing wave:

$$V_R = \frac{4}{9\eta} \left(\frac{\omega}{c_g}\right) r^2 \mu_g^2 \overline{E} \sin 2kx_0 \qquad (6.7)$$

In the first case, the particle executes a uniform motion, while in the second case, the motion is nonuniform, following the equation

$$\tan kx = e^{Bt} \tan kx_0. \qquad (6.8)$$

where

$$B = \frac{8}{9\eta} (kr)^2 \mu_g^2 \overline{E}.$$

Equation (6.8), first derived by St. Clair [179, 180], is easily arrived at if we integrate Eq. (6.7) with the initial condition $x = x_0$ at $t = 0$.

All the above equations hold if the following two conditions are satisfied:

First, the amplitude of the vibrations of the medium are small in comparison with the radius of the sphere (since otherwise the motion of the medium would cease to be of potential type).

Second, the viscous energy losses in the sound field in the boundary layer surrounding the sphere are comparatively small (since otherwise the sound wave would not get to the surface of the sphere and could not be scattered there). According to [61], the fraction of the acoustic energy absorbed in the boundary layer of a small sphere ($kr \ll 1$) is $6\nu/c_g r$ per cm^2 of cross section of the sphere. Hence it follows that the second condition is satisfied as long as we have the following inequalities:

$$\frac{11}{9} (kr)^4 > 6\nu/c_g r \qquad (6.9a)$$

45

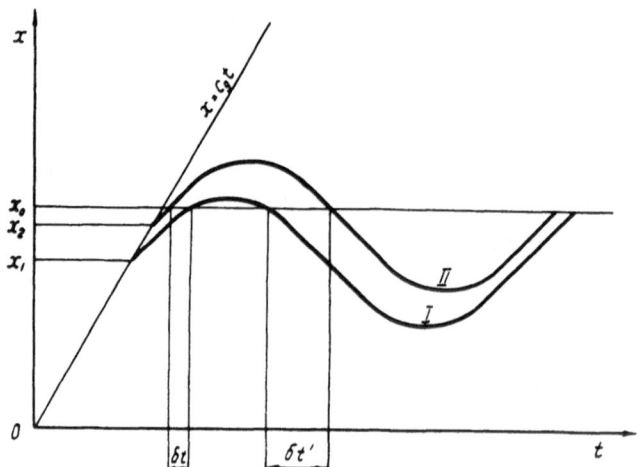

Fig. 21. Space-time diagram, illustrating how a resultant velocity occurs in the particles of the medium at a fixed point in a sound field.

for a traveling wave, and

$$\frac{8}{3}(kr) > 6v/c_g r \qquad (6.9b)$$

for a standing wave.

For air at a frequency of f = 10 kcps this gives: $r > 700\mu$ in a traveling wave, and $r > 25\mu$ in a standing wave. At lower frequencies, the dimensions of the aerosol particles will be even greater.

Hence, in the smaller sized primary particles of aerosols undergoing coagulation, the energy of the incident wave is not so much scattered as absorbed in the viscous boundary layer surrounding the particles. The result of this is to produce new types of drift, as discussed below. But radiation drift is only experienced by highly consolidated aerosol particles in a standing-wave field.

Drift Due to Periodic Change in Viscosity of the Medium. The adiabatic compression and rarefaction of the medium occurring in a sound field results in periodically raising and lowering the temperature of the medium. It is not difficult to show from the adiabatic equation pv$^\gamma$ = const and the perfect gas equation pv = R$_g$T that if the sound pressure is changing sinusoidally so that the pressure at the point in question in the medium varies according to the law p = P$_{st}$ + P$_g$ sin ωt, the absolute temperature of the medium changes, to a first approximation, in the following way:

$$T \approx T_0 \left(1 + \frac{\gamma - 1}{\gamma} \frac{P_g}{P_{st}} \sin \omega t \right), \qquad (a)$$

where T_0 is the absolute temperature of the medium in the surrounding space at the static pressure P_{st}.

For a sound intensity of J = 0.1-1.0 W/cm^2, which corresponds to P_g/P_{st} = 0.009-0.030, the temperature of the air (γ = 1.4) changes, under normal conditions, by the amount $\Delta T = \pm 0.75$-2.5°C between compression and rarefaction.

This large change in temperature produces a corresponding change in the viscosity of a gas. For perfect gases (in the thermodynamic sense), there is a simple relation between the temperature and the viscosity, thus:

$$\eta \sim T^{1/2}. \qquad (b)$$

46

This relation is easily arrived at if we recall the following two equations from the kinetic theory of gases:

$$\eta = \frac{1}{3} \, \rho_g l_m v_m, \tag{c}$$

$$\frac{m_m v_m^2}{2} = \frac{3}{2} k_B T \tag{d}$$

where m_m, v_m, and l_m are the averaged values of the mass, velocity, and mean free path of the molecules in the gas, and k_B is Boltzmann's constant.

From (a) and (b) above, we can write the following expression for the instantaneous viscosity of the medium at the instant of time t:

$$\eta = \eta_0 \left(1 + \frac{\gamma - 1}{2\gamma} \, \frac{P_g}{P_{st}} \, \sin \omega t \right). \tag{6.10}$$

It may be seen from this expression that the viscosity of the medium increases in compression, where the temperature is rising, while the viscosity of the medium decreases in rarefaction, where the temperature is dropping. The difference in viscosity of the medium between compression and rarefaction means that in the two half periods of the vibration, the forces exerted by the medium on a suspended particle in accordance with Stokes' law are definitely different.

This factor in the drift of aerosol particles in a sound field was first noted by Westervelt in [285], but it was dealt with in conjunction with the next factor, so that it did not receive proper treatment.

If an aerosol particle is not carried along at all in the vibrations of the medium, the drift force F_η acting on the particle is easily found by simply substituting Eq. (6.10) in Stokes' equation (4.3), using (1.8) and (1.10), and then averaging (4.3) over a period of the vibrations.

In the more general case where the particle is partly carried along by the vibrations of the medium, the same thing is done after first replacing the absolute velocity of the medium U_g by the relative velocity U_{gp}, which is equal to $\mu_g U_g$. This gives the following result:

$$F_\eta = 3\pi \, (\gamma - 1) \, \frac{\nu}{c_g} \, r \mu_g^2 \, \overline{E}. \tag{6.11}$$

By setting this expression equal to the resistive force $F_{St} = 6\pi r V_\eta$, we obtain a formula for the drift velocity of aerosol particles due to periodic viscosity changes in the medium:

$$V_\eta = \frac{\gamma - 1}{2\rho_g c_g} \, \mu_g^2 \, \overline{E}. \tag{6.12}$$

In a standing sound wave, averaging Stokes' equation gives the value zero, which means that the above type of aerosol particle drift is absent in this case. It has been tacitly assumed in the derivation that the instantaneous temperature of the particle follows the temperature of the medium.

Drift Due to Difference in Phase in the Vibrations of the Particles in the Medium in a Sound Wave. This type of aerosol particle drift in a sound field was found theoretically, along with the preceding type, in the paper by Westervelt [285]* while making a study of the mean static pressure and the mean velocity of the gas particles in a plane sound wave. This work took account of the fact that a change occurs in the coordinates of the vibrating particles in the medium in a sound wave, for finite vibration amplitudes. It was shown by transforming the coordinates from Lagrange to Euler form that the mean static pressure and the mean velocity of the particles in the medium at a fixed point in space differ from zero by some finite amount, so that an aerosol particle suspended in the medium experiences a unidirectional force, which causes it to drift.

Without reference to the problem of aerosol particle motion in a sound field, the question of mean values in acoustics — velocity, density, pressure, and temperature — is also treated in detail in the paper by A.A. Éikhenval'd [133] on large amplitude sound waves. The method of finding the mean values used in this paper, which are essentially identical, are extremely simple and easy to visualize, so that we shall use the method in our subsequent mathematical derivations.

However, before we go any further, let us stop to consider the physical meaning of the resultant velocity of the medium found at a fixed point in space for large amplitude vibrations.

For this purpose, we shall use the space-time diagram given in [285], which shows how the particles in the medium move in a traveling sound wave, as visualized by Fey (Fig. 21). The letters x_1 and x_2 in the diagram are the initial (equilibrium) coordinates of the two particles 1 and 2 in the medium, vibrating in the vicinity of some fixed point x_0 in space. Because of the fact that the sound wave propagates at finite velocity, the vibrations of particles 1 and 2 are displaced in time by the amount $\delta t = (x_2 - x_1)/c_g$. The vibrations of particle 1 describe the sinusoid I, while the vibrations of particle 2 describe the sinusoid II, the origin of which is displaced along the straight line $x = c_g t$.

It may be concluded from the diagram that for any particle in the medium passing through the point x_0 the linear velocity is the same whether going forward or backward (since the slopes of the tangents at the point x_0 are the same for both the rising and falling branches of the appropriate sinusoid). This means that there is no steady gas flow through the point x_0.

It may however be seen from the same diagram that when the particles in the medium between x_1 and x_2 are moving backward, they take a somewhat longer time to pass through the fixed point x_0 in space, than when they are moving forward, i.e., $\delta t' > \delta t$. This is equivalent to the medium having a resultant velocity of the point x_0, in the opposite direction to the direction of propagation of the sound wave.

Let us find the magnitude of the resultant velocity. In solving the problem, we shall proceed directly from the general solution of the wave equation (1.7), which describes the motion in time and space of a particle in the medium in a traveling sound wave:

$$u_g = U_g \sin \omega \left(t - \frac{x_0}{c_g} \right). \tag{6.13}$$

If the vibrations of the medium are of large amplitude, and the equation is to be kept in the Euler form, we must replace the fixed coordinate x_0 by $x - a_g$, where x is the variable coordinate of the particle in the medium in question at the instant t, and a_g is the displacement of the particle from its equilibrium position x_0.

In this case, Eq. (6.13) takes the form:

$$u_g = U_g \sin \omega \left(t - \frac{x - a_g}{c_g} \right). \tag{6.13'}$$

---

*In a subsequent paper by Westervelt [286], as well as in the book by Hueter and Bolt [205] and review [140], the two types of aerosol drift taken together are given the name "Stokes type drift," and are mistakenly considered to be related solely to the periodic viscosity changes in the medium, but the mathematical relations given below make it clear that the difference in phase of the vibrations of the particles in the medium is immeasureably more important.

Expanding this expression in Taylor's series about the equilibrium point x_0, and limiting the expression to the first two terms, we obtain the following expression for the instantaneous velocity of the medium at a fixed point in space:

$$u_g = U_g \sin \omega \left(t - \frac{x_0}{c_g} \right) - \frac{U_g^2}{c_g} \cos^2 \omega \left(t - \frac{x_0}{c_g} \right). \tag{6.13''}$$

Here, we do not take into consideration the periodic change in the velocity of sound c_g, which would be equivalent to taking account of the periodic change in viscosity of the medium ($\eta \sim c_g$, since both c_g and η are $\sim T^{1/2}$).

To get a value for the mean velocity of the medium, we average Eq. (6.13'') over a period of the vibration. The first term in this expression, which changes sign in the second half period, gives the value zero, while the second term which keeps the same sign throughout the whole period, gives the value $1/2$. Hence, we obtain the following expression for the mean velocity of the medium at a fixed point in space:

$$V_\varphi = - \frac{1}{\rho_g c_g} \overline{E}. \tag{6.14}$$

This is the drift velocity of large aerosol particles which are not carried along in the vibrations of the medium (but are completely carried along in the translational motion of the particles in the medium, for which see §7).

In the general case, where the aerosol particles are only partly carried along in the vibrations of the medium, the drift velocity, due to difference in phase of the vibrations of the particles in the medium in a traveling sound wave, is given by the expression:

$$V_\varphi = - \frac{\mu_g^2}{\rho_g c_g} \overline{E}. \tag{6.15}$$

Substituting this value in Stokes' formula gives the following equation for the force in this type of aerosol particle drift:

$$F_\varphi = - 6\pi \frac{\nu}{c_g} r \mu_g^2 \overline{E}. \tag{6.16}$$

If Eqs. (6.15) and (6.16) are compared with (6.12) and (6.11) respectively, derived for the previous type of particle drift, they are easily seen to be identical. The only difference is in the sign and magnitude of the coefficient in front of the equations, which is here almost an order of magnitude greater than in the previous case. This means that the previous type of drift cannot exist independently of the type we have just been talking about.

The resultant of the two different types of particle drift may thus be regarded as a single type of drift due to difference in phase of the vibrations of the particles in the medium in a sound wave, but somewhat retarded by the periodic viscosity changes in the medium.

The force and velocity of this combined type of aerosol particle drift in a traveling wave are given by the equations:

$$F_{\eta + \varphi} = - 3\pi (3 - \gamma) \frac{\nu}{c_g} r \mu_g^2 \overline{E}, \tag{6.17}$$

$$V_{\eta + \varphi} = -\frac{3-\gamma}{2\rho_g c_g} \mu_g^2 \, \overline{E}. \tag{6.18}$$

The force and velocity of the combined type of drift, as was to be expected, are in the opposite direction to the direction of propagation of the sound wave.

A characteristic detail is that the velocity of this type of aerosol particle drift only depends on the size of the particles through the flow-around factor μ_g, so that for large particles, which the medium flows around completely ($\mu_g \approx 1$), the drift velocity becomes completely independent of the particle size and the frequency, and takes on its maximum value:

$$V_{\eta + \varphi}^{max} = -\frac{3-\gamma}{2\rho_g c_g} \, \overline{E}. \tag{6.18'}$$

There is no drift of this type nor any of its components in a standing wave.

Drift Due to Distortion (Asymmetry) in the Sound Wave. If a sound wave is distorted so as to have a saw-tooth shape, as shown in Fig. 7, this means that the vibrations of the particles in the medium are not sinusoidal (see Fig. 8). In compression, which we shall call the forward motion (in the direction of the wave), the particles in the medium acquire velocity more rapidly, and, conversely, lose velocity more slowly than when the vibrations are sinusoidal. In rarefaction , where the motion is backward, the opposite phenomenon occurs: the particles in the medium acquire velocity more slowly than they lose it. This cannot help affecting the motion of a particle suspended in the medium.

An aerosol particle is more completely carried along in the motion when the medium is moving backward and the velocity is rising slowly than is the case when the velocity is rising in the "normal" sinusoidal way, and for this reason, the particle takes on a higher velocity. When the velocity in the medium subsequently drops, the particle "slides" somewhat farther than usual past the particles in the medium, since it has a higher momentum. This is also aided by the fact that the velocity of the medium is dropping off more sharply than usual. The opposite occurs when the medium moves forward: the aerosol particle lags behind the particles in the medium by the same amount. As a result, the aerosol particle does not return to its original position after completing one cycle of the vibrations, but stops at a point that is shifted in a direction opposite to the direction of the motion.

Let us find an expression for the drift velocity due to asymmetry in the sound wave. For this purpose, following Westervelt [286, 205], we use the second approximation in Stokes' equation, as given by Oseen:

$$F_{Oc} = 6\pi \eta r u_{gp} \left(1 + \frac{3}{16} \, \mathrm{Re} \right). \tag{6.19}$$

The second term in the correction factor of this equation gives the additional force ΔF which, unlike the mean Stokes' force F_{St}, is related to the velocity of flow around a sphere by the quadratic equation

$$\Delta F = \frac{9}{4} \, \pi r^2 \rho_g \overline{u}_{gp} \, | u_{gp} |, \tag{A}$$

where $\overline{u}_{gp}$ is the velocity vector of the flow, and $|u_{gp}|$ is the absolute value.

If the velocity of the flow around the sphere varies sinusoidally, averaging the force over any half-period of the vibration gives the value zero, from which it follows that the force has no effect on the periodicity of the particle motion. However, if the wave is asymmetrically distorted so as to produce harmonics (see §1), things change: averaging the force ΔF gives an aperiodic unidirectional force F_h.

If we limit our discussion to the second harmonic, we can write for the vibratory velocity of flow around the particle:

$$u_{gp} = \mu_g U_g [\sin \omega t + h_2 \sin (2\omega t + \psi)], \tag{B}$$

where $h_2 = u_2/U_g$ is the relative amplitude of the second harmonic component, and ψ is the phase angle ($\psi = -\pi/2$ in Fig. 7b).

Squaring this expression and substituting in Eq. (A) gives

$$\Delta F = \frac{9}{4} \pi r^2 \rho_g \mu_g^2 U_g^2 [\sin^2 \omega t + 2h_2 \sin \omega t \sin (2\omega t + \psi) + h_2^2 \sin^2 (2\omega t + \psi)]. \tag{C}$$

Averaging the terms in the square brackets over the first half-period gives:

$$\frac{1}{\pi} \int_0^\pi \sin^2 \omega t \, d\,(\omega t) = \frac{1}{2},$$

$$\frac{1}{\pi} \int_0^\pi 2h_2 \sin \omega t \sin (2\omega t + \psi) \, d\,(\omega t) = \frac{4h_2}{3\pi} \sin \psi,$$

$$\frac{1}{\pi} \int_0^\pi h_2^2 \sin^2 (2\omega t + \psi) \, d\,(\omega t) = \frac{h_2^2}{2}.$$

Averaging the same terms over the second half-period (from $\omega t = \pi$ to $\omega t = 2\pi$), where the velocity vector is pointing backward, gives identical results except for the second term, which takes on a negative sign. This shows that only the component of force ΔF associated with this term is in a direction opposite to the velocity vector, i.e., it alone stays in the same direction. As a result, we obtain the unidirectional or drift force:*

$$F_h = -6h_2 \sin \psi r^2 \mu_g^2 \overline{E}. \tag{6.20}$$

The force is in the direction of propagation of the sound wave if the phase shift angle ψ of the second harmonic is negative (as in Fig. 7b) and changes to the opposite direction if the angle ψ is positive, as is usually the case (see Fig. 8).

Setting the drift force (6.20) equal to the resistive force $F_{St} = 6\pi \eta r V_h$ gives the following equation for the drift velocity:

$$V_h = -\frac{h_2 \sin \psi}{\pi \eta} r \mu_g^2 \overline{E}. \tag{6.21}$$

It may be seen that the drift velocity V_h is directly proportional to the degree of distortion in the sound wave and the sine of the phase shift angle of the second harmonic, i.e., to the asymmetry in the wave form.

Getting a mathematical solution of the problem of particle drift in a standing wave presents serious difficulties, due to the fact that the wave form changes with time [133] for vibrations of finite amplitude. It may, however, be concluded from the graph given in [286] that the maximum values of the force F_h and the velocity V_h are of the same order of magnitude in a standing wave as in a traveling wave.

---

*In Westervelt's paper [286], the drift force is called a "force of Oseen type."

<u>Drift Due to Asymmetric Vibration of the Medium in a Standing Wave.</u> A distinctive feature of standing sound waves is, as we know, that the displacement and velocity of the particles in the medium, as well as the sound pressure, are functions of both time and space [see Fig. 1 and Eqs. (1.4)-(1.6)]. In going from a node to a loop, the amplitude of the displacement and the amplitude of the velocity increase sinusoidally with distance from the node. Because of this, if the particles in the medium are displaced toward a loop during vibration, the particles encounter a zone where the amplitudes of the vibrations are higher, while if displaced in the opposite direction, they encounter a zone where the amplitudes of the vibration are lower, as compared with the original amplitude existing at the start of the displacement. In other words, when the particles of the medium are moving toward a loop, they receive a certain amount of acceleration, while in the opposite direction they are somewhat decelerated as compared with the "normal" sinusoidal motion starting at each of the extreme positions. What we have here is asymmetry in the motion of the particles in the medium, due to the finite amplitude of the vibrations.

It is precisely when the aerosol particle is moving toward a loop, where acceleration of the medium occurs, that it lags more behind the motion of the particles of the medium than is the case in sinusoidal motion.

In going in the other direction, where the medium is being decelerated, the aerosol particle gets more ahead of the motion of the particles in the medium than occurs insinusoidal motion.

The result in both cases is that the aerosol particle gets closer to the node than the particles in the medium vibrating with it. The displacement of the aerosol particle with respect to the particles in the medium increases with each cycle of the vibration, and would soon carry the aerosol particle into the node, if it were not being acted upon at the same time by other forces in precisely the opposite direction.

The type of aerosol particle drift just described was predicted theoretically by S. S. Dukhin. A simplified mathematical solution of the problem of drift was given by A. Bagrinovskii in [3]. Recently, S. S. Dukhin got an exact solution of the problem [34]. We shall give both solutions.

To a first approximation, the equation of motion of an aerosol particle in a standing wave field, including (6.2), is of the form:

$$m_p \frac{d^2 x_p}{dt^2} = 6\pi \eta r \left(U_g \sin kx \sin \omega t - \frac{dx_p}{dt} \right), \tag{6.22}$$

or

$$\tau \frac{d^2 x_p}{dt^2} + \frac{dx_p}{dt} = U_g \sin kx \sin \omega t. \tag{6.22'}$$

If, to avoid the difficulties involved in making an exact integration of the equation, we use the approximate integrating formulas

$$\frac{dx_p}{dt} \approx \frac{x_{n+1} - x_n}{\Delta t}, \quad \frac{d^2 x_p}{dt^2} \approx \frac{x_{n+1} - 2x_n + x_{n-1}}{\Delta t^2},$$

Eq. (6.22') gives the following expression for the (n−1)-th ordinate

$$x_{n+1} = \frac{x_n \left(\frac{2\tau}{\Delta t^2} + \frac{1}{\Delta t} \right) + U_g \sin kx_n \sin \omega t - x_{n-1} \frac{\tau}{\Delta t^2}}{\frac{\tau}{\Delta t^2} + \frac{1}{\Delta t}}. \tag{6.23}$$

Using this equation, and fixing the initial conditions for the motion of the aerosol particle, we can successively construct a graph showing the drift of the particle in the absence of other forms of translational motion.

To get an exact solution of the problem of aerosol particle drift, let us, following S. S. Dukhin, consider the second approximation to the equation for the vibrations of the particle. If we bear in mind that the drift of the particle is anharmonic, we can proceed from the general expression (4.2) for the force F'' acting in a viscous medium where the velocity is varying in any arbitrary fashion. This gives the following equation of motion for the aerosol particle:

$$\left(m_p + \frac{m_g}{2}\right)\frac{d^2x_p}{dt^2} + 6\pi\eta r\left(\frac{dx_p}{dt} + \frac{r}{\sqrt{\pi\nu}}\int_{-\infty}^{t}\frac{d^2x_p}{dt_i^2}\frac{dt_i}{\sqrt{t-t_i}}\right) =$$

$$= \frac{3}{2}m_g\frac{d^2x_g}{dt^2} + 6\pi\eta r\left(\frac{dx_g}{dt} + \frac{r}{\sqrt{\pi\nu}}\int_{-\infty}^{t}\frac{d^2x_g}{dt_i^2}\frac{dt_i}{\sqrt{t-t_i}}\right),$$

(6.24)

where x_g and x_p are the distance from a node for the medium and the particle respectively, and $dx_g/dt = U_g \sin kx_0 \sin \omega t$.

Equation (6.24) describes the motion in a rapidly oscillating field, so that it may be solved by P. Kapitsa's method as given in [63]. Since the amplitude A_g of the vibrations is much less than the wavelength, the value of x_g on the right-hand side of the equation may be assumed constant during any one cycle of the vibrations, thus: $x_g = x_0$. In this case, the solution of Eq. (6.24) is the equation for the harmonic motion of a particle about the point $x_p = x_0$, namely:

$$x_p - x_0 = \mu_p A_g \sin kx_0 \cos[\omega t + (\varphi - \theta)],$$

(6.25)

where the degree of entrainment of the particle, μ_p, and the phase shift angel $(\varphi - \theta)$ are determined respectively by Eqs. (5.9) and (5.10) already derived.

The right-hand side of Eq. (6.24) may be regarded as a quasi-periodic force with a slowly varying amplitude of vibration in the medium, under which the particle vibrates, and is at the same time moved somewhat in each cycle, so that in place of the force we may take Stokes' equation (5.2). Since we are only interested in drift of the particle, we average Eq. (5.2) over a cycle of the vibrations. First, we expand $\sin kx_p$ in series about the point x_0:

$$\sin kx_p = \sin kx_0 + k \cos kx_0 (x_p - x_0),$$

(6.26)

where $x_p - x_0$ is given by Eq. (6.25)

After substituting this series in the expressions for u_p and du_p/dt occurring in Eq. (5.2), and averaging it over a period of the vibrations, for which a periodic motion gives the value zero, we get the following equation of motion for the aerosol particle:*

$$\left(m_p + \frac{m_g}{2}\right)\frac{d^2x_0}{dt^2} + 6\pi\eta r\left(\frac{dx_0}{dt} + \frac{r}{\sqrt{\pi\nu}}\int_{-\infty}^{t}\frac{d^2x_0}{dt_i^2}\frac{dt_i}{\sqrt{t-t_i}}\right) =$$

$$= \frac{k}{4}\mu_p U_g^2 m_g\left[\sin(\varphi - \theta)\cdot\frac{9}{4}(b^2+b) - \cos(\varphi-\theta)\left(\frac{3}{2} + \frac{9}{4}b\right)\right]\sin 2kx_0.$$

(6.27)

---

*The equation given in S. S. Dukhin's paper [34] contains an error: m_p is written instead of m_g.

It has already been pointed out that the first and third terms on the left-hand side of this equation are small in comparision with the second term (see §4). As a result, Eq. (6.27) may be written in the following form:

$$6\pi\eta r u_0 = \frac{k}{4}\mu_p U_g^2 \frac{4}{3}\pi r^3 \rho_g \left[\sin(\varphi-\theta)\frac{9}{4}(b^2+b) - \cos(\varphi-\theta)\left(\frac{3}{2}+\frac{9}{4}b\right) \right] \sin 2kx_0. \qquad (6.28)$$

Making use of Eqs. (5.23), (5.18), and (4.4), as well as the fact that the left-hand side of this expression has the meaning of a force, i.e., the drift force F_a, averaged over a period of the vibrations, we have:

$$F_a = \frac{\pi}{3}kr^3\mu_p \left[\frac{9}{2}(b^2+b)\mu_g - \left(3+\frac{9}{2}b\right)\mu_p \right] \overline{E} \sin 2kx_0. \qquad (6.29)$$

Setting the drift force (6.29) equal to the resistive force $F_{St} = 6\pi\eta r V_a$, we obtain the following equation for the drift velocity:

$$V_a = \frac{k}{18\,\eta}r^2\mu_p \left[\frac{9}{2}(b^2+b)\mu_g - \left(3+\frac{9}{2}b\right)\mu_p \right] \overline{E} \sin 2kx_0. \qquad (6.30)$$

It may be seen that the way in which the force and velocity in this type of particle drift change between a node and a loop is identical with the way in which the force and velocity change in a radiation drift. Otherwise there is no similarity. A characteristic detail is that each size particle has its own "favorite" frequency at which the drift velocity reaches its maximum value (see Fig. 22B).

Table 5 gives a collection of formulas for the force and velocity of all the types of aerosol particle drift in an acoustic field as discussed above. Note, with regard to the drift velocity formulas, that since they are all derived from the expressions for the drift force by means of Stokes' formula (4.3) they are only exact as long as the corresponding Reynolds number $Re = 2rV/\nu$ is not greater than 1. Otherwise (for large particles or high sound intensity) the velocity must be corrected by Oseen's method, using the formula:

$$V_{Oc} = -\frac{4\nu}{3r} + \sqrt{\left(\frac{4\nu}{3r}\right)^2 + \frac{8\nu}{3r}V_{st}}. \qquad (6.31)$$

This formula is easily arrived at by setting the right-hand sides of the expressions for the resistive force of a sphere in the usual form, as given by Stokes, equal to the corrected form as given by Oseen.

Values calculated by the above formulas are given below for the absolute drift velocity of spherical aerosol particles of unit density ($\rho_p = 1$), in atmospheric air with J = 0.1 W/cm^2 for a traveling wave (Fig. 22A), and an undistorted standing wave (Fig. 22B). In addition, Fig. 23 gives comparative graphs illustrating the nature, direction, and relative velocity of all the types of aerosol particle drift discussed above, in a traveling and standing sound wave.

A number of important conclusions may be drawn from an examination of the graphs.

1. In an undistorted traveling wave, the predominant type of drift is that due to difference in phase of the vibrations of the particles in the medium, the absolute value of the velocity being small ($V_{\eta+\varphi}^{max} = 0.55$ cm/sec). The drift velocity due to acoustic radiation pressure is insignificant and may be neglected in all cases.

2. In a distorted traveling wave the predominant type of drift is usually that due to wave-form distortion, with the absolute velocity reaching high values (of up to $V_h^{max} \approx 10$ cm/sec and above) if the amount of distortions and the asymmetry are quite large.

In an undistorted standing wave with small sized particles, the predominant type of drift is that due to asymmetry in the vibrations of the medium while for large sized particles it is the drift due to acoustic radia-

TABLE 5

Cause of particle drift	Force and velocity of particle drift	
	In a traveling wave	In a standing wave
Acoustic radiation pressure	$F_R = \dfrac{11\pi}{9}\left(\dfrac{\omega}{c_g}\right)^4 r^6 \mu_g^2 \overline{E}$ $V_R = \dfrac{11}{54\eta}\left(\dfrac{\omega}{c_g}\right)^4 r^5 \mu_g^2 \overline{E}$	$F_R = \dfrac{8\pi}{3}\left(\dfrac{\omega}{c_g}\right) r^3 \mu_g^2 \overline{E}\sin 2kx_0$ $V_R = \dfrac{4}{9\eta}\left(\dfrac{\omega}{c_g}\right) r^2 \mu_g^2 \overline{E}\sin 2kx_0$
Periodic viscosity change in the medium	$F_\eta = 3\pi \dfrac{(\gamma-1)}{c_g}\nu r \mu_g^2 \overline{E}$ $V_\eta = \dfrac{\gamma-1}{2\rho_g c_g}\mu_g^2 \overline{E}$	
Difference in phase of the vibrations of the particles in the medium	$F_\varphi = -6\pi \dfrac{\nu}{c_g} r \mu_g^2 \overline{E}$ $V_\varphi = -\dfrac{1}{\rho_g c_g}\mu_g^2 \overline{E}$	
Asymmetric vibrations of the medium		$F_a = \dfrac{\pi}{3}\left(\dfrac{\omega}{c_g}\right) r^3 \mu_p\left[\dfrac{9}{2}(b^2+b)\mu_g - \left(3+\dfrac{9}{2}b\right)\mu_p\right]\overline{E}\sin 2kx_0$ $V_a = \dfrac{1}{18\eta}\left(\dfrac{\omega}{c_g}\right) r^2 \mu_p\left[\dfrac{9}{2}(b^2+b)\mu_g - \left(3+\dfrac{9}{2}b\right)\mu_p\right]\overline{E}\sin 2kx_0$
Distortion of sound wave	$F_h = -6h_2 \sin\psi\, r^2 \mu_g^2 \overline{E}$ $V_h = -\dfrac{h_2 \sin\psi}{\pi\eta}r\mu_g^2 \overline{E}$	No analytical solution

55

tion pressure. The absolute drift velocity in the first case is not large ($V_a^{max} \approx 0.17$ cm/sec; $V_\eta^{max} \approx 0.55$ cm/sec), while in the second case it may reach high values ($r = 100\mu$, $V_R^{max} = 7-40$ cm/sec, $f = 5-50$ kcps).

4. In a badly distorted standing wave with very small sized particles, the predominant type of drift is that due to asymmetry in the vibrations of the medium while for larger sized particles it is the drift due to distortion of the sound wave. In this case, the absolute velocity of the last type of particle drift may reach high values [$r > 5\ \mu$, $V_h^{max} > 10$ cm/sec], in excess of the radiation drift velocity of the particles. The direction of this type of drift depends on the phase shift angle of the harmonic components.

5. The drift velocity of aerosol particles is strongly dependent on the particle size and the frequency. As a rule, high drift velocities only occur for large sized particles or at high ultrasonic frequencies.

6. The velocity of all types of aerosol particle drift is directly proportional to the acoustic energy density, and hence to the sound intensity. If the sound intensity is raised to $J = 1$ W/cm^2, the particle drift velocity increases by a factor of 10, if the Reynolds number does not exceed 1 in the process. Otherwise, the increase in the drift velocity is not quite so large.

§ 7. Circulating and Pulsating Motion of Aerosol Particles

Circulating motion is the name that we give to the motion which aerosol particles execute under the action of an acoustic wind. The length of time during which the velocity of the acoustic wind changes is much greater than the relaxation time of the aerosol particles. Accordingly, as in the case of drift, it is reasonable to assume that the particles acquire the velocity of the medium practically instantaneously, and, thus, follow

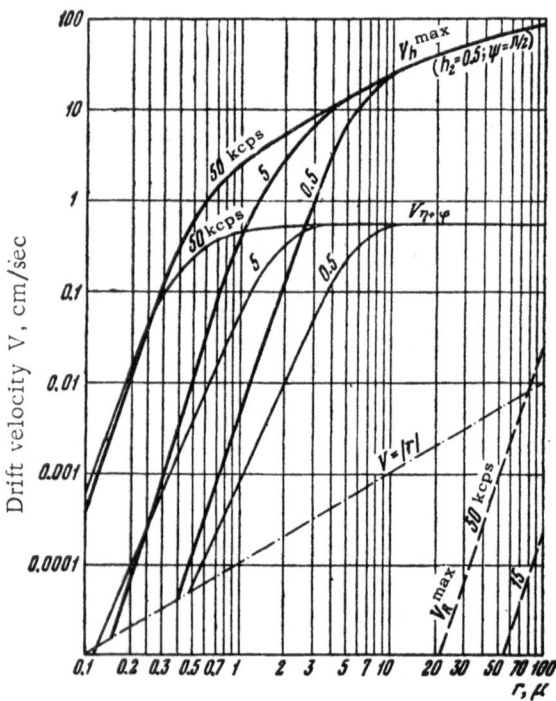

Fig. 22A. Drift velocity of aerosol particles in a traveling sound wave for $J = 0.1$ W/cm^2 ($\rho_p = 1$ g/cm^3, the medium is air). V_R) Drift velocity due to radiation pressure of sound; $V_{\eta+\varphi}$) drift velocity due to difference in phase of the vibrations of the particles in the medium and periodic viscosity changes in the medium; V_h) drift velocity due to distortion of the wave form ($\psi = \pm \pi/2$; $h_2 = 0.5$).

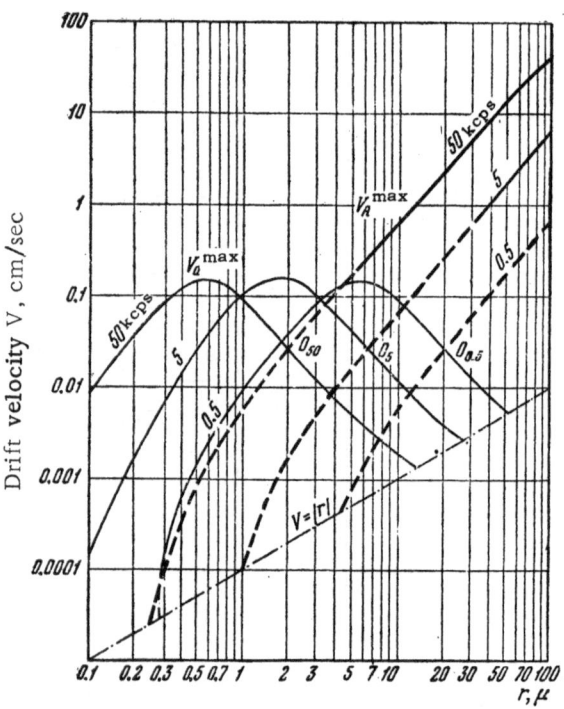

Fig. 22B. Maximum values of the drift velocity of aerosol particles in an undistorted standing sound wave for $J = 0.1$ W/cm^2 ($\rho_p = 1$ g/cm^3, the medium is air). V_R^{max} is the drift velocity due to acoustic radiation pressure; V_a^{max} is the drift velocity due to asymmetric vibrations of the medium (the drift velocities from wave form distortion V_h^{max}, are found from Fig. 22A).

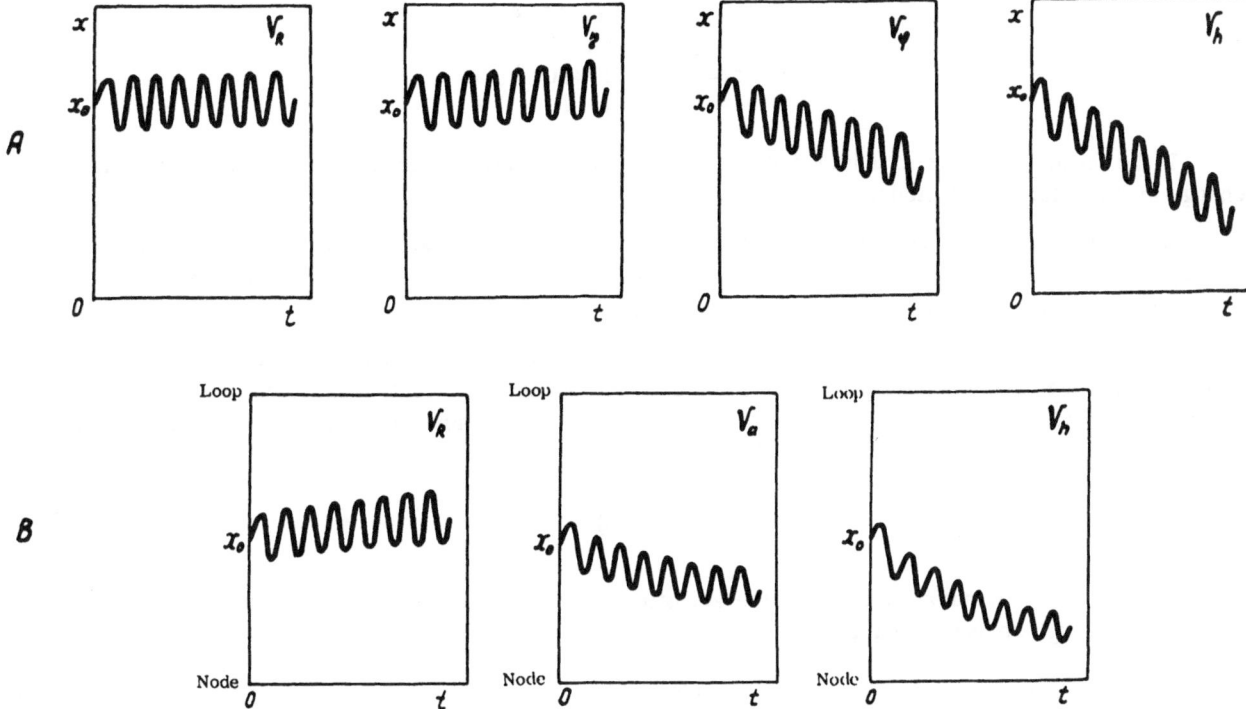

Fig. 23. Comparative graphs for the drift of aerosol particles in a sound field. A) In a traveling sound wave; B) in a standing sound wave.

the motion of the medium completely. To make this idea more tangible, consider the equation of motion of a particle acted upon by a force coming from the medium. If the velocity of the acoustic wind is w_a, then neglecting the second and third terms in Eq. (4.2) for simplicity, the equation of motion of the aerosol particle may be written in the following form:

$$m_p \frac{dw_p}{dt} = 6\pi\eta r (w_a - w_p), \qquad (7.1)$$

or

$$\frac{dw_p}{dt} + \frac{w_p}{\tau} - \frac{w_a}{\tau} = 0. \qquad (7.1')$$

Assume that the velocity of the wind does not change in the time interval under discussion, i.e., w_a = const. In this case, the solution of Eq. (7.1') which vanishes for t = 0, is [39]:

$$w_p = w_a(1 - e^{-t/\tau}).$$

This equation shows that at the time $t = \tau$, the velocity of the aerosol particle differs from that of the acoustic wind by 37%, while at t = 5τ the difference is only 0.6%, and for t = 10τ, the difference is less than 0.005%. Hence it follows that for practical purposes aerosol particles are moving at the acoustic wind velocity in the following fractions of a second:

$$
\begin{aligned}
&\text{for} \quad r = 0.1\ \mu \quad t \approx 10^{-6}\ \text{sec} \\
&\quad \text{»} \quad r = 1\ \ \mu \quad t \approx 10^{-4}\ \ \text{»} \\
&\quad \text{»} \quad r = 10\ \mu \quad t \approx 10^{-2}\ \ \text{»} \\
&\quad \text{»} \quad r = 100\,\mu \quad t \approx 1 \quad\ \ \text{»}
\end{aligned}
$$

If the third, integral term is included in Eq. (4.2), the correction is not more than 4%, which makes no change in the order of magnitude.

It may be shown that the same thing occurs when aerosol particles are moving under any other slowly varying force, including the drift forces discussed in the previous section. Aerosol particles are carried along just as quickly in the general gas flow through the acoustic treating chamber.

Consider the behavior of aerosol particles toward the reversals of acoustic flow occurring in a standing sound wave. Here, every aerosol particle is acted upon in addition by a centrifugal force, with the result that the particle moves in a radial direction at a velocity which may be found from the familiar formula [121]:

$$
V_c = \frac{w_a^2 \tau}{R}\,, \tag{7.3}
$$

where R is the radius of curvature at which the acoustic flow turns around. The radial motion of the particle for rotation through an angle φ (in radians) is

$$
\Delta R = V_c t_w\,, \tag{7.4}
$$

where t_w is the time during which the particle moves in the curved path, given by $t_w = \varphi R / w_a$. Substituting this last expression, as well as Eq. (7.3) in (7.4) gives

$$
\Delta R = \varphi \tau w_a. \tag{7.5}
$$

In the paper [73] by the author of this book, which discusses the question, and gives velocity curves and trajectories for the motion of the acoustic flow in a standing wave field at a frequency of 4.25 kcps as calculated from Rayleigh's formulas (1.24)–(1.26), it is shown that the velocity drops when the flow turns around (for J = 1 W/cm^2, it is not greater than w_a = 1 cm/sec). Hence it follows that the radial displacement of the particles for a rotation of $\varphi = \pi/2$ is not greater in order of magnitude than the relaxation time, which, as we know, lies in the range $\tau \approx 1.2 \cdot (10^{-7} - 10^{-3})$ sec for the primary particles in aerosols subjected to sonic treatment. Hence, any radial displacement of the aerosol particles that occurs when an acoustic disturbance turns around may safely be neglected, as long as the particles have not already been consolidated by coagulation into large sized aggregates.

Detailed experimental studies of the circulating motion of aerosol particles in a sonic field have been made by Andrade [140] who used aerosol particles to get beautiful "prints" of the trajectories followed by the acoustic wind between the nodes and loops of a standing sound wave with λ = 56.5 and λ = 91.8 cm. This phenomenon has subsequently been observed by many people working on acoustic coagulation of aerosols.

There is some interest in comparing the direction of the circulation motion of aerosol particles with the direction in which they drift as discussed in the previous section.

In an undistorted traveling wave, the direction of the circulating motion of aerosol particles due to the acoustic wind is opposite to the drift of the particles in the central part of the sound beam, so that the resultant particle velocity is the arithmetic difference between the velocity of the acoustic wind and the drift velocity at the point in question. On the edge of the sound beam the types of particle motion that we are comparing are in the same direction, so that the resulting particle velocity is the sum of the acoustic wind and particle drift velocities. If the wave form is not greatly distorted, the velocity of the acoustic wind is usually greater than the drift velocity, so that the motion of the particles is away from the sound source in this case.

In a standing sound wave, the resultant velocity depends on the size of the aerosol particles. Small particles, where the drift is predominantly due to asymmetric vibration of the medium and is of low velocity, move toward a vibration loop in both the central part and on the edge of the sound beam but at the center the velocity is decreased by V_a and at the edge is increased by V_a, where V_a is the acoustic streaming at the point in question. Large particles, where the drift is predominantly due to acoustic radiation pressure move toward a loop in the central part of the beam, while on the edge they move toward a node, or toward a loop, if V_R is very large.

In the intermediate part of the sound field where the acoustic flux is primarily transverse to the direction of the aerosol particle drift, the magnitude and direction of the motion of the particles longitudinally are completely determined by the magnitude and direction of the drift velocity, while in the transverse direction, they are determined by the velocity of the acoustic streaming. As a result the motion of the aerosol particles here makes some angle with the direction of the sound wave.

By taking part in the vibratory and circulating motion of the medium, the aerosol particles are at the same time caught up in the pulsations of the acoustic flow due to acoustic turbulence. This has been observed visually by many investigators [167, 76, 30, 156, 231, 232].

To what extent are the aerosol particles caught up in the turbulent pulsations of the vibrating medium? This problem has still not been studied experimentally, but some idea may be obtained from the theory of acoustic turbulence which we developed in §1.

If, following the example of N. A. Fuks in [121], we think of the turbulent pulsations of the medium as being harmonic vibrations with the angular frequency ω_l it is not difficult to grasp how the degree to which the aerosol particles are caught up in the pulsations may be calculated from the equation (5.9) already derived.

If we assume that the spectrum of the turbulent pulsations lies in the low-frequency range [see Eqs. (1.38) and (1.39)] so that $\omega\tau \ll 1$, we may use the simplified equation (5.16). According to this equation, the degree to which turbulent pulsations of frequency ω_l flow around the aerosol particles is given by

$$\mu_g^l = \omega_l \tau. \tag{7.6}$$

The mean square velocity of the relative motion between the particle and the medium is given by

$$v_{pg} = \mu_g^l v_l = \omega_l v_l \tau, \tag{7.7}$$

where v_l is the mean square pulsational velocity in the medium.

Making use of the fact that the product $\omega_l v_l$ is nothing other than the acceleration a_l of the pulsations in the medium, Eq. (7.7) may also be written as:

$$v_{pg} = a_l \tau. \tag{7.8}$$

Relative motion between a particle in the medium is only possible for pulsations on a scale $l < l_0$, the frequency of which, as may be seen from (1.39) is independent of the scale.

The highest acceleration is naturally found in pulsations in the scale l_0, which, from (1.36), have the highest pulsational velocity:

$$v_{l_0} \simeq \frac{1}{4}\left(\varepsilon\, \frac{b}{\rho_g}\right)^{1/4} \simeq \frac{1}{4}\,\frac{\xi^{1/4} b^{1/4}}{(\rho_g c_g)^{3/4}}\, J^{3/4} f^{1/4}. \tag{7.9}$$

From this, we can write for the maximum acceleration in the pulsations:

$$(a_l)_{max} = \omega_{l_0} v_{l_0} \approx \frac{v_{l_0}^2}{l_0} \approx \frac{1}{15}\,\frac{\varepsilon^{3/4}}{(b/\rho_g)^{1/4}}. \tag{7.10}$$

From (7.8) and (7.10), the maximum relative pulsational velocity between a particle and the medium is equal to

$$(v_{pg})_{max} \simeq \frac{2}{135} \frac{\rho_p}{\eta} \frac{\varepsilon^{3/4}}{(b/\rho_g)^{1/4}} r^2 \simeq \frac{2}{135} \frac{\xi^{3/4}\rho_p J^{3/4}f^{1/4}}{b^{1/4}\rho_g^{7/4}c_g^{15/4}\eta} r^2. \tag{7.11}$$

V. G. Levich [68, 69], citing Yaglom's calculations, takes the numerical coefficient in (7.10) to be $\sqrt{3}$, so that, instead of Eq. (7.11), we get the following equation:

$$(v_{pg})_{max} \simeq \frac{2\sqrt{3}}{9} \cdot \frac{\rho_p}{\eta} \frac{\varepsilon^{3/4}}{(b/\rho_g)^{1/4}} r^2. \tag{7.11'}$$

However, this equation, derived on the assumption that $v_{pg} \ll v_{l_0}$, leads to much too high values for the relative velocity between the particle and the medium, and thus to much too high an absolute value for the velocity of the pulsations, which is sometimes even greater than the particle velocity in the medium, a completely implausible condition [as may be shown by setting (7.11) equal to (7.7), and thence finding the value of v_l]. Accordingly, in what follows, we shall use Eq. (7.11) exclusively. We are strengthened in this decision by a simple experimental fact: particles, suspended in a sonic field, as a rule trace out densely overlaid tracks, rather than the stretched-out sinusoid which would be found if the velocity of the pulsations were the more important.

Table 6 gives values calculated from Eqs. (7.6) and (7.11) for the amount of flow around the aerosol particle, and the maximum relative pulsational velocity between the particles ($\rho_p = 1$) and the medium in a sound field at frequencies of $f = 1$ kcps and 10 kcps for the normal sound intensity of $J = 0.1$ W/cm^2 (the numerators in the "fractions" are for $f = 1$ kcps, while the denominators are for $f = 10$ kcps).

It may be seen from Table 6 that the relative pulsational velocity between the particles in the medium is of moderate value for the range 1-10 kcps, and is not greater than 0.15-0.88 cm/sec for particles with $r < 5\mu$, this velocity being 0.1-0.6% of the particle velocity in the medium. These values are correct with an accuracy up to the factor ξ.

TABLE 6

r, μ	τ, sec	ω_{l_0}, rad/sec	μ_g^l From the exact formula (5.9)	From the simplified formula (5.16)	v_{l_0} cm/sec	(v_{pg}) max cm/sec
1	$1.2 \cdot 10^{-5}$		$\dfrac{0.0017}{0.0055}$	$\dfrac{0.0017}{0.0055}$		$\dfrac{0.006}{0.035}$
3	$1.08 \cdot 10^{-4}$	$\dfrac{140}{440}$	$\dfrac{0.0151}{0.0497}$	$\dfrac{0.0151}{0.0497}$	$\dfrac{3.6}{6.4}$	$\dfrac{0.055}{0.317}$
5	$3.0 \cdot 10^{-4}$		$\dfrac{0.0420}{0.1366}$	$\dfrac{0.0420}{0.1380}$		$\dfrac{0.150}{0.880}$
10	$1.2 \cdot 10^{-3}$		$\dfrac{0.1655}{0.4830}$	$\dfrac{0.1680}{0.5520}$		$\dfrac{0.600}{3.050}$

§8. Scattering and Absorption of Acoustic Energy by Aerosol Particles

Every aerosol particle, however small, constitutes a definite obstacle to sound waves, which can only be overcome at the expense of a certain amount of the vibrational energy in the medium. This is due, first, to the fact that the incident beam of sound waves is scattered into the surrounding space by the particle, second, vibrational energy of the medium is absorbed in the boundary layer of the particle, and, third, the particle acts as a source of irreversible heat losses in the medium due to periodic temperature changes. As a result, when sound waves pass through an aerosol, an appreciably greater reduction in sound intensity occurs than is the case when the waves pass through a pure gas.

The theory of scattering of sound waves by spherical and cylindrical obstacles was discussed by Rayleigh [107], and further developed in the work of Lamb [61], Rzhevkin [105], and others.

The theory [62] shows that the energy carried off per second by waves scattered by a spherical particle, for the condition $r \ll \lambda$, is equal to

$$J_s = \frac{7\pi}{9} \frac{\omega^4}{c_g^3} r^6 E_{gp}. \tag{8.1}$$

The total energy flux transmitted by sound waves per second per square centimeter of wave front is given by (1.22) as:

$$J = \overline{E} c_g. \tag{8.2}$$

As in the case of sound absorption by the medium, the fraction of the energy supplied that is lost by scattering in an aerosol layer is proportional to the thickness of the layer:

$$\frac{J_s n \, dx}{J} = \alpha_p^s \, dx, \tag{8.3}$$

where α_p^s is the scattering factor for acoustic energy by aerosol particles.

Substituting Eqs. (8.1) and (8.2), and using the fact that $E_{gp} = \mu_g^2 \overline{E}$, we have

$$\alpha_p^s = \frac{112\pi^5}{9} \frac{f^4 r^6 \mu_g^2}{c_g^4} n. \tag{8.4}$$

Instead of the count concentration, it is more practical to use the concentration of particles by weight, and then, from Eq. (9.1), we obtain the following expression for the scattering factor of acoustic energy by aerosol particles:

$$\alpha_p^s = \frac{28}{3} \left(\frac{\pi f}{c_g} \right)^4 \frac{r^3}{\rho_p} \mu_g^2 k 10^{-6}. \tag{8.5}$$

For particles of unit density, suspended in air, we have

$$\alpha_p^s \approx 0.68 \cdot 10^{-21} k r_\mu^3 \cdot \mu_g^2 f_{kcps}^4 \tag{8.5'}$$

(r_μ is the radius of the particles in μ, and f_{kcps} is the frequency in kcps).

It is not difficult to see that under ordinary conditions the scattering factor for acoustic energy by aerosol particles is an insignificantly small quantity, of the order $\alpha_p^s \approx 10^{-20}$, which can always be neglected in practical calculations.

The theory of the absorption of acoustic energy by stationary spherical and cylindrical obstacles was first developed by Sewell [265]. The coefficient of absorption of acoustic energy by spherical particles as a result of viscous losses is given, including the degree of flow around the particles, by the following expression:

$$\alpha_p^v = \frac{6\pi\nu r n}{c_g}\,\mu_g^2\left(1 + r\sqrt{\frac{\omega}{2\nu}}\right), \tag{8.6}$$

or, replacing n by k in Eq. (9.1), by

$$\alpha_p^v = 4.5\,\frac{\nu k\,10^{-6}}{c_g\rho_p r^2}\,\mu_g^2\left(1 + r\sqrt{\frac{\omega}{2\nu}}\right). \tag{8.7}$$

The second term in parentheses in both expressions is usually much less than one, and so may be neglected. In this case, we obtain the following formulas for the coefficient of absorption of acoustic energy:

$$\alpha_p^v = \frac{6\pi\nu r n}{c_g}\,\mu_g^2, \tag{8.8}$$

$$\alpha_p^v = 4.5\,\frac{\nu k\,10^{-6}}{c_g\rho_p r^2}\,\mu_g^2. \tag{8.9}$$

For particles of unit density, suspended in air, the last formula takes the form

$$\alpha_p^v \simeq 1.73 k\,\frac{\mu_g^2}{r_\mu^2}\,\text{db/m} \tag{8.9'}$$

(r_μ is the radius of the particles in μ).

These formulas may be easily arrived at in the following elementary way, as given by Brandt, Freund, and Hiedemann [162, 168].

The energy absorbed when a viscous medium flows around an aerosol particle is numerically equal to the work done by the resistive forces exerted by the particle on the motion of the medium. Assuming that the resistive force is given at any instant of time by Stokes' formula (4.3), where the relative velocity of the medium varies with time according to the sinusoidal law (5.22), we find that the energy absorbed per second by the particle is equal to

$$J_a = \int_0^1 F_{St} u_{gp}\,dt = 6\pi\eta r\mu_g^2 U_g^2 \int_0^1 \cos^2(\omega t - \varphi)\,dt = 3\pi\eta r\mu_g^2 U_g^2. \tag{8.10}$$

The ratio of the energy absorbed to the total energy flux (8.2) passing through an aerosol layer of the thickness dx is given by a formula identical with Eq. (8.3), which, after substituting (8.10), gives Eq. (8.8), and, after making use of (9.1), gives Eq. (8.9). Figure 24 gives values of the coefficient of viscous sound absorption by aerosol particles of unit density in air as a function of radius for k = 1 g/m³, calculated from Eq. (8.9) (for particles with r < 1μ, Cunningham's correction is made for the discrete properties of the medium).

We see that for every frequency there is a critical particle radius at which the sound absorption is a maximum. The critical radius is easily found by setting the derivative $d\alpha_p^v/dr$ equal to zero, giving

$$r_{cr} = \sqrt{\frac{9\eta}{4\pi\rho_p f}}. \tag{8.11}$$

For air, with $\rho_p = 1$, the formula takes the form

$$r_{cr} = \frac{3.65}{\sqrt{f_{kcps}}} \mu.$$ (8.11')

At the critical radius, the degree of flow around the particle μ_g is equal to $\sqrt{2}/2$, and, taking account of this fact, the maximum viscous absorption coefficient may, from (8.9) be written in the following form:

$$(\alpha_p^\nu)\max = k\,\frac{f_{kcps}}{15.4}\ db/m.$$ (8.12)

In the range 0.5-50 kcps, $(\alpha_p^\nu)_{max}$ is from 0.0325 to 3.25 db/m per gram of aerosol particles. Hence, it may be concluded that, even in comparatively low concentration by weight, particles of the critical dimension will give an absorption coefficient α_p^ν that is much in excess of the acoustic absorption coefficient α_g of a gas alone, and reaches enormous values at high frequencies. The value of α_p^ν may be lowered by simply reducing the frequency so that it lies off to one side of the critical frequency as given by Eqs. (8.11) or (8.11').

For the coefficient of the sound absorption due to periodic irreversible heat exchange between the particle and the medium, and the corresponding increase in entropy and loss in free energy of the medium, we have the following expression, derived by Epstein and Carhart [188, 122]:*

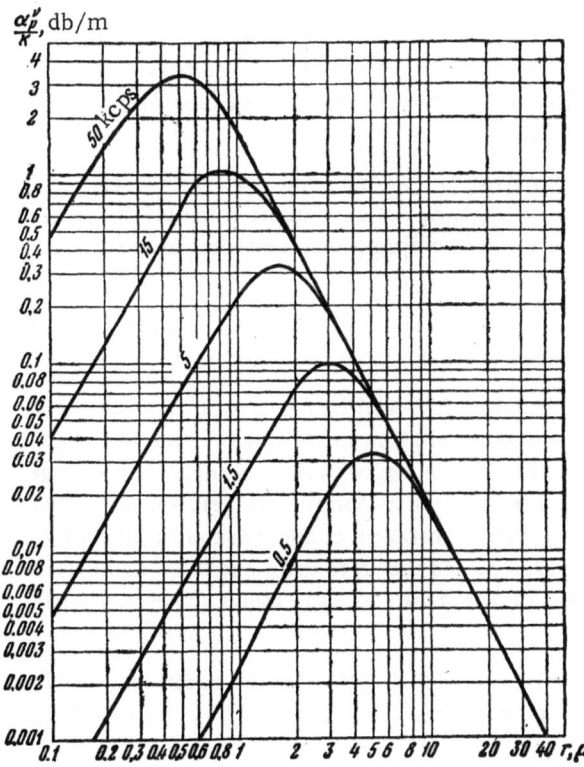

$\dfrac{\alpha_p^\nu}{k}$, db/m

Fig. 24. Theoretical values for the reduced coefficient of absorption of sound of aerosols of different frequencies.

$$\alpha_p^\chi = \frac{4\pi\chi rn}{c_g}(\gamma - 1)\left(1 + r\sqrt{\frac{\omega}{2\nu}}\right)\mu_{g\chi}^2,$$ (8.13)

where χ is the coefficient of thermal conductivity of the medium, $\lambda_q/\rho_g c_g$; $\mu_{g\chi}$ is the degree of equilization between the temperatures of the particle and the medium, as given by an equation identical with the equation for the degree of flow around the particles the only difference being that instead of $b = (1/r)(2\nu/\omega)^{1/2}$, we have $\theta = (1/r)(2\chi/\omega)^{1/2}$ thus:

$$\mu_{g\chi} = \sqrt{\frac{a^2}{a^2 + 3a\theta + \frac{9}{2}\theta^2 + \frac{9}{2}\theta^3 + \frac{9}{4}\theta^4}}.$$ (8.14)

Replacing n by k in (8.13), and making use of the fact that generally $r(\omega/2\nu)^{1/2} \ll 1$, we can write the following expression:

$$\alpha_p^\chi = \frac{3\chi k \cdot 10^{-6}}{c_g \rho_p r^3}(\gamma - 1)\,\mu_{g\chi}^2.$$ (8.15)

For particles of unit density, suspended in air ($\chi \simeq 0.2$; $\gamma = 1.4$), this formula takes the form:

$$\alpha_p^\chi \approx \frac{6 \cdot 10^3 k}{r_\mu^3}\,\mu_{g\chi}^2\ db/m.$$ (8.15')

(r_μ is the radius of the particles in μ).

*This problem was again discussed recently by Soo [326].

63

For large values of θ, the particle and the medium are at almost the same temperature, and the decrease in free energy is insignificant, so that $\mu_{g\chi} \simeq 0$. For very small values of θ, the temperature of the particle remains almost constant, and the temperature drop and the free energy decrease reach practically their maximum possible value, so that $\mu_{g\chi} \simeq 1$.

The total coefficient of sound absorption due to aerosol particles, is equal to

$$\alpha_p = \alpha_p^s + \alpha_p^v + \alpha_p^\chi \simeq \alpha_p^v + \alpha_p^\chi. \tag{8.16}$$

All the absorption coefficients under discussion remain additive for particle concentrations $n < 10^6$, for the condition $(\gamma - 1)(\omega\chi/c_g) \ll 1$, which gives for air: $\omega \ll 4 \cdot 10^5$.

In a water fog, α_p^χ is about 40% of the value of α_p^v.

The total sound attenuation factor in aerosols including absorption by the medium, is given by the sum

$$\alpha' = \alpha_g' + \alpha_p. \tag{8.17}$$

In this case the change in sound intensity with distance is given by the same exponential relation (1.15'), or (1.21), as for the pure medium.

Ostwald also showed that in addition to the above phenomena, alternate evaporation and condensation of vapor occurs periodically on the droplets when sound waves pass through aerosols having a liquid disperse phase (fogs). The evaporation is due to the rise in temperature of the medium that occurs during compression, while the condensation is due to the reduction in temperature that occurs in rarefaction.

Evaporation and condensation, which lag in phase behind the oscillations in temperature of the medium, are thermodynamically irreversible processes, which serve to convert the mechanical energy of the sound vibrations into heat, and, hence, lead to loss of energy. As a result, the attenuation of sound in fogs is correspondingly higher than the attenuation in smokes and dusts. This has been established experimentally at low audio frequencies (33 cps) by Makhe, as well as by Schmaus [2].

In a fog, the sound absorption coefficient due to the above evaporation and condensation processes is strongly dependent on the frequency of the sound, as well as on whether or not condensation nuclei are present, and on what phase transformations the fog undergoes during sound wave propagation (transition from the wet to the dry region, or from the wet region to the water stage).

If there are only a small number of condensation nuclei, the water vapor only diffuses to and from the nuclei, while if there are a large number of nuclei, both condensation and evaporation will occur.

The theory of the attenuation of sound in fogs has been discussed in detail by Oswatitsch in [245]. It follows from the theory that the additional sound absorption has a maximum lying in the range of ten or twenty or more cps. At lower frequencies, falling in the subsonic range, the time during which the temperature change in the medium occurs is large, so that an equilibrium state may be set up between the droplets and the vapor. At higher frequencies, on the other hand, the time during which the temperature changes is too small for this, so that evaporation and condensation do not get a chance to develop, and the state turns out to be adiabatically dry (a similar state also occurs if the number of condensation nuclei is small) and the sound absorption coefficient is insignificant.

As an illustration of this fact take the results of the calculation made in [213] for the additional coefficient of attenuation of sound $\Delta\beta$ in a water fog, containing droplets of mean radius $r_m = 6.25\mu$, with $k = 2\,g/m^3$:

$f =$	25	50	100	500	cps
$\Delta\beta =$	4	3	2	0.2	db·sec^{-1}.

It was shown by Wei Chun-Tsue [21, 22] that Oswatitsch's theory gives results that are too low. Nevertheless, it may be considered to have been established that even at a frequency of 0.5 kcps, the additional sound attenuation may be completely neglected in comparison with the usual attenuation of sound in a fog, as given by the formulas for a solid phase (see below Table 7).

It is, as a rule, the higher frequencies that are used in practice in acoustic coagulation of aerosols, so that it may be assumed that no additional attenuation of the sound occurs in the fogs undergoing coagulation, and the formulas given above for aerosols with a solid disperse phase may be used.

In addition to increasing the attenuation, having suspended particles present produces a certain amount of reduction in the velocity of propagation of sound. Zink and Delsasso [297] derived the following formula for the reduction Δc_g in the velocity of sound due to the presence of aerosol particles:

$$\Delta c_g = \frac{1}{2} c_g \frac{M_p}{M_g} \left(\mu_p^2 + \gamma_{pg} \frac{\mu_{px}^2}{C_{pg}} R_g \right),$$

(8.18)

where M_p/M_g is the ratio of masses of the disperse and dispersing phases, γ_{pg} is the specific heat ratio C_{vp}/C_v of the two phases, C_{pg} is the molar specific heat of the gas at constant pressure, and R_g is the gas constant.

The first term in the equation gives the reduction in the velocity of sound due to the increase in density of the system, while the second term gives the reduction due to the increase in specific heat of the system. It may be seen from the equation that these factors do not affect the velocity of sound unless the aerosol particles take part in the vibratory motion of the medium ($\mu_p > 0$), and absorb and give off heat ($\mu_{gx} > 0$). Thus, the two effects of attenuation and reduction in the velocity of sound are complimentary.

It is interesting to note that the first, purely qualitative experimental studies on the attenuation of sound in aerosols (natural fogs), as described by Tindal in [117], did not show that the suspended particles have any adverse effect on the passage of sound. On the other hand, it was noticed that sound was transmitted to a greater distance in thick fogs than in a transparent atmosphere. The reason for this, at first glance paradoxical, phenomenon, as was found out much later (see §1), is hidden in the fact that the absorption of sound depends on the moisture content of the air, which changes greatly when a fog is formed. It must be pointed out in general that experimental measurements of the attenuation of sound in natural fogs are extremely unreliable, since, under these conditions, the sound is very much weakened by the expansion of the wave front, and by variations in density and humidity of the atmosphere, which cannot be taken account of rigorously.

The first quantitative measurements of the absorption of sound by aerosols were made by Altberg and Holtzmann [138]. The experiments were made at frequencies of 5-22 kcps. The aerosol used was tobacco smoke. The particle sizes were not determined, and further, tobacco smoke contains a large amount of CO_2, which greatly increases the absorbing power of the medium. It is thus difficult to compare the results obtained by these authors with the theory of the attenuation of sound waves in aerosols as given above.

Laidler and Richardson [220], made an experimental study, at high ultrasonic frequencies (42, 98, and 695 kcps) of the absorption in magnesium oxide and stearic acid smokes, as well as in a lycopodium spore aerosol. The first two aerosols were composed of particles of greatly different sizes, but the lycopodium spores were quite uniform in size, with a mean radius of $r \approx 2.5\mu$, and the count concentration reached $n = 1.5 \cdot 10^6$. The degree of flow around the particles was $\mu_g \approx 1$, i.e., the particles were practically stationary.

The following values were found for the coefficient of absorption of sound by aerosol particles consisting of lycopodium spores: at 42 kcps, $\alpha_p = 0.029$, and at 98 kcps, $\alpha_p = 0.031$. The theoretical values of the coefficients are, as calculated by N. A. Fuks [121], 0.038 and 0.042 respectively. We see that the difference between the results of the theoretical calculations and the experimental data reaches 30-35%. We shall consider the reasons for this later on.

In the experimental paper by Knudsen, Wilson, and Anderson [213], a measurement was made of the rate of attenuation of sound in a resonant chamber filled with a water or oil fog (produced by mechanical atomiza-

TABLE 7

Frequency, kcps	Attenuation coefficient β, db $\cdot$ sec^{-1}		
	Experiment	Theory	
		Knudsen et al. [213]	Epstein and Carhart [188]
0.5	5	10.1	5.0
1.0	7	13.8	5.7
2.0	9.4	16.0	6.3
4.0	10.1	17.1	6.9
6.0	12.0	18.2	7.5
8.0	13.2	18.8	7.7

tion of the liquid), as well as with amonium chloride smoke. Here, a determination was made of the sound attenuation coefficient β (in db $\cdot$ sec^{-1}), which is related to α_p in the following way:

$$\beta_p = 10 \log_{10} e \cdot \alpha_p c_g. \qquad (8.19)$$

For a water fog containing droplets of mean radius $r_m = 6.25\mu$ in the amount $k = 2$ g/m^3, the results obtained are given in **Table 7**.

For a mineral oil fog ($r_m = 5\mu$, $k = 1.17$ g/m^3), and an amonium chloride smoke ($r_m = 0.5$-1.0μ, $k = 0.26$-1.03 g/m^3), results were obtained as given in Tables 8 and 9 respectively.

In addition to the above experiments, measurements were made on the attenuation of sound in a water fog at lower frequencies. The results of the measurements are given below.

Frequency, cps	Attenuation coefficient β, db $\cdot$ sec^{-1}
27.5	4.8
58.0	3.5
112.0	2.8
150.0	3.6
200.0	6.7
350.0	7.2

A reduction in the attenuation of sound was found to occur in the vicinity of 112 cps.

It may be seen from Tables 7, 8, and 9 that the differences between theoretical calculations of Knudsen et al. and experiment are quite large. This may be accounted for as follows. First, in calculating the theoretical coefficients of attenuation of the sound, Knudsen et al. neglected the attenuation due to irreversible heat losses in the medium to heating and cooling the aerosol particles, which was not investigated theoretically until later. Second as N. A. Fuks pointed out in [121], the authors neglected the large effect which the range of sizes of the aerosol particles has on the results of theoretical calculations of the coefficient of attenuation of sound. As the particle radius to be used in the calculation, the authors took the arithmetic mean value $\bar{r}$, found from the relation $\sum_i n_i r_i = n\bar{r}$, while instead of the quantity $1/r^2$ used in Eq. (8.9), what must be used is the ratio of the arithmetic mean radius $\bar{r}$ to the root-mean-cube radius raised to the third power, thus: $\bar{r}/r_3^3$. Since the root-mean-cube radius is always greater than the arithmetic mean in aerosols with a wide range of particle sizes, making $r_3 > \bar{r}$, neglecting this fact usually leads to results that are much too high.

Epstein and Carhart made the theoretical calculations of the coefficient of attenuation of sound shown in the last column of Table 7 separately by fractions, and including the thermal conductivity of the medium by

TABLE 8

Frequency, kcps	Absorption coefficient β, db·sec⁻¹			
	First series of experiments	Second series of experiments	Mean value of result	Theoretical calculation
0.25	–	0.5	0.5	2.3
0.50	1.5	1.8	1.6	6.3
1.0	3.6	4.0	3.8	11.2
2.0	7.7	7.7	7.7	14.4
4.0	13.6	12.8	13.2	16.3
6.0	15.0	14.4	14.7	17.3
8.0	21.2	20.6	20.9	18.3

TABLE 9

Frequency, kcps	Attenuation coefficient β, db·sec⁻¹					Calculated coefficient for k = 1.03 g/m³
	k = 0.26 g/m³	k = 0.46 g/m³	k = 0.52 g/m³	k = 0.86 g/m³	k = 1.03 g/m³	
0.5	0.2	0.4	0.3	0.2	1.0	0.7
1.0	0.5	0.8	1.5	3.0	3.0	2.8
2.0	2.0	4.6	6.0	11.0	12.6	10.4
4.0	7.0	15.5	16.0	30.5	37.0	35.8
6.0	11.0	25.0	26.0	51.0	58.0	65.5

Eq. (8.13). However, the results turned out to be too low. From all appearances, this may be accounted for by the fact that evaporation and condensation of vapor on the particles in the fog were neglected.

Wei Chun-Tsue [22] made measurements on the coefficient of attenuation of low-frequency sound in an artificial water fog, containing, predominantly, droplets with a radius of the order of $r = 5$-9μ, in amount $n = 0.5 \cdot 10^4$ - $1.5 \cdot 10^4$. The frequency varied from 25 to 250 cps. The measurements were made by the standing-wave method, using a sound level meter. The values of the coefficient of attenuation of sound turned out to lie in the range $\beta = 8.8$-20.8 db·sec⁻¹ (the largest absorption was found for 35-50 cps). These values are much in excess of the sound absorption coefficients given by Oswatitsch's theory.

Exceedingly good agreement between the theoretical and experimental data on the attenuation of sound in aerosols at audio-frequencies was found by Zink and Delsasso [297]. The method of measurement was based on comparing a sound pulse that had gone through the aerosol with a pulse that had gone through the pure gas. The pulse consisted of ten or twenty or more sinusoidal waves. The amplitude ratio gave the attenuation coefficient, while the distance between the sinusoids, which determines the change in arrival time of the pulse, gave the velocity of sound in the aerosol.

A study was made of the way in which the attenuation and the change in velocity of the sound varied with frequency for different gases, such as air, argon, oxygen, and helium. The aerosol particles used were aluminum oxide powder consisting of spherical particles of radii $r = 2.5$-7.5 at a concentration of $n = 3 \cdot 10^4$. In calculating the theoretical values of the coefficient of attenuation of sound, the particles were divided into four groups of radii 2.5, 3.75, 5, and 7.5 μ.

Figure 25 shows values of the coefficient of attenuation of sound in an aerosol in air, as found experimentally and theoretically by these authors. The experimental and theoretical values seem to be in almost complete agreement. Just as good agreement is found for helium, while in argon and oxygen, the experimental points lie somewhat above the theoretical curves (5 or 10%). At the same time, good agreement was found between the experimental data on the velocity of sound in aerosols and the theoretical values for the velocity as given by Eq. (8.18).

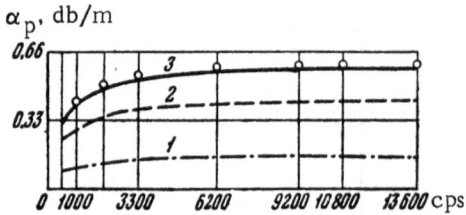

Fig. 25. Absorption of sound in an aluminum oxide aerosol
(from Zink and Delsasso). 1) Theoretical coefficient of the
absorption of sound due to all losses (α_p^{ν}); 2) theoretical coefficient of absorption of sound due to irreversible heat
transfer back and forth between the particle and the medium
(α_p^{χ}); 3) total theoretical sound absorption coefficient
$\alpha_p = \alpha_p^{\nu} + \alpha_p^{\chi}$; circles—experimental values.

The experiments by Zink and Delsasso go to show that the theory of attenuation of sound in aerosols having a solid disperse phase (smokes and dusts) has reached a high degree of perfection at the present time, and
may be reliably used as a basis for practical calculations.

Of the other experimental studies in the field of attenuation of sound in aerosols, we may mention the
paper by B. F. Podoshevnikov and B. D. Tartakovskii [97], who measured the coefficient of attenuation of sound
at 13 kcps in a highly disperse dioctylphthalate fog ($r_m = 0.28\mu$), where the particles were to a very large extent carried along in the vibratory motion of the medium (for details see §15). The attenuation coefficient
turned out to be higher in this case, by 2.7 db/m on the average, than in pure air. The results were not found
to be greatly dependent on the droplet concentration, which is undoubtedly a result of imperfection in the
measurements.

CHAPTER 3

INTERACTION BETWEEN AEROSOL PARTICLES
IN AN ACOUSTIC FIELD

§9. Preliminary Information

In the preceding chapter, a discussion was given of the laws governing the motion of individual aerosol particles without considering how they interact with one another. No such state of affairs exists under actual conditions. The mean distance between the particles in aerosols undergoing coagulation is such that as a result of differences in the rates of vibratory motion, the particles are able to overtake one another or to interact with one another through the medium and thus spoil the ideal picture of particle motion discussed in the last chapter.

It is well known that aerosols differ exceedingly from one another in their physical properties, in particular in dispersion composition, density, and concentration by weight of particles. Because of this, the number of aerosol particles per unit volume of gas varies over wide limits, as well as the mean distance between particles, the specific surface of the particles, the provisional mean radius of the particles, the volume of the disperse phase, etc. The geometric factors just mentioned exert a very important effect on the kinetics of coagulation processes in general and on acoustic coagulation of aerosols in particular. The effect is less important but nevertheless perfectly appreciable in evaporation, drying, desorption, and combustion of a disperse phase in an acoustic field.

Consider the geometry of an ideal aerodisperse system, with particles all of the same size in a nonevaporating fog, where the droplets are strictly spherical and, when they coalesce, form another sphere of larger radius but of the same density. By using the relations derived for this case it is not difficult to get some idea of the geometric factors involved in polydisperse systems (including solid particle aggregates exhibiting loose, light packing of the primary particles), if the calculation is made for successive fractions.

If we know the concentration by weight $k(g/m^3)$, the radius r, and density ρ_p of the particles in a monodisperse aerosol, the number of particles per cubic centimeter, the particle "count" concentration, is given by the formula:

$$n = \frac{k \cdot 10^{-6}}{\frac{4}{3}\pi r^3 \rho_p} \simeq 0.24 \cdot 10^{-6} \frac{k}{r^3 \rho_p} . \qquad (9.1)$$

The count concentration reaches very high values, of the order of 10^{10} or more, for very small particles. However, as a result of intense Brownian coagulation of the primary particles, even the first few seconds "in the world" of highly disperse aerosol particles finds them joined together into aggregates, so that the count concentration drops to a value of the order of 10^7-10^8. We shall now give an example of this. Let the radius of the primary particles formed as a result of condensation or sublimation of a material be $r = 0.02 \mu = 2 \cdot 10^{-6}$ cm, while the concentration by weight is k = 10 g/m^3. From Eq. (9.1), this corresponds to a value of $n_0 \simeq 3.5 \cdot 10^{11}$. The rate of Brownian coagulation of aerosols, according to Smoluchowski, is given by the quadratic relation [121]:

$$\frac{dn}{dt} = - K_{Br} n^2, \qquad (9.2)$$

which, when integrated, gives

$$n = \frac{n_0}{1 + K_{Br} n_0 t},$$ (9.3)

where K_{Br} is the coagulation constant, equal, for the particles under discussion, to $1.8 \cdot 10^{-9}$ cm$^3 \cdot$ sec^{-1}.

A calculation made from this formula shows that the particle count concentration drops with time in the following way:

$$\begin{array}{lll} \text{in } t = 1 \text{ sec} & n = 5.5 \cdot 10^8 & \text{(i.e. a factor of 640 res),} \\ \text{in } t = 10 \text{ sec} & n = 5.5 \cdot 10^7 & \text{(i.e. a factor of 6400 res),} \\ \text{in } t = 100 \text{ sec} & n = 5.5 \cdot 10^6 & \text{(i.e. a factor of 64000 res).} \end{array}$$

Here, the particle radius increases respectively to r = 0.17, 0.5, and 1.5μ (i.e., by factors of 8.5, 25, and 75). Hence it follows, among other things, that there are only rare cases in which highly disperse industrial fogs contain droplets of radius less than 0.2-0.5μ, while finely disperse smokes, as a rule, consist of aggregates of even larger dimensions.

Let us imagine that n particles are uniformly distributed throughout 1 cm^3, and let us divide this volume into a number of little cubes in such a way that each cube contains just one aerosol particle. In this case, there are $\sqrt[3]{n}$ particles on one side of each face, and, hence, the mean distance S_m between particles is:

$$s_m = \frac{1}{\sqrt[3]{n}}.$$ (9.4)

Substituting the expression (9.1) in this equation, we find, after simple algebra, an expression for the "reduced" distance $\mathbf{S}_m = S_m/r$ [73, 74]:

$$s_m \simeq 160 \sqrt[3]{\frac{\rho_p}{k}}.$$ (9.5)

This is the fundamental equation of aerosol geometry. Figure 26 gives values calculated from Eq. (9.5) for the reduced mean distance $\mathbf{S}_m$ between aerosol particles as a function of the concentration by weight k for different densitites ρ_p. It may be seen that the reduced mean distance between particles changes comparatively little with change in concentration by weight and density of the particles.

For concentrations by weight of k = 1-100 g/cm^3 and ρ_p = 1, the reduced mean distance lies in the range S_m = 160-35. Equation (9.5), strictly speaking, only holds for monodisperse aerosols but it makes it possible to follow clearly how the mean distance changes as the particles increase in size during aerosol coagulation (for the condition that the particles all stay the same size). As a matter of fact, in coagulation of ideal aerosols, ρ_p and k = const, and, hence,

$$s_m = \text{const.}$$ (9.6)

Hence it follows that at any stage of particle consolidation, the distance between the particles is a linear function of the instantaneous radius r, thus:

$$s_m = s_m r.$$ (9.7)

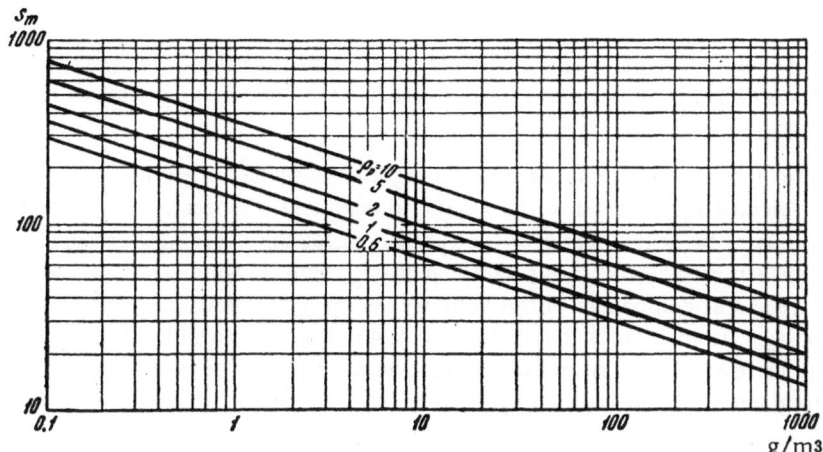

Fig. 26. Mean reduced distance between aerosol particles for different densities and concentrations by weight.

As the droplets in an ideal aerosol coalesce, the radius varies in the following way. When droplets of the same radius r_0 coalesce, with the result that the initial count concentration n_0 drops to n, we have, from the material balance:

$$\frac{3}{4} \pi r_0^3 \, \rho_p \, n_0 = \frac{3}{4} \pi r^3 \, \rho_p \, n,$$

we have:

$$r = r_0 \sqrt[3]{\frac{n_0}{n}}. \tag{9.8}$$

If n_2 small droplets of radius r_2 coalesce with n_1 large droplets of radius r_1 acting as coagulation centers, then, from the material balance:

$$\frac{3}{4} \pi r_2^3 \, \rho_p \, n_2 + \frac{3}{4} \pi r_1^3 \, \rho_p \, n_1 = \frac{3}{4} \pi r^3 \, \rho_p \, n_1,$$

we have:

$$r = r_1 \sqrt[3]{\frac{n_2}{n_1} r_{2rr}^3 + 1}, \tag{9.9}$$

where $r_{2rr} = r_2/r_1$ (the "reduced" radius of the small particles). If the concentration by weight k_2 of the small droplets is much greater than the concentration by weight k_1 of the large droplets, unity may be neglected, and Eq. (9.9) then reduces to Eq. (9.8), where $r_0 = r_2$, $n_0 = n_2$, and $n = n_1$.

Solid particles form loose aggregates with the low density ρ_p'. If the aggregates are approximately spherical, Eqs. (9.8) and (9.9) take the form:

$$r = r_0 \sqrt[3]{\frac{n_0}{n} \frac{\rho_p}{\rho_p'}}, \tag{9.8'}$$

$$r = r_1 \sqrt[3]{\left(1 + \frac{n_2}{n_1} r_{2rr}^3\right) \frac{\rho_p}{\rho_p'}}. \tag{9.8"}$$

71

We now pass to the theory of viscous flow around spherical bodies.

In viscous flow around bodies, the gas stream undergoes very important changes which are not limited to the immediate surroundings, but extend to distances greater than the mean distances between the aerosol particles.

Consider the velocity field set up in the surrounding medium when a gas stream moving forward at the unperturbed relative velocity u_{gp} parallel to the x axis flows around a spherical obstacle of radius r (Fig. 27). Let the origin of coordinates be at the center of the sphere and let the coordinates of the point in question in the velocity field be determined by the radius vector ρ of the angle θ, which the radius vector forms with the positive x axis. Let the radial component of the velocity vector at the point in question be v_ρ, and the tangential component be v_θ. From Oseen's theory [243, 244, 45, and 111], which, unlike Stokes' theory, takes partial account of the inertia of the gas stream incident on the sphere, the components of the velocity of flow around the sphere are given by the following expressions:

$$v_\rho = \frac{3}{4} \frac{u_{gp} r}{m\rho^2} \{1 - [1 + m\rho(1 + \cos\theta)] e^{-m\rho(1-\cos\theta)} \} + u_{gp} \cos\theta, \qquad (9.10)$$

$$v_\theta = \frac{3}{4} \frac{u_{gp} r}{\rho} \sin\theta e^{-m\rho(1-\cos\theta)} - u_{gp} \sin\theta, \qquad (9.11)$$

where $m = u_{gp}/2\nu$. The last terms in these equations represent an addition to the equations given in the literature cited, due to the fact that our case is diametrically opposite to the case of motion of a sphere in a viscous medium at rest, as discussed by the theory (see [45]; p. 393).

Let us make a transformation in Eqs. (9.10) and (9.11), by setting $\rho_{rr} = \rho/r$ (the "reduced" radius vector, referred to the radius of the particle), so that $m\rho = \text{Re } \rho_{rr}/4$. After substitution of these quantities, Eqs. (9.10) and (9.11) also take on a "reduced" dimensionless form:

$$v_{\rho_{rr}} = \frac{v_\rho}{u_{gp}} = \frac{3}{\text{Re } \rho_{rr}^2} \{1 - [1 + \frac{1}{4}\text{Re } \rho_{rr}(1 + \cos\theta)] e^{-\frac{1}{4}\text{Re } \rho_{rr}(1-\cos\theta)}\} + \cos\theta, \qquad (9.12)$$

$$v_{\theta_{rr}} = \frac{v_\theta}{u_{gp}} = \frac{3}{4\rho_{rr}} \sin\theta \, e^{-\frac{1}{4}\text{Re } \rho_{rr}(1-\cos\theta)} - \sin\theta. \qquad (9.13)$$

The equations for the components of the velocity of flow around a sphere are incomparably more convenient for theoretical analysis in this form.

The resultant "reduced" flow around the sphere is given by the usual formula:

$$v_{rr} = \sqrt{v_{\rho_{rr}}^2 + v_{\theta_{rr}}^2}. \qquad (9.14)$$

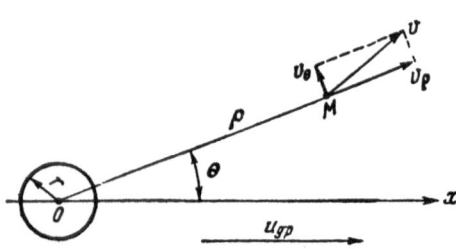

Fig. 27. Diagram used in calculating the velocity field around a particle in a gas stream.

Figure 28 shows a diagram of the velocity field set up in a medium by the motion of a sphere for Re = 1, equivalent to our case, as calculated by Pearcy and McHugh [251] on the basis of a refined solution of Oseen's initial equations made by Goldstein [194]. The solid lines show the location of points in the medium having the same reduced velocity, i.e., the velocity referred to the maximum value, which is that of the sphere itself. The dotted lines show the direction of the reduced velocity (the angle, written on each line is the angle that the velocity makes with the direction of motion of the sphere at infinity). The distances written horizontally and vertically are "reduced" distances, i.e., referred to the radius of the sphere.

A number of important conclusions may be drawn from an examination of Fig. 28. The first conclusion which forces itself on our attention with only the most cursory glance at the figure is that the velocity field set up around the sphere is highly asymmetric in the direction of motion, with a long parabolic "trail" behind the sphere, forming a "stagnant" zone, where the rate of flow around the particle is small. A second conclusion: the "boundary" layer formed around the sphere is unusually well developed, so that the velocity is appreciably different from the velocity at infinity at distances greater than ten or twenty or more times the radius of the sphere, while in the region of the "trail", it differs by factors of hundreds. It may be seen from the figure given that 1% of the velocity of the sphere is found at a distance of about 20r ahead of and at the sides of the sphere and about 150r behind the sphere, in the region of the "trail." The third conclusion, following from an analysis of the figure together with Eqs. (9.12) and (9.13) is that the boundary layer around the sphere becomes thicker, while the asymmetry decreases as the Reynolds number becomes smaller, but even at the lower values of Re the asymmetry makes itself felt right down to Re = 0 at even greater distances than those shown in the figure.

As an illustration of this last fact, let us supplement the information given by the following calculation: using Eqs. (9.12) and (9.13), let us find the value for the reduced velocity of flow around a sphere at a lower value of Re, ahead of the sphere ($\theta = 180°$), at the sides of the sphere ($\theta = 90°$ and $270°$), and behind the sphere ($\theta = 0°$) at the distances of $\rho_{rr} = 75$ (which corresponds to the mean value of the reduced distance S_m between aerosol particles for k = 10 g/m^3).

To do this note that Eqs. (9.12) and (9.13) may be greatly simplified* for large values of ρ_{rr} and fixed values of the angle θ. For $\theta = 0°$:

$$v_{x_{rr}} = 1 - \frac{3}{2x_{rr}}, \quad v_{y_{rr}} = 0; \tag{9.15}$$

for $\theta = 90$ and $270°$

$$v_{y_{rr}} = 0, \quad v_{x_{rr}} = \frac{-3}{4y_{rr}} + 1 \ (\text{for} \ \ Re \to 0), \tag{9.16}$$

$$v_{y_{rr}} = \frac{3}{Re \ y_{rr}^2}, \quad v_{x_{rr}} = +1 \quad (\text{for} \ Re \, |\, y_{rr}\, | \gg 2); \tag{9.16'}$$

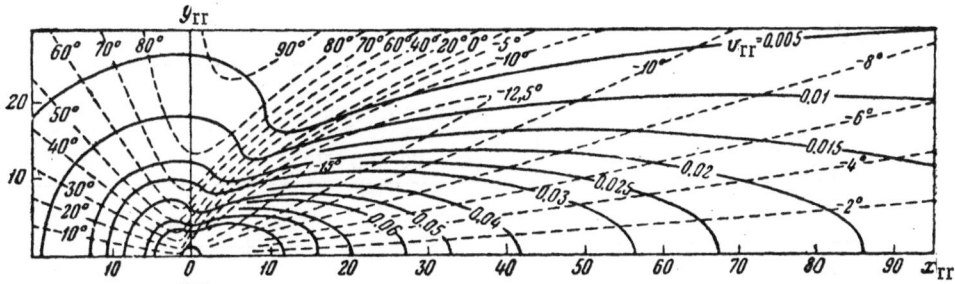

Fig. 28. Velocity field around a moving spherical particle at large distances for Re = 1.

---

*Unlike Eqs. (9.12) and (9.13), the direction of the velocity v_x is here taken to coincide with the x axis.

for $\theta = 180°$:

$$v_{x_{rr}} = 1 - \frac{3}{2x_{rr}}, \quad v_{y_{rr}} = 0 \quad (\text{for} \quad Re \to 0), \tag{9.17}$$

$$v_{x_{rr}} = \frac{-3}{Re\, x_{rr}^2} + 1, \quad v_{y_{rr}} = 0 \quad (\text{for } Re\,|x_{rr}| \gg 2). \tag{9.17'}$$

Thus we see that the velocity in front of the sphere decreases as $1/x_{rr}^2$, while behind the sphere the velocity decreases $1/x_{rr}$, i.e., more slowly. The results of the calculations are given in Table 10.

It may be seen from Table 10 that even for $Re = 0.25$, the difference between the velocities of flow in front of and behind the sphere is ~ 2% of the rate of flow around the sphere.

The fourth conclusion that follows from a consideration of Fig. 28 together with Eqs. (9.12) and (9.13) is that at large distances from a sphere in a gas stream, the flow is in a radial direction in front of the sphere and in a narrow region behind the sphere so that as $\theta \to 0$ and $\theta \to 180°$, the tangential components may be neglected for practical purposes, i.e., $v_\theta \approx 0$, while the radial components are given by the simplified equations (9.15) and (9.17).

Consider now the trajectory of the motion of the particles in the medium around the sphere. This case has been treated specially by Tomotika and Aoi in [280], who used an approximate solution of Oseen's equation as refined by Goldstein to find the following expression for the reduced flow function $\psi_{rr} = \psi/r^2 u_{gp}$:

$$\psi_{rr} = -\left\{ \frac{3}{4}\left(\rho_{rr} - \frac{1}{\rho_{rr}}\right) - \frac{16+3Re}{32}\left(\rho_{rr}^2 - \frac{1}{\rho_{rr}}\right) + \frac{3Re}{32}\left(\rho_{rr}^2 - \frac{1}{\rho_{rr}^2}\right)\cos\theta \right\}\sin^2\theta. \tag{9.18}$$

As $Re \to 0$, this equation reduces to the function for Stokes flow, which is perfectly symmetric, thus:

$$\psi_{rr} = \frac{1}{2}\left(1 - \frac{3}{2\rho_{rr}} + \frac{1}{2\rho_{rr}^3}\right)\rho_{rr}^2 \sin^2\theta. \tag{9.19}$$

Figure 29 gives flow lines around a sphere for $Re = 1$, as calculated in the paper [280] just cited. It may be seen from the figure that the flow lines are appreciably asymmetric even close to the sphere.

Let us find to what extent the above relations, derived on the assumption of steady-state flow around bodies, apply to our case, which is that of a vibrating gas flowing around particles.

TABLE 10

Reynolds number, Re	In front of sphere ($\theta = 180°$)		At sides of sphere ($\theta = 90$ and $270°$)		Behind sphere ($\theta = 0°$)	
	$v_{x_{rr}}$	$v_{y_{rr}}$	$v_{y_{rr}}$	$v_{x_{rr}}$	$v_{x_{rr}}$	$v_{y_{rr}}$
0	0.980		0	0.99		
0.25	0.998		0.0020			
0.50	0.999	0	0.0010	1.00	0.98	0
0.75	1.000		0.0007			
1.00	1.000		0.0005			

There are two peculiarities of the flow around aerosol particles in a high intensity sonic field. First, the particles are small in comparison with the thickness δ of the boundary layer ("depth of penetration" of the vortex motion), as given by Eq. (1.40), i.e., we have the condition

$$(2r)^2 \omega \ll \nu. \qquad (9.20)$$

Second, the Reynolds number is small: Re < 1, i.e., we have the condition

$$\frac{2r\omega A_{gp}}{\nu} \ll 1. \qquad (9.21)$$

This is at the same time equivalent to the condition: $A_{gp} \gg 2r$.

As is pointed out in [62], this is the low-frequency case where the motion of the medium around the obstacle may be regarded as steady-state at any given instant of time. In this case, Eq. (1.40) ceases to hold, and the thickness of the boundary layer around the sphere is given by Eqs. (9.12) and (9.13) for steady-state flow, in which there is no frequency dependence (this fact is not always taken into consideration by investigators, see, for example, [12]).

If a vibrating gas flows repeatedly around aerosol particles, new, specific features show up which will be dealt with specially in §11.

The difference between the velocities of vibratory motion of the aerosol particles, the existence of extensive fields of flow around them, and, finally, the general turbulence of the vibrating medium cannot fail to have an effect on the behavior of the particles. A complex type of hydrodynamic interaction is set up between the aerosol particles, which can only be made clear if the elementary types of interaction are considered separately. Such types of interaction are:

1) orthokinetic interaction between particles,
2) parakinetic interaction between particles,
3) attractional interaction between particles, and
4) pulsational interaction between particles.

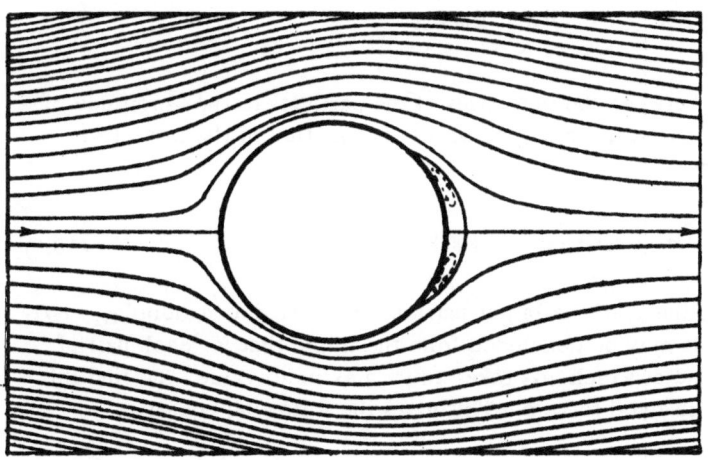

Fig. 29. Flow lines around a streamlined spherical particle for Re = 1 (ψ_{π} = 0.005; 0.05; 0.1; 0.2; 0.3·0.4; 0.5 etc.).

The subsequent sections of the book deal in order with all the above elementary types of interaction between aerosol particles in a sonic field.

§ 10. Orthokinetic Interaction between Aerosol Particles

If there are two particles one behind the other of different dimensions (or densities), so that they are moving at different velocities, they will, in the course of this motion, get closer together or separate from each other. This type of longitudinal approach or separation is given the name orthokinetic* particle interaction. It occurs during vibratory, drift, and pulsational motion of the particles.

The most interesting type of orthokinetic interaction is that which occurs when the particles are executing vibratory motion. When all is said and done, this effect tops all the other kinds of orthokinetic interaction since the vibratory motion occurs at a rate incomparably higher than the drift or pulsating motion of the particles. Let us consider the conditions under which it becomes possible for orthokinetic approach to occur between two particles until they touch, i.e., the particles collide during vibratory motion.

It is not infrequently assumed [167] that orthokinetic collision between two vibrating particles becomes possible when the smaller particle gets into the "aggregation volume" of the larger particle, which consists of a cylinder with a radius equal to the sum of the radii of the two particles, $r_a = r_1 + r_2$, and an altitude equal to twice the difference between the amplitudes of the displacements that the particles undergo during vibration thus $h_a = 2(A_{p_2} - A_{p_1}) = 2(\mu_{p_2} - \mu_{p_1}) A_g$, and with hemispheres at the ends. But this scheme needs substantial modification. First, it neglects the phase differences between the vibrations of the interacting particles, and second, it ignores flow in the medium around the particles, which results in the particles being deflected somewhat to the side as they approach one another.

We shall now deal with these two questions in succession.

If the velocity of the particles in the medium follows the law $u_g = U_g \sin \omega t$, the absolute difference between the velocities of two spherical particles 1 and 2 of radii r_1 and r_2 at the instant of time t may be found in the following way:

$$\Delta u_p = u_{p_1} - u_{p_2} = \mu_{p_1} U_g \sin(\omega t - \varphi_1) - \mu_{p_2} U_g \sin(\omega t - \varphi_2), \tag{10.1}$$

where μ_{p_1} and μ_{p_2} are the degree to which the first and second particles are carried along in the vibratory motion of the medium, as found from Eq. (5.16), while φ_1 and φ_2 are the phase angles of the vibrations of the particles as found from (5.14).

The maximum (or amplitude) value of the difference ΔU_p between the velocities of the particles is reached at a time t_0 and a phase angle φ_0 which may be found by taking the derivative $d(\Delta u_p)/dt$ and setting it equal to zero, thus:

$$\tan \omega t_0 = \tan\left(\frac{\pi}{2} + \varphi_0\right) = \frac{\mu_{p_2}^2 - \mu_{p_1}^2}{\mu_{p_1} \mu_{g_1} - \mu_{p_2} \mu_{g_2}}. \tag{10.2}$$

The ratio of the maximum value of the difference between the velocities of the particles to the amplitude of the particle velocity U_g in the medium, or, in other words, the degree of relative motion of the particles, $\mu_{12} = \Delta U_p/U_g$, is given by the following expression:

$$\mu_{12} = \{\mu_{p_1}^2 + \mu_{p_2}^2 - 2\mu_{p_1} \mu_{p_2} (\mu_{p_1} \mu_{p_2} + \mu_{g_1} \mu_{g_2})\}^{1/2}. \tag{10.3}$$

Figure 30 gives values of μ_{12} as a function of the radius r_1 of the larger particle and the reduced radius $r_{2rr} = r_2/r_1$ of the smaller particle for different frequencies. It may be concluded from the figure that for each pair of particles, there is an optimum frequency of the sound at which μ_{12} takes on its maximum value. To find this frequency, we take the derivative $d\mu_{12}/d\omega$ and set it equal to zero. This gives the following equation:

$$\omega_{opt} = \frac{1}{r_{2rr} \tau_1}, \tag{10.4}$$

or, explicity:

$$f_{opt} = \frac{9\eta}{4\pi \rho_p r_2^2} r_{2rr}. \tag{10.5}$$

---

*This term (from the Greek orthos, straight, and kinetikos, relating to motion) comes closer to expressing the essence of the phenomenon than the term "kinematic" from the Greek kinema, motion) proposed in [121], as will become especially obvious from § 11.

76

For a particle of unit density suspended in air, if r is expressed in μ and f is expressed in kcps, this formula is of the form:

$$f_{\text{opt}} = \left(\frac{13.2}{r_{2\mu}^2} \right) r_{2\text{rr}} \quad \text{kcps} \tag{10.5'}$$

At the optimum frequency the constants of the vibratory motion of the particles and of the medium are given by the expressions:

$$\mu_{p_1} = \mu_{g_2} = \cos \varphi_1 = \frac{r_{2\text{rr}}}{\sqrt{1 + r_{2\text{rr}}^2}}, \tag{10.6}$$

$$\mu_{p_2} = \mu_{g_1} = \cos \varphi_2 = \frac{1}{\sqrt{1 + r_{2\text{rr}}^2}}, \tag{10.7}$$

$$\tan \varphi_1 = \frac{1}{r_{2\text{rr}}}, \quad \tan \varphi_2 = r_{2\text{rr}}, \tag{10.8}$$

$$\omega t_0 = \frac{\pi}{2}, \quad \varphi_0 = 0, \tag{10.9}$$

$$\mu_{12} = \frac{1 - r_{2\text{rr}}^2}{1 + r_{2\text{rr}}^2}. \tag{10.10}$$

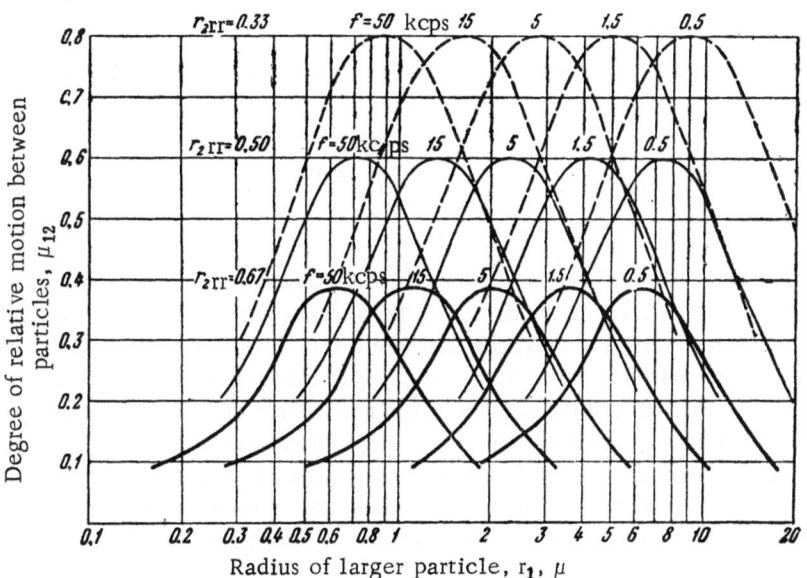

Fig. 30. Degree of relative motion μ_{12} between two aerosol particles for different frequencies and dimension ratios.

At the instant the relative motion between the particles reaches its maximum value, the flow-around factors of the particles by the medium are equal to:

$$\mu_{g_1}^0 = \mu_{g_1}^2 = \frac{1}{1 + r_{2rr}^2}, \tag{10.11}$$

$$\mu_{g_2}^0 = \mu_{g_2}^2 = \frac{r_{2rr}^2}{1 + r_{2rr}^2}. \tag{10.12}$$

Similar expressions are also found for the relative displacement of the particles, since the displacement and the velocity are proportional [see Eq. (1.11)]. Accordingly, it may be seen that the limiting distance between particles (in the direction of vibratory flow), at which orthokinetic collision is possible, is given by

$$A_{12} = \mu_{12} A_g, \tag{10.13}$$

and, hence, the altitude of the aggregation volume is equal to

$$h_a = 2\mu_{12} A_g. \tag{10.14}$$

The altitude of the aggregation volume calculated from this formula is substantially greater than twice the difference between the amplitudes of the vibratory displacements of the particles (if we leave out of consideration the fact that the particles are slowed down by the highly developed boundary layers surrounding them).

Let us now consider the trajectory of the smaller particle as it approaches the larger particle.

If the smaller particle is infinitesimally small absolutely and relatively, it follows the motion of the gas "obediently" along its original line of flow and the possibility of its being captured by the larger particle is equal to zero, since all the flow lines go around the larger particle without intersecting it (except the central line).

However, aerosol particles are of finite dimensions and mass, so that because of its inertia, the smaller particle is deflected from its original flow line, as shown in Fig. 31. In this case, the aggregation volume is of the form shown by the dotted line.

The capture coefficient of particles, as we know from [66, 121, 122, and 129], is given by the relation:

$$\vartheta = \left(\frac{y}{r_1} \right)^2 = y_{rr}^2 \tag{10.15}$$

Unfortunately, when it comes to calculating the capture coefficient, the existing formulas, and particularly the familiar Langmuir formula [120], are no good. First, the formula is for the case where the characteristic dimensions of the particle are small in comparison with the dimensions of the sphere that the gas is flowing around, but in our case both particles are as a rule of comparable size, so that the "hooking" effect [121] is very large. Second, it is assumed that the motion of the particles is uniform, while our particles are executing nonuniform motion according to a sinusoidal or more complicated law, and, moreover, from different initial positions. Third, it is assumed that the thickness of the boundary layer around the sphere is negligibly small in comparison with its dimensions, but in our case the thickness of the boundary layer is considerably greater than the dimensions of the interacting particles, so that the smaller particle is pulled in as it approaches the larger particle.

Finding a rigorous mathematical solution of the problem of the capture coefficient of aerosol particles in a single orthokinetic approach in a sonic field presents considerable difficulties. Fortunately, there is no

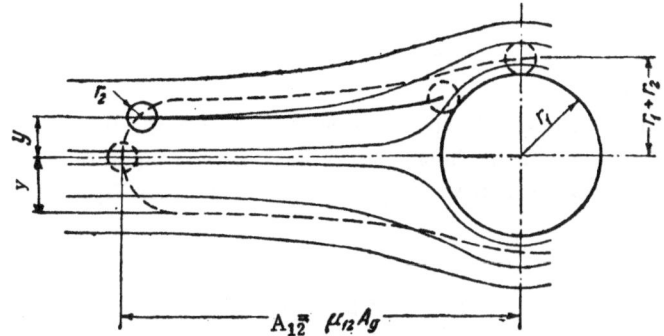

Fig. 31. Orthokinetic collision of aerosol particles. The "aggregation" volume for a single approach of particles is shown by the dotted line.

particular need to overcome the difficulties, since, in a sonic field, where multiple orthokinetic approaches and withdrawals of particles are occurring, the concept of capture coefficient, as will be shown later on (§11), loses its usual meaning. However, in order to trace out the form of the aggregation volume, we shall make an approximate calculation of the limiting values of the "one-time" capture coefficient, giving the minimum and maximum values of the cross-sectional area of the aggregation volume.

Inertial deflection of a particle from its original line of flow occurs principally in close approach to the sphere in the gas stream, where the radii of curvature of the flow lines are very small (see Fig. 29). At the more remote parts of the flow lines, the inertial displacement of the particle per approach cycle is small, since the flow lines have much less curvature.

Hence it may be concluded that the minimum value of the capture coefficient ϑ_{min} occurs for the case where the particle is far from the sphere, and is reached at the instant its relative velocity drops to zero, so that it may be assumed in tentative calculations that the particle moves without being deflected from its original line of flow.

If the reduced radius of the particle is r_{2rr}, at the instant it touches the sphere, the radius vector is equal to $\rho_{rr} = 1 + r_{2rr}$. Assume for simplicity that contact occurs for $\theta = 90°$ (actually $\theta \approx 98°$, but this has little effect on our calculations). The function for the flow line passing through the point $\rho_{rr} = 1 + r_{2rr}$ and $\theta = 90°$, will, from (9.22), be as follows:

$$\psi_{rr} = \frac{r_{2rr}}{2(1 + r_{2rr})} \left[r_{2rr}^2 + \frac{3}{2} r_{2rr} + \frac{3\mathrm{Re}}{16} (r_{2rr}^2 + 3r_{2rr} + 3) \right]. \tag{10.16}$$

In order to calculate ϑ_{min}, we must, by means of Eq. (9.18) find the ordinate of the point of the flow line which is at the distance $\rho_{rr} = A_{12} = \mu_{12}A_g$.

At large distances from the sphere ($\rho_{rr} > 10$) the terms $1/\rho_{rr}^2$ and $1/\rho_{rr}$ in Eq. (9.18) may be neglected, so that the equation for the flow function takes the form:

$$\psi_{rr} = \left[\frac{1}{2} \rho_{rr}^2 - \frac{3}{4} \rho_{rr} + \frac{3\mathrm{Re}}{32} (1 - \cos\theta) \rho_{rr}^2 \right] \sin^2\theta. \tag{10.17}$$

Since the problem involves flow lines passing close to the central line, we may set $\rho_{rr} \approx x_{rr}$ and $\sin^2\theta = (y_{rr}/\rho_{rr})^2 \approx (y_{rr}/x_{rr})^2$. Further, under these conditions, the angle θ formed by the radius vector with the center line is small, so that, for the left branch of the flow line, where $\theta \to \pi$, we set $\cos\theta \approx -1$, while for the right-hand branch, where $\theta \to 0$, we may set $\cos\theta \approx +1$.

As a result of these simplifications, the equation for the flow function takes the following form:

$$\psi_{rr} = \left(\frac{1}{2} - \frac{3}{4} |x_{rr}^{-1}| + \frac{3\mathrm{Re}}{16} \right) y_{rr}^2 \qquad (\text{as } \theta \to \pi), \tag{10.18}$$

79

$$\psi_{rr} = \left(\frac{1}{2} - \frac{3}{4} \left| x_{rr}^{-1} \right| \right) y_{rr}^2 \quad (\text{as} \quad \theta \to 0). \tag{10.19}$$

When we are dealing with particle approach, we have to use the first equation, while for withdrawal of particles we use the second, which is nothing more or less than the equation for the Stokes flow line function. Usually, the distance x_{rr} is so large that we may set $x_{rr}^{-1} \approx 0$, and then Eqs. (10.18) and (10.19) become even simpler:

$$\psi_{rr} = \left(\frac{1}{2} + \frac{3}{16} \text{Re} \right) y_{rr \infty}^2 \quad (\text{for} \quad \theta \to \pi), \tag{10.18'}$$

$$\psi_{rr} = \frac{1}{2} y_{rr \infty}^2 \quad (\text{for} \quad \theta \to 0). \tag{10.19'}$$

Setting Eq. (10.16) equal to (10.18'), and using (10.15), we obtain

$$\vartheta_{\min} = \frac{8 r_{2rr}}{(1 + r_{2rr})(8 + 3\text{Re})} \left[r_{2rr}^2 + \frac{3}{2} r_{2rr} + \frac{3\text{Re}}{16} (r_{2rr}^2 + 3r_{2rr} + 3) \right]. \tag{10.20}$$

This expression takes on its minimum value as $\text{Re} \to 0$. Hence, to calculate $\vartheta_{\min}$, we must use the following formula:

$$\vartheta_{\min} = \frac{r_{2rr} + 1.5}{r_{2rr} + 1} r_{2rr}^2 \simeq (1.25 - 1.50) r_{2rr}^2. \tag{10.20'}$$

Since the inertial deflection of the particle from its original line of flow was completely neglected in deriving this formula, the results are somewhat too low.

The maximum value of the capture coefficient $\vartheta_{\max}$ occurs for the case where the small particle is close to the sphere and reaches it with the maximum (or amplitude) value of the relative velocity. The value of $\vartheta_{\max}$ may be calculated approximately in the following way.

Assume that we know the value of the capture coefficient ϑ_L, as calculated from Langmuir's formula, neglecting the hooking effect. In this case, the origin of the starting point of the trajectory of the particle has the following value, from (10.15):

$$y_{rr}^L = \sqrt{\vartheta_L}. \tag{10.21}$$

If the particle is of finite dimensions, the trajectory changes somewhat in that it shifts upwards. If we look at Fig. 29, which gives the flow lines around a sphere in a gas stream, we come to the conclusion that if y_L is not too small ($y_L \gtrsim 0.4$-0.5, or, what is the same thing, $\vartheta_L \gtrsim 0.16$-0.25), the increase in the ordinate of the initial point of the trajectory of the particle is equal, roughly speaking, to the radius r_{2rr} of the particle. Accordingly, if we include the hooking effect, the initial ordinate on the trajectory of the particle is approximately equal to:

$$y_{rr} \approx y_{rr}^L + r_{2rr} \approx \sqrt{\vartheta_L} + r_{2rr}, \tag{10.22}$$

while the capture coefficient, from (10.15), is equal to:

$$\vartheta_{max} \approx (\sqrt{\vartheta_L} + r_{2rr})^2.$$

(10.23)

Langmuir's formula, which is to be used in calculating the capture coefficient ϑ_L neglecting the hooking effect, is of the form [120, 121][*]

$$\vartheta_L = \left(1 + \frac{0.75 \log 2k}{k - k_{cr}} \right)^{-2},$$

(10.24)

where k is the coefficient of inertia of the small particle:

$$k = \frac{u_{21} \tau_2}{r_1}$$

(10.25)

(u_{21} and τ_2 are the relative velocity and the relaxation time of the small particle, r_1 is the radius of the large particle), and k_{cr} is the critical coefficient of inertia given, for Oseen flow, according to L. M. Levin [66], by the formula

$$k_{cr} = 1.49 \sqrt{\frac{16 - 3Re}{24 + 12Re}}.$$

(10.26)

Table 11 gives the minimum and maximum capture coefficients calculated by the above method for one-time orthokinetic particle approach in a sonic field of normal intensity ($J = 0.1$ W/cm^2, $U_g = 220$ cm/sec), at the optimum frequency for each pair of particles. The relative velocity u_{21} of the small particle was found from the equation $u_{21} = \mu_{12} v_{\theta rr} U_g$, where $v_{\theta rr}$ is a correction for retardation in the boundary layer, assumed equal to the reduced velocity at the distance $y_{rr} = 1 + r_{2rr}$ and $\theta = 90°$, as given by (9.13)

$$v_{\theta rr} = \frac{0.75}{1 + r_{2rr}} e^{-\frac{1}{4} Re (1 + r_{2rr})} - 1.$$

(10.27)

The Reynolds number Re was found for the absolute velocity of flow of the medium around a large particle, given by $u_{gp} = \mu_{g1}^0 u_g$ where μ_{g1}^0 is the flow-around factor of the particle at the instant the unperturbed vibrational velocity reaches its maximum value, as given by Eq. (10.11).

It may be concluded from Table 11 that for particles of radius $r_1 = 0.5 \div 1\mu$, we have $\vartheta = 0.3 - 0.7$, while for larger particles, $\vartheta = 0.7 - 1.5$. Accordingly, the aggregation volume of the large particle is a long cylinder, having the cross section $\vartheta_{min} \pi r_1^2$ at the ends, and then broadening out toward the middle and reaching the cross section $\vartheta_{max} \pi r_1^2$ at the sphere. The cross section is even larger right at the center level of the particle. Here it is equal to $(1 + r_{2rr})^2 \pi r_1^2$.

Thus, the aggregation volume in this case turns out to be at any rate considerably less than the volume of a cylinder of radius $r_1 + r_2$, to reach which, the capture coefficient would have to have the value $\vartheta_{cyl} = (1 + r_{2rr})^2$.

The orthokinetic interaction occurring during particle drift is generally associated with small velocities, so that it may be assumed that in this case the capture coefficient of the particles is close to the values of ϑ min, which lie in the range 0.99−0.82.

---

[*]N. S. Shishkin's simplified formula [129], gives results that are too high for our comparatively large values of k.

TABLE 11

r_1, μ	r_2, μ	r_{2rr}	τ_2, sec	μ_g^0	ugp cm/sec	Re_1	k_{cr}	μ_{12}	$v\theta_{rr}$	u_2 cm/sec	k	Θ_L^{max}	Θ_{min}	Θ_{max}
1.0	0.25	0.25	$7.5 \cdot 10^{-7}$	0.94	207	0.276	1.110	0.88	0.496	96.0	0.72	0	0.09	0.09
	0.50	0.50	$3 \cdot 10^{-6}$	0.80	176	0.235	1.125	0.60	0.580	76.5	2.29	0.255	0.33	1.00
2.0	0.5	0.25	$3 \cdot 10^{-6}$	0.94	207	0.552	1.020	0.88	0.575	111.2	1.67	0.175	0.09	0.45
	1.0	0.50	$1.2 \cdot 10^{-5}$	0.80	176	0.470	1.045	0.60	0.650	85.8	5.15	0.492	0.33	1.45
	1.5	0.75	$2.7 \cdot 10^{-5}$	0.64	141	0.376	1.076	0.28	0.692	42.6	5.75	0.041	0.72	0.90
3.0	1.0	0.33	$1.2 \cdot 10^{-5}$	0.90	198	0.792	0.951	0.80	0.668	117.5	4.70	0.478	0.15	1.05
	1.5	0.50	$2.7 \cdot 10^{-5}$	0.80	176	0.705	0.976	0.60	0.705	93.0	8.37	0.607	0.33	1.65
	2.0	0.67	$4.8 \cdot 10^{-5}$	0.69	152	0.608	1.004	0.38	0.730	61.0	9.76	0.637	0.58	2.15
4.0	1.0	0.25	$1.2 \cdot 10^{-5}$	0.94	207	1.104	0.874	0.88	0.700	135.4	4.06	0.450	0.09	0.85
	2.0	0.50	$4.8 \cdot 10^{-5}$	0.80	176	0.940	0.912	0.60	0.753	99.4	11.93	0.678	0.33	1.75
	3.0	0.75	$1.08 \cdot 10^{-4}$	0.64	141	0.752	0.963	0.28	0.777	47.9	12.94	0.690	0.72	2.50
5.0	1.0	0.20	$1.2 \cdot 10^{-5}$	0.96	211	1.410	0.800	0.92	0.731	148.0	3.55	0.426	0.06	0.75
	2.0	0.40	$4.8 \cdot 10^{-5}$	0.86	189	1.260	0.835	0.72	0.778	123.2	11.82	0.676	0.22	1.50
	3.0	0.60	$1.08 \cdot 10^{-4}$	0.73	160	1.067	0.880	0.47	0.799	81.6	22.10	0.778	0.47	2.20
	4.0	0.80	$1.92 \cdot 10^{-4}$	0.61	134	0.893	0.925	0.22	0.814	39.4	15.12	0.719	0.82	2.70

§ 11. Parakinetic Interaction between Aerosol Particles

If there are two aerosol particles of different sizes (or density), arranged such that the line joining their centers is not in the same direction as the vibratory motion, a transverse, or, more exactly, longitudinal-transverse interaction is set up between them, which is given the name parakinetic.*

This type of interaction, first discussed in our paper [82], is set up as a result of unilateral, or bilateral distortion of the fields of flow around the particles during relative motion, and is due to the difference in dimensions (or densities). It will be shown below that as a result of the Oseen asymmetry and the curvature of the flow lines, the particles are somewhat deflected from their original forward trajectory when they move backward. Since the flow around aerosol particles in a sound field is of a repetitious back-and-forth nature, the first deflection is followed by a second deflection, and the second by a third, and so on cycle after cycle. As a result, the particles get moved about relative to one another in a very short time.

The geometric picture of parakinetic particle motion is rather complicated. If we are going to understand it, we need some additional information on the theory of flow around particles, dealing with the steady state flow lines at large distances from a sphere, of the order of the mean distance between the particles in natural aerosols. In this case, the simplified equation (10.17) for the flow function may be used to construct the flow lines.

For flow lines passing close to the center line (x axis), we can, if we exclude the immediate field ($x_{rr} < 10$), use the even simpler equations (10.18) and (10.19) for the flow function, and if these equations are solved for y_{rr}, we obtain the following expressions:

$$y_{rr} = \left(\frac{\psi_{rr}}{\frac{1}{2} + \frac{3}{4} x_{rr}^{-1} + \frac{3Re}{16}} \right)^{1/2} \quad \text{for} \quad x < 0. \tag{11.1}$$

$$y_{rr} = \left(\frac{\psi_{rr}}{\frac{1}{2} - \frac{3}{4} x_{rr}^{-1}} \right)^{1/2} \quad \text{for} \quad x > 0. \tag{11.2}$$

The second equation is the equation of a Stokes flow line, and may be obtained from the first equation by setting Re = 0. The ordinates at which these flow lines start, $y_{rr - \infty}$, are found by setting $x_{rr} = \infty$.

Table 12 gives values of y_{rr} and $\Delta y_{rr} = y_{rr} - y_{rr - \infty}$ calculated from Eqs. (11.1) and (11.2) for $\psi_{rr} = 0.1$ and $\psi_{rr} = 1$ with Re = 0 and Re = 1. Figure 32 shows flow lines plotted in greatly exaggerated form (the scale of the increments Δy_{rr} is a factor of 100 greater than the scale of the distances along the x axis). For the two cases we have $y_{rr - \infty}$ 0.381 − 0.447, and $y_{rr - \infty} = 1.205 - 1.415$ respectively. The curves at the bottom of Fig. 32 gives values of the reduced radii of curvature of the flow lines shown at the top, namely, $R_{1rr} = R_1/r_1$, as calculated from the formula (see, for example [11]):

$$R_{1rr} = \frac{(1 + y_{rr}'^2)^{3/2}}{y_{rr}''} = \frac{-\left(\frac{1}{2} + \frac{3}{4} x_{rr}^{-1} + \frac{3Re}{16} \right)^{3/2} x_{rr}^3}{\frac{3}{4} \psi_{rr}^{1/2} \left[1 - \frac{9}{16} x_{rr}^{-1} \left(\frac{1}{2} + \frac{3}{4} x_{rr}^{-1} + \frac{3Re}{16} \right)^{-1} \right]} \tag{11.3}$$

(y_{rr}' and y_{rr}'' are the first and second derivatives, the first of which is so small that it may be neglected).

For the flow lines far from the center line, we use Eq. (10.17), which, when solved for ρ_{rr}, gives the equation for the flow line in explicit form. For large values of ψ_{rr}, and close approach, it may be written in the form

─────────

*From the Greek para, alongside of, around, or bypassing; and kinetikos, relationg to motion.

TABLE 12

x_{rr}	$-\infty$	-200	-100	-50	-25	-15	-10	0	$+10$	$+15$	$+25$	$+50$	$+100$	$+200$	$+\infty$
I. $\psi_{rr} = 0.1$															
Re = 0 $\{\ y_{rr}$	0.447	0.448	0.451	0.454	0.461	0.471	0.485		0.485	0.471	0.461	0.454	0.451	0.448	0.447
Δy_{rr}	0	0.001	0.004	0.007	0.014	0.024	0.038		0.038	0.024	0.014	0.007	0.004	0.001	0
Re = 1 $\{\ y_{rr}$	0.381	0.382	0.383	0.385	0.390	0.395	0.404								
Δy_{rr}	0	0.001	0.002	0.004	0.009	0.014	0.023								
II. $\psi_{rr} = 1$															
Re = 0 $\{\ y_{rr}$	1.415	1.418	1.424	1.435	1.455	1.486	1.533		1.533	1.486	1.455	1.435	1.424	1.418	1.415
Δy_{rr}	0	0.003	0.009	0.020	0.040	0.071	0.118		0.118	0.071	0.040	0.020	0.009	0.003	0
Re = 1 $\{\ y_{rr}$	1.205	1.206	1.210	1.216	1.233	1.249	1.278								
Δy_{rr}	0	0.001	0.005	0.011	0.028	0.044	0.073								

$$p_{rr} = 12G^{-1} + \sqrt{32\psi_{rr}}\, G^{-\frac{1}{2}} \sin^{-1}\theta, \tag{11.4}$$

where $G = 16 + 3\mathrm{Re}\,(1 - \cos\theta)$.

Figure 33 shows in exaggerated form (the scale of the increment Δy_{rr} is a factor of 20 greater than the scale of the distances along the x_{rr} axis), the flow lines calculated from Eq. (11.4) for $\psi_{rr} = 100$ and $\psi_{rr} = 1000$ for the "limiting" types of flow: a) Re = 0, and b) Re = 1 (the dotted lines show the flow in the opposite direction).

All the flow lines pass at a considerable distance from the center line (x axis). The ordinates at which they start (at infinite), marked at the left end of each of the lines, were found from (11.4), using the formula:

$$y_{rr\,-\infty} = \left(\frac{2\psi_{rr}}{1 + 0.375\mathrm{Re}}\right)^{1/2}. \tag{11.5}$$

For $\psi_{rr} = 100$, we have $y_{rr\,-\,\infty} = 12-14$, and for $\psi_{rr} = 1000$, we have $y_{rr\,-\,\infty} = 38-45$.

To complete the picture, the curves at the bottom of Figs. 33a and 33b give values of the reduced radii of curvature of the flow lines, $R_{1rr} = R_1/r_1$. They were calculated from the familiar formula [11]:

$$R_{1rr} = \frac{(\rho_{rr}^2 + \rho_{rr}'^2)^{3/2}}{\rho_{rr}^2 + 2\rho_{rr}'^2 - \rho_{rr}\,\rho_{rr}''}, \tag{11.6}$$

where ρ_{rr}' and ρ_{rr}'' are the first and second derivatives of the radius vector, as found by differentiating Eq. (11.4):

$$\rho_{rr}' = -36\mathrm{Re}\sin\theta\, G^{-2} - \sqrt{32\psi_{rr}}\, G^{-\frac{1}{2}}\left(\sin^{-2}\theta\cos\theta + \frac{3}{2}\mathrm{Re}\, G^{-1}\right),$$

$$\rho_{rr}'' = 36\,\mathrm{Re}\, G^{-2}(6\mathrm{Re}G^{-1}\sin^2\theta - \cos\theta) + \sqrt{32\psi_{rr}}\, G^{-\frac{1}{2}}\sin\theta\left[2\sin^{-4}\theta - \sin^{-2}\theta\right.$$

$$\left. + \frac{3}{2}\,\mathrm{Re}\, G^{-1}\left(\sin^{-2}\theta\cos\theta + \frac{9}{2}\mathrm{Re}\, G^{-1}\right)\right].$$

The conclusion may be drawn from what has been presented that flow lines passing close to the center line undergo comparatively little deformation, excluding the immediate field, which may be neglected in one-time flow around the sphere. However, the important thing for us is the following:

a) The flow lines occuring in Oseen flow (Re > 0), are appreciably asymmetric, the right branch being much steeper than the left. Thus, in the range $x_{rr} = 10-50$, for Re = 1, the ordinate increment Δy_{rr} on the right is greater than the one on the left by the amount $(0.003-0.015)\, r_1$ for $\psi_{rr} = 0.1$, and by the amount $(0.009-0.045)\, r_1$ for $\psi_{rr} = 1$ (see Table 12),

b) The radius of curvature of the flow lines, except for those that are quite far away, is not large, and lines mostly in the range $(10^3-10^5)\, r_1$, which gives $R_1 = 0.35-35$ cm, even for the "limiting" radius of the sphere, $r_1 = 3.5\mu$,

c) The asymmetry, steepness, and curvature of the flow lines increases rapidly as we approach the sphere in the gas stream.

As for the flow lines far from the center line, it may be seen that they undergo a great deal more deformation than the flow lines near the sphere (compare Fig. 29).

Here the asymmetry of the flow lines takes on large dimensions. As we get away from the center line, the incident gas stream flows around the sphere with ever-increasing delay and ever-increasing steepness, and after a flow line has risen it no longer comes back to its original level (within the range of the figure), with the

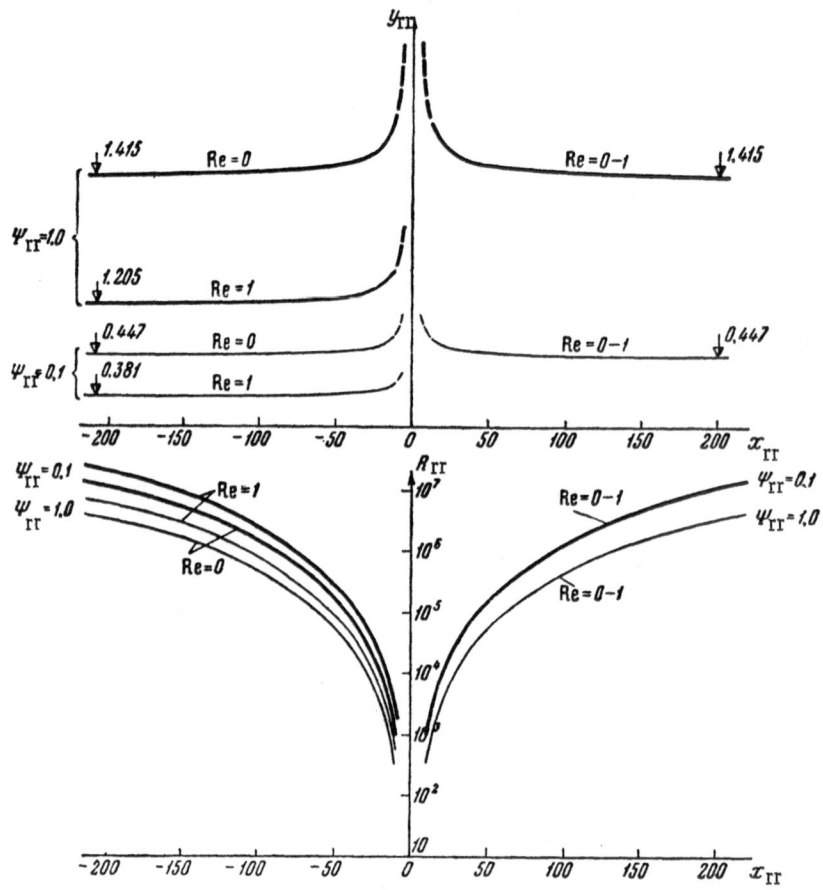

Fig. 32. Steady-state flow lines and radii of curvature for a spherical particle near the center line ($\psi'_{rr} = 0.1$, and $\psi''_{rr} = 1.0$).

result that the right-hand branch is always flatter than the left-hand branch. The radius of curvature of the flow lines, except for the flex points, is of approximately the same order of magnitude as in the first case. This is the steady-state picture of the flow around aerosol particles at large distances.

Let us now imagine that the medium is executing vibrations of amplitude A_g, and follow the behavior of a particle in the medium vibrating:

1) Near the center line, in remote approach to the sphere, where the steady-state flow lines are of the sort given by Eqs. (11.1) and (11.2) and shown in Fig. 32,

2) Far from the center line, and symmetrically about the sphere, where the steady-state flow lines are of the type given by Eq. (11.4), and shown in Fig. 33.

These to cases are remarkable for the fact that they give the best possible illustration of the two diametrically opposite tendencies found in viscous back-and-forth flow by obstacles, which, together, constitute one aspect of parakinetic interaction between aerosol particles in a sonic field.

So that the form and substance of these tendencies may be immediately obvious, let us consider first the behavior of particles in a medium executing a steady-state successive back-and-forth motion, always at the same velocity: $|\vec{u}_g| = |u| = $ const. In this case, in discussing the forward motion of any particle in the medium we may be guided by the steady state flow pattern shown in Figs. 32 and 33, but if we are talking about the backward motion, we use as a pattern the mirror image of these figures about the y axis.

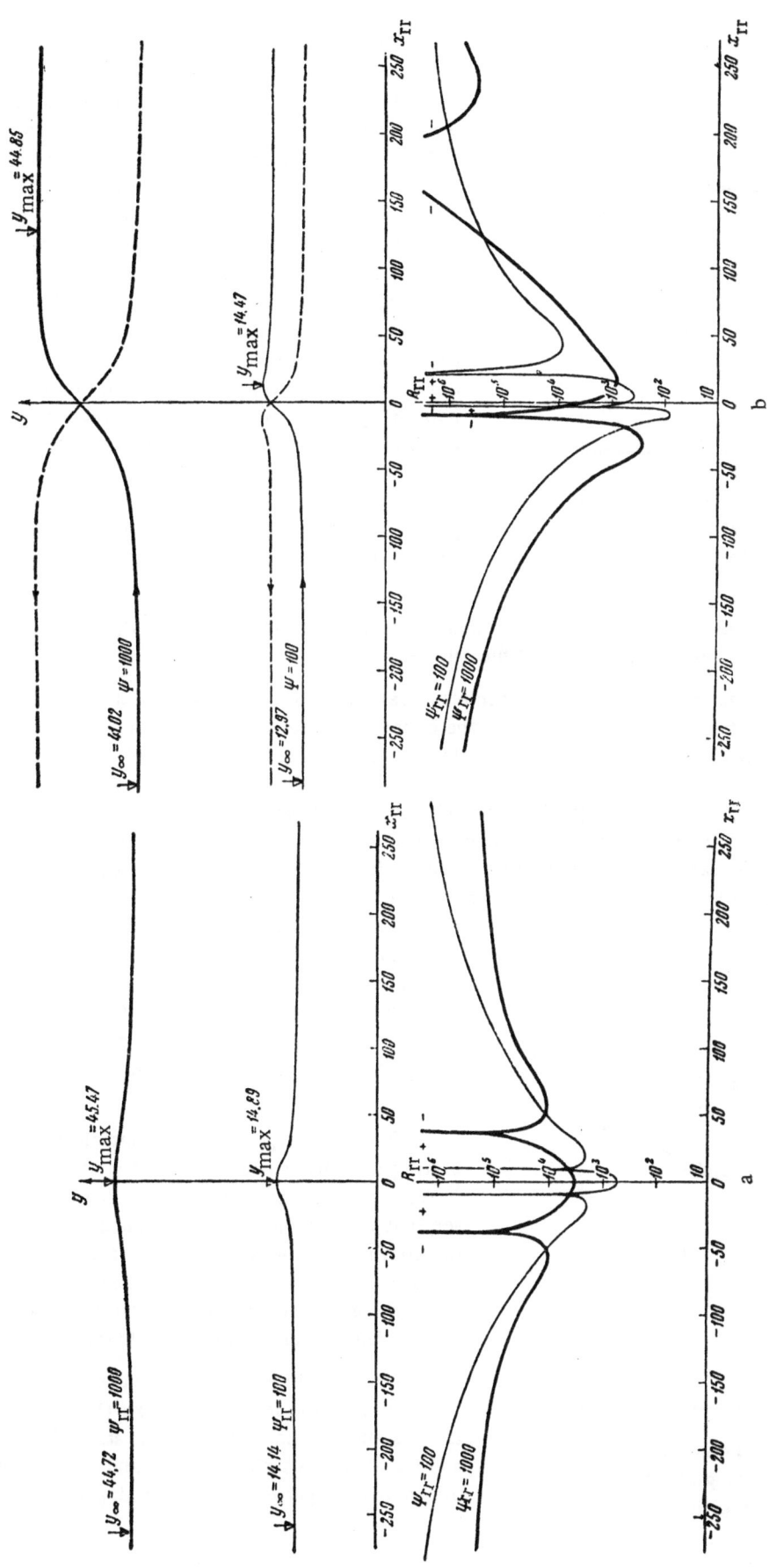

Fig. 33. Steady-state flow lines and radii of curvature for a spherical particle at large distances from the center line ($\psi_{rr} = 100$ and $\psi_{rr} = 1000$), a) for Re = 0; b) for Re = 1 (the dotted lines show the flow lines in the opposite direction).

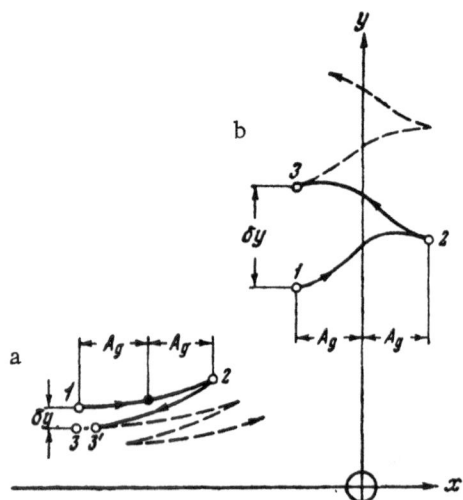

Fig. 34. Hysteresis in the flow around an aerosol particle. a) Near the center line, b) far from the center line.

Consider first the behavior of a particle in the medium which, at the instant the forward motion starts, is at the point 1, close to the center line, and far to the left of the y axis (Fig. 34a). If the velocity and therefore the value of Re are finite, the motion of the particle occurs along the straight, Oseen flow line shown in Fig. 32. Moving along this line, the particle reaches the point 2 at the end of its path. The backward motion of the particle occurs along a flow line which is the mirror image of the Stokes flow line passing through the symmetric point 2. As has already been pointed out, this flow line is steeper than the Oseen line. Because of this, when the particle in the medium is moving backward, it moves in the direction of the point 3, lying below the original point 1 by some small, but finite amount, δy. We know however that the velocity is lower behind an obstacle in a gas stream than in front of it (see §9 and 12). As a result, instead of reaching the point 3, the particle reaches the point 3', which is somewhat closer to the center of the obstacle.

In succeeding cycles of the motion, the displacement is repeated many times, with the result that the particle zig-zags up close to the center line of the sphere.

If, at the instant the motion starts, the particle in question in the medium as at the point 1, far from the center line and to the left of the y axis (Fig. 34b), the behavior of the particle takes a different turn. In the forward motion, the particle in the medium moves along a straight Oseen flow line, of the type shown in Fig. 33b, and, as a result, ends its path at the point 2. However, in the backward motion, the particle follows a flow line consisting of the mirror image of the straight Oseen line passing through the point 2. This line causes the particle to end its backward path at the higher point 3, displaced with respect to the original point by some amount δy. The same phenomenon is repeated again and again in successive cycles of the motion, and, as a result, the particle zig-zags farther and farther from the center line. The reason for the phenomenon [81] is the same as that for the Oseen asymmetry in the flow around a sphere, namely, the inertia of the medium (that a vibrating medium is susceptible to flow hysteresis is shown by the velocity field itself as given in Fig. 28, since the slope of the velocity at a point on the right is always different from the slope at the symmetric point on the left).

Practically speaking, the particle motion in a vibrating medium is not constant, but varies sinusoidally or in some more complex way. It is, however, not difficult to see that even in these cases the phenomenon that we are considering continues to act. It is true though that some specific features show up. If the particle velocity in the medium varies according to the sinusoidal law $u_g = U_g \sin \omega t$, the features are simply as follows.

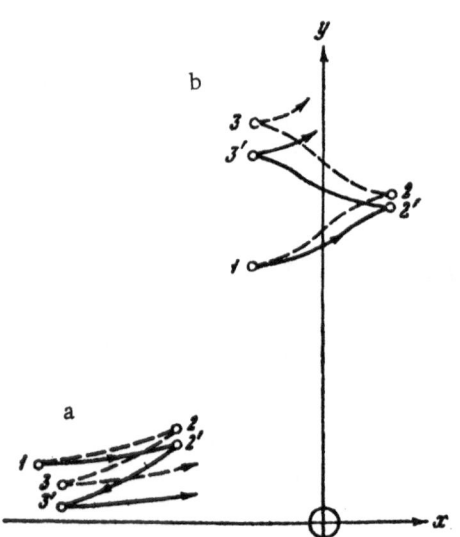

Fig. 35. Diagram showing how self-centering (a) and self-decentering (b) of aerosol particles occurs in a sonic field.

Let a particle, vibrating near the center line, be at some point to the left of the y axis (Fig. 35a), at the initial instant of time. Then, at the start of the displacement, as long as the particle velocity, and with it the Re number, are small, the particle will naturally move along a steady-state Stokes line. However, as the stream velocity and hence the Re number, increase, the particle begins to move in a flatter and flatter trajectory, since it is passing to a more pronounced Oseen line. Then, after reaching the maximum velocity (at the point through which the "maximum" Oseen line passes), the steepness of the trajectory begins to increase in reverse order, and, at the end point 2, the particle is following a new Stokes line. The particle in the medium executes its backward motion from start to finish along the new Stokes flow line, and ends up at the point 3, which is below the original point 1 by a somewhat smaller amount than that shown in Fig. 34a. The equation of the trajectory of the particle for the above type of "sinusoidally developing" Oseen flow in the medium may be found, if we neglect the retarding effect of the boundary layer (i.e., far from the sphere), from Eqs. (11.1) and (11.2), by setting Re = $\mathbf{Re} \sin \omega$ and making use of the fact that $\sin \omega t = \sqrt{1 - \cos^2 \omega t}$, where $\cos \omega t = (x_1 - A_g - x)/A_g = 1 - (x_{rr} - x_{1rr})/A_{g_{rr}}$ ($\mathbf{Re}$ is the "amplitude" of the Reynolds number equal to $2r_1 U_g/\nu$ and $A_{g_{rr}}$ is the reduced amplitude of the vibrations, equal to A_g/r_1).

Equation (11.1), which applies to the forward motion, takes the following form:

$$y_{rr} = \left\{ \frac{\psi_{rr}}{\frac{1}{2} + \frac{3}{4} x_{rr}^{-1} + \frac{3\text{Re}}{16} \left[1 - \left(1 - \frac{x_{rr} - x_{1rr}}{A_{g_{rr}}} \right)^2 \right]} \right\}^{1/2} \tag{11.7}$$

Equation (11.2), which applies to the reverse motion, remains unchanged.

A particle in the medium, vibrating sinusoidally far from the center line, to the left of the y axis, also begins its motion along a Stokes line (Fig. 35b). However, as the stream velocity, and hence the Re number, increase, the particle begins to go more and more steeply, since it is passing to a more and more clearly defined Oseen flow line. Then, after the maximum velocity has been reached (at the point through which the "amplitude" of the Oseen line passes), the steepness begins to drop in the reverse order, and, at the end point 2, which is to the right of the y axis, the particle is following a new Stokes line.

The equation of the trajectory of a particle in the medium for the above type of "sinusoidally developing" Oseen flow around a sphere (if we neglect retardation of the stream) may be found from Eq. (10.17) by making the previous substitution Re = $\text{Re} \sin \omega t$, using the relation

$$\cos \omega t = \frac{x_1 - A_g - \rho \cos \theta}{A_g} = 1 - \frac{\rho_{rr} \cos \theta - x_{1rr}}{A_{g_{rr}}}.$$

As a result, we have:

$$\psi_{rr} = \left\{ \frac{1}{2} \rho_{rr}^2 - \frac{3}{4} \rho_{rr} + \frac{3\,\mathbf{Re}}{32} \rho_{rr}^2 (1 - \cos\theta) \left[2 \frac{\rho_{rr} \cos\theta - x_{1rr}}{A_{g_{rr}}} - \left(\frac{\rho_{rr} \cos\theta - x_{1rr}}{A_{g_{rr}}} \right)^2 \right] \right\}^{1/2}. \tag{11.8}$$

The backward motion of the particle begins along the same Stokes line, but it then passes to a more and more clearly defined backward Oseen line (of the type shown dotted in Fig. 33b), which has a steeper slope. As a result, at the end of this backward path, the particle, passing through the new "amplitude" point, arrives at the higher point 3, through which a new Stokes line passes. Thus, what we have here is exactly the same tendency to get farther from the center line of the sphere. The experimental confirmation of this fact is provided by the pictures shown in the paper by Schlichting [261].

The result of the above type of hysteresis in the flow around a sphere is to set up a peculiar type of acoustic streaming in the direction shown by the arrows in Fig. 36, where the closed lines are simply relative. The peculiar feature of the streaming is that the vortices are on a scale comparable with the amplitude of the vibrations, while they are in exactly the opposite direction to that observed for $A_g \ll r$ by Andrade in [140], who found that the conditions for vortices to be formed is to have $\text{Re} > 5$. Later on, Schlichting [261] showed that at the surface of an obstacle, these conditions should also give internal streaming in the opposite direction, as predicted by Carriere in [174]. This idea was confirmed experimentally by the work of West [284] which was done for values of $\text{Re} > 40$.

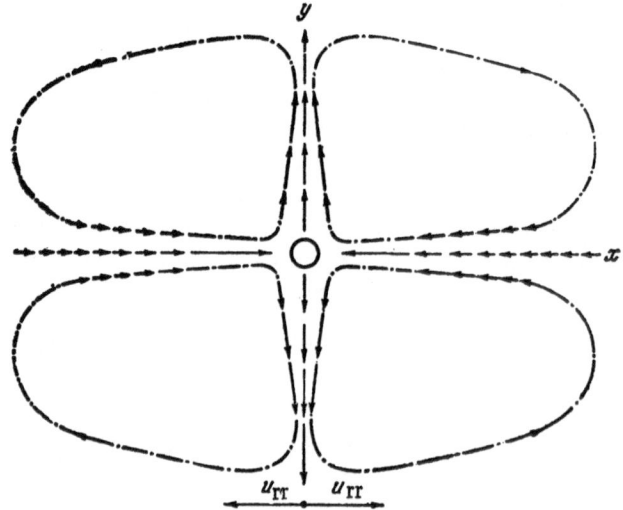

Fig. 36. Diagram of acoustic streaming around an aerosol particle suspended in a sonic field.

Subsequent theoretical and experimental studies, made by Andres and Ingard [144], Holtsmark et al. [201], and Westervelt [255], as well as by Lane [222], have shown that on passing to viscous flow around an object, the scale of the internal vortices increases rapidly, driving the external vortices far out, so that they reduce to nothing (since the vortices are further washed out by the turbulent pulsations of the medium). Strictly speaking, external vortices also exist in our case, where $A_g \gg r$, which is, however, different for the reason that:

a) The scale of the vortices bears no relation to the frequency of the vibrations in the medium (which follows from our assumption that the flow is quasi-steady-state), and,

b) The configuration of the vortices depends on the amplitude of the vibrations in the medium (which, for the present, may only be shown geometrically, since making an analytic solution of the problem of acoustic streaming around small obstacles for $A_g \gg r$ represents serious mathematical difficulties).

Let us now suppose that in the above field of flow around the spherical particle, we have another aerosol particle of radius r_2 in place of a particle in the medium. Suppose first, for simplicity, that the degree of entrainment of the particle in the vibratory motion is nearly unity, so that there is no field of flow about the particle itself to distort the above flow pattern around the sphere.

If our aerosol particle is infinitesimally small, it will behave in a way that is practically indistinguishable from the behavior of the particles in the medium, and during the vibratory motion, it will follow the same zig-zag path followed by the particles in the medium, as discussed above.* If, however, our particle has appreciable inertia, its behavior in the field of flow takes on some new features. As it moves along the curved parts of a flow line, the particle experiences more or less large centrifugal forces, with the result that it is deflected from its original parth in the direction of convexity.

Accordingly, in the first case (Fig. 35a), as the aerosol particle is moving with the forward flow, it does not arrive at the point 2, but at the point 2' which is somewhat lower, and this happens cycle after cycle. Thus, it may be seen that the inertia tends to cause hysteresis in the approach of the particle to the center line.

---

*This fact can unfortunately not be used to find the trajectories of the vortices, as investigators commonly do in the case of larger obstacles, where $r \gg A_g$ (see [140, 261], etc.). Long particle tracks, of a scale comparable with the vortices, come along one after the other, forming a continuous background on the picture. The problem of finding the trajectories of the vortices for the case $r \ll A_g$ may only be solved by synchronizing the camera shutter with the source of sound.

In the second case (Fig. 35b), the result of the centrifugal force is that the particle does not arrive at the point 2 but at the point 2', which is somewhat below the point 2. When moving backward, the particle arrives at the point 3', which is below the point 3, and so on cycle after cycle. Thus, it may be seen in this case, that the inertia keeps the particle from moving away from the center line as the flow hysteresis tends to make it do.

The zig-zag way in which a vibrating aerosol particle approaches the center line of a particle in a gas stream, due, on the one hand to flow hysteresis, and on the other, to the inertia of the particle, was given the name "self-centering" in our paper [82]. Conversely, the phenomenon in which the particles move away from the center line may be given the name "self-decentering."

It is not theoretically unthinkable that the particles could move into a state of parakinetic opposition, where neither of the above diametrically opposed tendencies is predominant. All these phenomena taken together is what we mean by parakinetic interaction between aerosol particles in a sonic field.

In which of the above forms does the parakinetic interaction between particles occur in any concrete case?

This depends on the relative arrangement of the aerosol particles, on the dimensions and density of the particles, and on the viscosity of the medium and the way the sonic treatment is being conducted. Unfortunately, it does not seem that a general analytic solution of the problem can be made without using computer techniques.

However, there is no particular difficulty about getting a value for the parakinetic interaction rate between aerosol particles in a sonic field, if we limit ourselves to the case where the change in particle velocity follows the law $|\vec{u}_g| = |\overleftarrow{u}_g|$ = const. All the values will be correspondingly less if the change is sinusoidal.

The hysteresis component of the parakinetic displacement rate of a vibrating aerosol particle may be calculated from the formula

$$V_g = f\delta y_g, \tag{11.9}$$

where δy_g is the amount of hysteresis in the forward and backward flow lines around the particle in the gas per cycle of the vibration.

The inertial component of the parakinetic displacement rate of a vibrating aerosol particle may be found from the formula (7.3)

$$V_c = \frac{u_{p2}^2 \tau_2}{R_1} = \frac{\mu_{12}^2 U_g^2 \tau_2}{R_{1rr} r_1}, \tag{11.10}$$

where u_{p2} and τ_2 are the relative velocity and the relaxation time of the small particle, and R_1 and R_{1rr} are the absolute and reduced radii of curvature of the flow line around the large particle at the point in question.

For the self-centering case (Fig. 35a), V_g may be found analytically be means of the formula

$$\delta y_{rr} = \sqrt{\frac{\vec{\psi}_{rr}}{\frac{1}{2} + \frac{3Re}{16}}} - \sqrt{\frac{\vec{\psi}_{rr}\left(1 - \frac{3}{2}x_{2rr}^{-1}\right)}{\frac{1}{2} - \frac{3}{4}x_{2rr}^{-1} + \frac{3Re}{16}}}, \tag{11.11}$$

which is easily derived from Eqs. (11.1) and (11.2) by assuming that $x_{1rr}^{-1} \approx 0$.

If Re = 1, and $x_{2rr} = -10$, we have: for ψ_{rr} = 0.1, δy_{13} = 0.0095 r_1, and for ψ_{rr} = 1, δy_{13} = 0.030 r_1. For particles with the "limiting" radius r_1 = 3.5 μ at a frequency of f = 1 - 10 kcps, we obtain the following values for the velocity:

$$V_g^{max} = 0.03\text{-}0.30 \text{ cm/sec for } \psi_{rr} = 0.1,$$
$$V_g^{max} = 0.10\text{-}1.00 \text{ cm/sec for } \psi_{rr} = 1.$$

The magnitude and sign of V_c are different for each point on the trajectory of the vibrating particle. For a particle with the reduced radius $r_{2rr} = 0.33$ ($\mu_{12} = 0.8$), and $r_1 = 3.5\mu$ for $U_g = 220$ cm/sec ($J = 0.1$ W/cm^2) in the range $R_{1rr} = 10^3-10^5$, we find the following values for the inertial deflection rate of the particles:

$$V_c = 0.015 - 1.5 \text{ cm/sec.}$$

For the second case, where the particles move apart (Fig. 35b), the value of V_g is found by graphical analysis, using Fig. 33b as a guide. If Re = 1, and $A_{grr} = 50$, we have for $\psi_{rr} = 100$, $\delta y_{grr} \approx 1$, and for $\psi_{rr} = 1000$, $\delta y_{grr} \approx 3$. Accordingly, for particles with the "limiting" radius $r_1 = 3.5\ \mu$, at a frequency of f = 1-10 kcps, we obtain the following maximum values for the rate of hysteretic divergence of the particles:

$$V_g^{max} \approx 0.35\text{-}3.5 \text{ cm/sec for } \psi_{rr} = 100,$$
$$V_g^{max} \approx 1.05\text{-}10.5 \text{ cm/sec for } \psi_{rr} = 1000.$$

The order of magnitude of V_c lies within the same limits as in the first case, for the same radii of curvature.

In order to get a clearer picture of the parakinetic self-centering rate of the particles, it is well to introduce the concept of a "reduced" rate of interaction by which we mean the ratio of the absolute rate to the distance passed through, in the present case, the ratio $V_g / y_{-\infty}$. This parameter shows how many times the distance may be gone through per second for the existing interaction velocity. The reciprocal of this quantity, $y_{-\infty} / V_g$ gives the time required for the center lines of the particles to come into complete coincidence for the same absolute interaction velocity.

The following formula for the reduced hysteretic self-centering velocity may be derived from Eqs. (11.1), (11.2), and (11.5):

$$\frac{V_g}{y_{-\infty}} = \left[1 - \sqrt{\frac{\left(\frac{1}{2} + \frac{3Re}{16}\right)\left(1 - \frac{3}{2} x_{2rr}^{-1}\right)}{\frac{1}{2} - \frac{3}{4} x_{rr}^{-1} + \frac{3Re}{16}}} \right] f. \qquad (11.12)$$

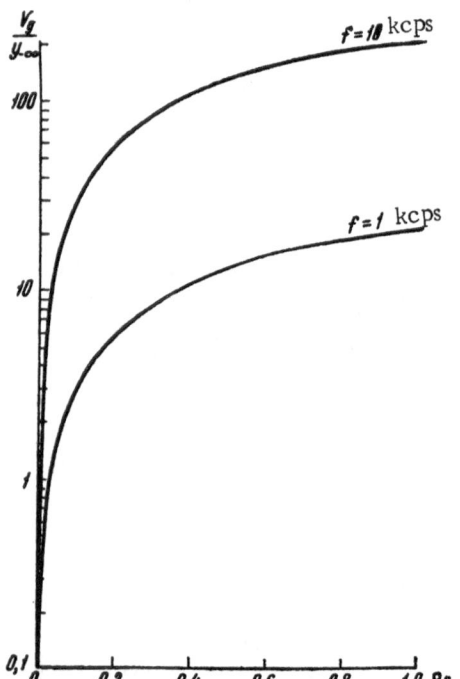

Fig. 37. Reduced hysteretic self-centering velocity of aerosol particles in a sonic field for J = 0.1 W/cm^2.

Figure 37 gives values of the reduced hysteretic self-centering velocity of the particles as a function of Re for a constant value of $x_{2rr} = 10$. It may be concluded from the graph that if Re $\neq$ 0, the center lines of the two particles may be brought into coincidence by hysteresis in tenths or hundredths of a second (divergence occurs even faster).

If it is assumed that the parakinetic interaction is occurring at the optimum frequency for a given pair of particles, so that the value of μ_{12} is given by Eq. (10.10), the reduced inertial self-centering velocity, $V_c/y_{-\infty}$, may, using (11.10) and (11.5), be found from the following formula:

$$\frac{V_c}{y_{-\infty}} = \frac{\sqrt{2}}{9} \frac{\rho_p}{\eta} \left(r_{2rr} \frac{1 - r_{2rr}^2}{1 + r_{2rr}^2} \right)^2 \frac{U_g^2}{\sqrt{\psi_{rr}}} \frac{\sqrt{1 + 0.375 Re}}{R_{1rr}} \cdot \quad (11.13)$$

Figure 38 gives values of the reduced inertial self-centering velocity as a function of the reduced radius of curvature R_{1rr} of the flow lines for different values of the reduced radius r_{2rr} of the vibrating particle for $U_g = 220$ cm/sec (J = 0.1 W/cm^2), with $\psi = 1$, and Re = 0. It may be concluded from the graph that inertial processes bring the center lines into coincidence even more rapidly, namely in hundredths and thousandths of a second, although the absolute

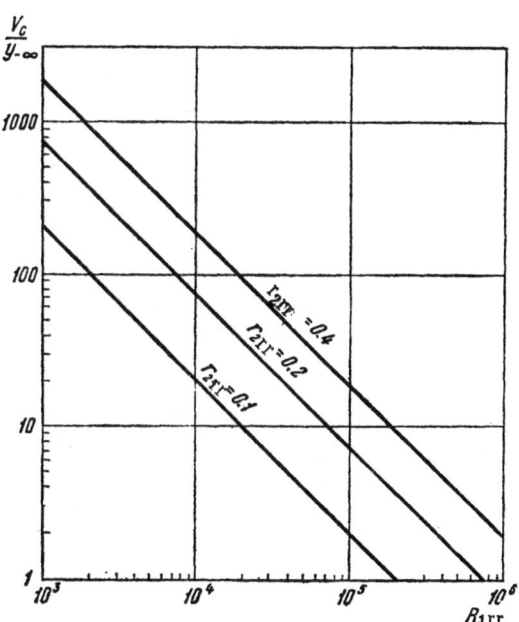

Fig. 38. Reduced inertial self-centering velocity of aerosol particles in a sonic field for $J = 0.1$ W/cm^2.

value of the velocity V_c is comparatively low. It follows from everything that has been presented that the parakinetic interaction between aerosol particles is extremely large. As a result, the concept of capture coefficient in a sonic field loses its usual sense and meaning. As a result of the self-centering phenomenon, orthokinetic collision is not limited to vibrating particles initially in the aggregation volume with the particle in the stream, but is also possible for particles that are far outside.

The magnitude of the capture coefficient, if such a term may be used in the present case, is now primarily determined by the time required for the particles to come together, and even in a very short time may become such as to exceed the maximum values of the capture coefficient for steady-state flow around bodies (such, for example, as the capture coefficient of falling drops calculated from the Oseen attractive forces by Pearcey and Hill in [250]).

§12. Attractional Interaction Between Aerosol Particles

By attractional* interaction between aerosol particles in a sonic field we mean that the particles come together under the action of the hydrodynamic forces resulting from mutual distortion of the fields of flow around the particles, which we shall, for our purposes call forces of attraction. One after the other, these forces have been considered to be Bernoulli forces [141a], Bjerknes forces [109], and finally, Oseen forces [103] and Stokes forces [116]. The first two types of forces were brought into the acoustic aerosol coagulation picture without sufficient reason, so that we shall deal with them briefly at the end of the section, and only in so far as they are mentioned in many of the earlier published papers.

The basis for attractional interaction between aerosol particles of the same size in a sonic field is provided by Oseen hydrodynamic forces, as was shown by S. V. Pshenai-Severin in [103]. The forces owe their origin to the asymmetry in the velocity field formed around each of the interacting particles.

It was shown in §9 (see Fig. 28) that the velocity field set up in the flow around each of the particles is asymmetric in the direction of motion of the steady-state flow, so that there is an extensive parabolic "dead" zone behind the particle, at every point of which the velocity of the medium is appreciably lower than at the symmetrically located point in the slightly retarded "frontal" zone formed ahead of the particle.

Imagine two aerosol particles 1 and 2 (Fig. 39) moving under the action of an acoustic flow in such a way that one of them, namely particle 2, is moving in the dead zone of the other particle 1. In this case, particle 1 is in the slightly retarded frontal zone of particle 2. It is not difficult to see that each particle slows

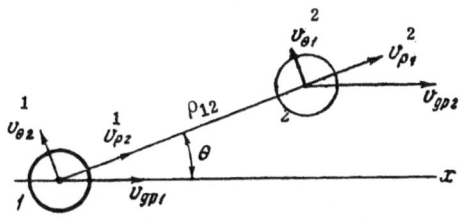

Fig. 39. Superposition of the velocity fields of two aerosol particles.

down the motion of the other when they are in this position. The "leading" particle 1 is naturally much less slowed down than the "trailing" particle 2, with the result that they tend to come together and the particles seem to be attracting one another. When the medium is moving in the other direction, the particles exchange roles, particle 2 becoming the "leading" particle, and particle 1 the "trailing" particle. The distance between them again becomes less, and this goes on for cycle after cycle of the vibrations in the medium.

---

* This type of interaction is often given the name "hydrodynamic" in the literature, which, in our option, is less satisfactory, since the term is too all-inclusive, and not very definite.

Since Oseen's hydrodynamic equation is linear, in considering attractive particle interaction, we may proceed from the assumption that the fields of flow around the particles are superimposable. In this case, the force acting on the particle in question in the direction of the line joining the centers during steady state motion of the medium may be found from the formula:

$$F_\rho = 6\pi\eta r \left(u_{gp}\cos\theta - \Delta v_\rho\right),\tag{12.1}$$

where u_{gp} is the unperturbed flow velocity around the particle, as given by Eq. (5.22), while Δv_ρ is the perturbation to the velocity at the point where the center of the particle is located, due to the presence of the second particle. This quantity is equal to the difference between the projection of the unperturbed flow velocity u_{gp} around the particle, and the flow velocity around the second particle at the point in question v_ρ, as given by Eq. (9.10).

Accordingly, the expression in parenthesis in (12.1) is nothing more or less than the flow velocity around the second particle v_ρ at the center of the other particle, since $(u_{gp}\cos\theta - \Delta v_\rho) = u_{gp}\cos 0 - (u_{gp}\cos\theta - v_\rho) = v_\rho$.

From the above, we may write, for the force, acting between centers on the "leading" particle 1:

$$F_\rho^1 = 6\pi\eta r v_{\rho 2}^1\tag{12.2}$$

and, on the "trailing" particle 2:

$$F_\rho^2 = 6\pi\eta r v_{\rho 1}^2,\tag{12.3}$$

where $v_{\rho 2}^1$ is the radial component of the velocity around particle 2 at the point where the center of particle 1 is located, as given by Eq. (9.10) for $\rho = \rho_{12}$, and $\theta = \theta_{12} + \pi$, and $v_{\rho 1}^2$ is the radial component of the velocity around the particle 1 at the point where the center of particle 2 is located, as given by Eq. (9.10) for $\rho = \rho_{12}$, and $\theta = \theta_{12}$.

The difference between the velocities at which the two particles are moving is numerically equal to the difference between the velocities at which the medium is flowing around them, so that for the rate of attractional approach of the particles, we may write:

$$V_{attr} = v_{\rho 1}^2 - v_{\rho 2}^1 = \left(v_{\rho 1 \text{rr}}^2 - v_{\rho 2 \text{rr}}^1\right) u_{gp}.\tag{12.4}$$

If the one particle is behind the other such that $\theta \to 0$, the velocities $v_{\rho 1}^2$ and $v_{\rho 2}^1$ are given, for Re = 0, by Eqs. (9.15) and (9.17) respectively, while for Re > 0, they are given by (9.15) and (9.17').

For Re = 0, where we have Stokes flow around the particles and the velocity fields are completely symmetric, the particles slow one another up by the same amount $(v_{xrr}^2 = v_{xrr}^1 = 1 - \tfrac{3}{2}\, x_{rr})$, and the attractional approach rate of the particles is equal to zero: $V_{attr}^x = 0$.

For Re > 0, the velocity fields are no longer symmetric and the attractional approach rate of the particles becomes equal to:

$$V_{attr}^x = \frac{3}{2x_{rr}} - \frac{3}{\text{Re}\cdot x_{rr}^2}\left(1 - e^{-\,\text{Re}\cdot x_{rr}/2}\right)u_{gp}.\tag{12.5}$$

In a sonic field, as we know, the flow rate around the particles varies in magnitude and direction, so that the Reynolds number varies, and, with it, from (12.5) the rate of attractional approach of the particles.

At the start of the vibratory motion in the medium, where Re is small, the velocity V_{attr}^x is nearly zero (or greater than zero), but then, as the velocity of the vibratory motion builds up, Re rises rapidly, and, when it reaches is maximum value, the velocity V_{attr}^x is also a maximum.

When we have the product $\mathrm{Re}x_{rr} \gg 2$, the second term in parenthesis (representing the velocity $v_{\rho_2}^1$, in Eq. (12.15) may be neglected, so that the expression for the rate of attractional approach of the particles is greatly simplified:

$$V_{attr} \simeq \frac{3}{2x_{rr}} u_{gp}. \tag{12.6}$$

In this case, we arrive at the case where the "leading" particle is exerting a unilateral hydrodynamic effect on the "trailing" particle.

By using Eq. (12.6), we can find the order of magnitude of the instantaneous rate of attractional approach of the particles for a mean distance between the particles of $x_{rr} = 100$, and a shortest distance of the order of $x_{rr} = 10$, for which the equation still holds. We have:

$$\text{for } x_{rr} = 100, \quad V_{attr}^x = 0.015\, u_{gp};$$
$$\text{for } x_{rr} = 10, \quad V_{attr}^x = 0.15\, u_{gp}.$$

Thus we see that the instantaneous rate of attractional approach of the particles is a comparatively small fraction of the instantaneous velocity of the flow around them. In absolute value, however, we get quite substantial figures. Thus, for a flow velocity of $u_{gp} = 100$ cm/sec, the rate of attractive approach V_{attr}^x of the particles takes on the values 1.5 and 15 cm/sec respectively.

Let us now calculate the mean attractional approach rate of the particles during a half-period of the vibration for the case where $\theta = 0$. Using Eqs. (12.5), which contain the variation Re, for this purpose leads to insuperable difficulties in integrating the equation of particle approach. In order to get around these difficulties, S. V. Pshenai-Severin [103] suggested using Eq. (12.6), assuming that particle approach begins at some instant of time t_1 where Re has reached some definite, quite appreciable value, Re_{cr}.

Up to the instant of time $t = t_1$, the rate of flow around the two particles follows the law (5.22), while for $t_1 \leq t \leq \frac{1}{2} T$, the rate of flow v_x^1 around the "leading" particle 1 continues to follow Eq. (5.22), and the rate of flow around the "trailing" particle 2 follows the law:

$$v_x^2 = (u_g - u_p) - \frac{3}{2x_{rr}} v_x^1 . \tag{12.7}$$

The equations of motion of the particles in this case are: for the leading particle 1:

$$m_p \frac{du_p^1}{dt} = 6\pi\eta r (u_g - u_p^1), \tag{12.8}$$

and, for the trailing particle 2:

$$m_p \frac{du_p^2}{dt} = 6\pi\eta r (u_g - u_p^2). \tag{12.9}$$

Subtracting the second equation from the first, and passing to the dimensionless variables $V_{attr} = V_{attr}/U_g$ and $t_{rr} = t/\tau$, we have:

$$\frac{d(V_{attr}^{rr})}{dt_{rr}} + V_{attr}^{rr} = \frac{3\mu_g}{2x_{rr}} \cos(\omega\tau t_{1rr} - \varphi). \tag{12.10}$$

The initial conditions are: $V_{attr}^{rr} = 0$, and $\Delta x_{rr} = 0$ at $t_{rr} = t_{1rr}$.

Integrating Eq. (12.10) gives the displacement Δx_{12} during the time interval $\Delta t = \frac{1}{2} T - t_1$ in the form:

$$\frac{\Delta x_{12}}{A_g} = -1.5 \frac{\mu_p \mu_g}{x_{rr}} \{[2\mu_p \mu_g \cos \omega \tau \, t_{rr\,1} - (\mu_p^2 - \mu_g^2) \sin \omega \tau \, t_{rr\,2}]$$

$$- \frac{\mu_g}{\mu_p} \left[2\mu_p \mu_g \sin \omega \tau \, t_{rr\,1} + \mu_p^2 - \mu_g^2) \cos \omega \tau \, t_{rr\,1} \right] e^{-\left(\frac{1}{2} T_{rr} - t_{rr}\right)} \qquad (12.11)$$

$$+ \left(\sin \omega \tau \, t_{rr\,1} - \frac{\mu_g}{\mu_p} \cos \omega \tau \, t_{rr\,1} \right) \}.$$

Figure 40 gives the results of calculations of Δx_{12} which Pshenai-Severin made from Eq. (12.11) for droplets in a water fog with $x_{rr} = 100 = $ const. The critical Reynolds number was taken very high, namely $Re_{cr} = 1$, which forced him to make his calculation of attractional particle approach for high sound intensities in the field.

The values of the attractional displacement Δx_{12} were found by Pshenai-Severin in terms of the particle radius r, and to obtain values comparable at different frequencies, were multiplied by the fraction f/x_{rr}. This gave values of the reduced attractional approach rate of the particles $V_{attr}/\Delta x_{12}$ to be plotted as ordinates, as we show in the graph.

It may be concluded from an examination of Fig. 40 that the attractional approach rate of the particles is very large. Even at the lowest sound intensity, we got a displacement per second that is ten or more times the distance between the particles. Hence it follows that it only takes tenths of a second or less to bring the particles into contact by the attractional approach mechanism.

It may be seen from the graph that the attractional approach rate of aerosol particles is strongly dependent on the frequency. For each particle size there is an optimum frequency at which the attractional approach rate of the particles has its maximum possible value. The optimum frequency is higher the smaller the particles, so that for particles of radii $r = 5\text{-}15\mu$, low frequencies of the order of several hundred cycles are best, while for particles of radii $r < 5\mu$, frequencies in the kilocycle range are required. It is fairly difficult to compare these values with the optimum frequencies observed experimentally, since acoustic coagulation of aerosols is, as a rule, carried out industrially at lower sound intensities than those used by Pshenai-Severin.

That there is an optimum frequency is shown immediately by Eq. (12.5), from which it may be seen that there are two cases in which there is no attractional particle approach ($V_{attr} = 0$):

a) When the particles are completely carried along by the vibratory motion of the medium, such that $u_{gp} = 0$ and Re = 0 and,

b) When the medium simply flows around the particles, and the particles are not moved out of place at all.

From this it follows that the particles are only brought together in the intermediate case where they are not completely carried along by the motion, and this only occurs for definite values of the frequency.

Two other features of the curves shown deserve attention, namely: how the curves get pushed together along the axis of abscissas, i.e., the particle radii, as the particles become smaller, and how the optimum shifts toward smaller particle radii as the sound intensity is increased.

Some limitations on the above conclusions have been pointed out by N. A. Fuks in his review[122].

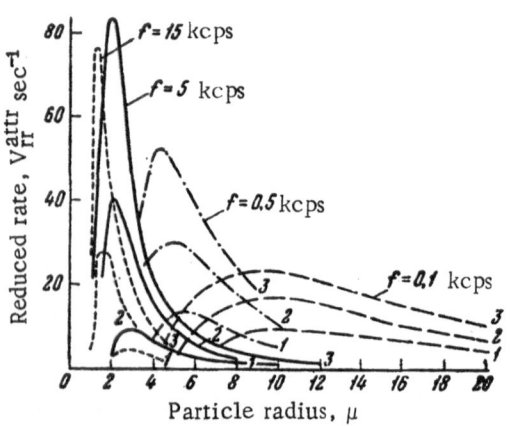

Fig. 40. Reduced attractional approach rate of aerosol particles at large arbitrary velocities: 1) for $U_g = 400$ cm/sec ($J \approx 0.33$ W/cm^2); 2) for $U_g = 700$ cm/sec ($J \approx 1.0$ W/cm^2); 3) for $u_g = 1000$ cm/sec ($J \approx 2.0$ W/cm^2).

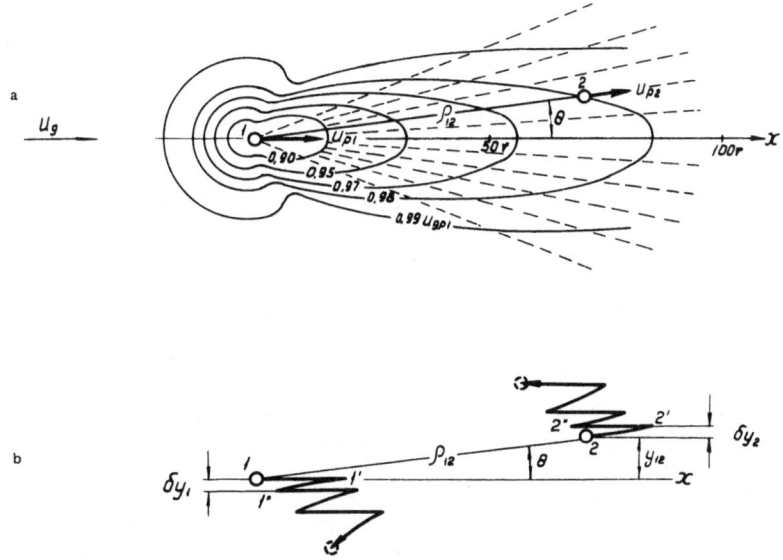

Fig. 41. Attractional interaction between two aerosol particles of the same size in a sonic field for $\theta > 0$. a) Velocity field set up as the result of the unilateral effect of the leading particle 1 on the trailing particle 2, when the medium is moving forward for Re = 1, b) attractional particle approach in a sonic field.

As an experimental proof the reality of attractional interaction between particles in a sonic field as described above, the experiments of S. V. Gorbachev and A. B. Severnii [26, 195] may be cited. These authors made a study of the elementary interaction between two water droplets of radii r=100 μ, suspended on glass threads at a reduced distance of $\rho_{12rr} = 26$ in a low-frequency sonic field produced by an "Akkord" loudspeaker. The particle velocity in the medium was, naturally, very low, so that it could be confidently asserted that viscous flow was occurring around the droplets.

These authors also found that when the droplets were located one behind the other ($\theta = 0°$), attraction occurs, while when they are placed side by side ($\theta = 90°$), on the other hand, repulsion occurs. This type of particle interaction in a sonic field is precisely what is characteristic of the attractional interaction produced by Oseen asymmetry in the flow around the particles, and this is what the investigators themselves and their subsequent commentators failed to see.

Let us now consider the attractional interaction between particles of the same size in a sonic field that occurs in the more general case where $\theta > 0$ [305].

Assume, as before, that the distance between the centers of the particles is initially so large in comparison that the radii that in making the analysis we can start with the idea that the leading particle is exerting a unilateral hydrodynamic effect on the second, trailing particle. In this case, the velocity field set up around the particles when the medium is moving forward is shown in Fig. 41a, which is for the case Re = 1 [251]. Here the light solid lines give the location of the points where the flow velocity of the medium around the leading particle 1 is the same (u_{gp_1} is the unperturbed velocity along the x axis).

It may be seen that the medium experiences appreciable retardation in the extensive parabolic zone behind the leading particle, where the trailing particle 2 is located, with the result that the velocity of particle 2 is less than that of particle 1: $u_{p_2} < u_{p_1}$. At the same time the velocity of the medium in the zone is in a substantially different direction for $\theta > 0$ than the motion of the unperturbed flow, and is inclined in the way shown by the dotted lines in the figure.

For small values of the angle θ, the direction of the velocity in the medium, and with it the velocity of the particle 2, is approximately radial for all values of Re < 1, i.e., it is in the same direction as the line joining the centers of the particles. This means that the direction in which the trailing particle moves in this case is independent of the rate of motion of the medium, and, hence, remains constant for either steady-state or transient motion of the medium.

In a sonic field, where the medium is moving back and forth, i.e., moving alternately forward and backward, the result is as follows (Fig. 41b).

When the medium is moving forward, the leading particle 1 moves (together with the velocity field as perturbed by the particle) linearly from the point 1 to the point 1', while the trailing particle 2 moves diagonally, along the line joining the centers, and a shorter distance, from the point 2 to the point 2'.

When the medium is moving backward, the role of leading particle is played by particle 2, while the trailing particle is 1, with the result that the velocity field is of a form diametrically opposite to that shown in Fig. 41a (rotated 180°). Since it is now leading, the particle 2 moves backward in a straight line from the point 2' to the point 2", shifted sideways from the original point 2 by the amount δ_{y_2}, while the trailing 1 moves diagonally from the point 1' to the point 1 ", shifted by the same amount, $\delta_{y_1} = \delta_{y_2}$.

As a result, after completing one cycle of the vibrations, the particles are closer together longitudinally (along the x axis), but are at the same time farther apart in the transverse direction. In the course of successive vibrations, the above phenomenon is repeated again and again, as shown in exaggerated form in Fig. 41b, and before long the approaching particles are so far apart sideways that we can no longer speak of them coming into contact.

It is not difficult to see that the above zig-zag particle motion also occurs for larger values of the angle θ, the only difference being that the zig-zags get sinuous too, as a result of the slope of the velocity of the medium in the parabolic zone changing with change in stream velocity.

For small values of the angle θ, it may be assumed approximately that the transverse distance between the particles is given by $\delta y = \delta y_1 + \delta y_2 \approx 4A_p \sin \theta = 4(y_{12}/\rho_{12})A_p$, while the instantaneous rate of divergence is given by $(2\sqrt{2}/\pi) u_p \sin \theta = (2\sqrt{2}/\pi)(y_{12}/\rho_{12}) u_p$, where A_p is the amplitude of the vibrations of the particles, and u_p is the vibratory velocity.

If the distance between the particles is originally of the order $\rho_{12} = 100r$, and the angle is $\theta = 0.5°$, which corresponds to $y_{12} \approx r$, the transverse separation δy between the particles after only the first ten cycles of the vibration with $A_p = 100\mu$ is (if we neglect the change in the angle θ) about 40μ, which is many times greater than the initial radius ($r \leq 5-7 \mu$) of the aerosol particles being coagulated in the sonic field. The rate of separation of the particles is, in this case, for a frequency of $f = 1-10$ kcps, about $0.4-4.0$ cm/sec to start with, but as they come closer together and the angle θ increases, the rate of separation reaches the values for longitudinal particle approach, or higher.

It may be concluded from what has been said that attractional approach of aerosol particles of the same size in a sound field presents a radically different picture from the approach of falling cloud particles, since the particles do not actually come into contact. The only exception is the case discussed earlier, where $\theta = 0$. Here the particles may actually come into contact, but only for the condition that the maximum value of the Reynolds number is $Re > 1$. However, the probability of the particles being located in this way is infinitesimally small, so that it may be asserted that the type of approach between particles of different sizes discussed above, resulting from Oseen hydrodynamic forces, is not directly responsible for the particle aggregation observed in a sonic field, as was suggested by the author of [103].

We now pass to the more general case of attractional interaction between aerosol particles which occurs when they are of different dimensions.

The treatment of this case for $\theta > 0$ presents an unusually complex problem, since, first, it is necessary to take account of the difference in degree of entrainment and phase of the oscillations of the particles, and, second, it is so closely interrelated with the orthokinetic and parakinetic interaction of the particles that it cannot be subjected to any sort of analysis without resorting to computer techniques.

Unlike particles of the same size, particles of different sizes show attractional interaction even in Stokes flow, where there is no Oseen asymmetry in the velocity fields. This is due to the fact that the velocity fields of particles of different sizes are not identical, but have a different space scale and configuration. The second feature is that the interaction ends up partly in orthokinetic aggregation of the particles even for $\theta > 0$.

In setting up the equations of motion of aerosol particles in Stokes flow, the formulas to be used as the starting points are, for $\theta = 0$, those of Faxen [Arkiv Mat. Astr. Fys., 19A (22): 1-10 (1925)], which are discussed in detail in the paper by S. V. Pshenai-Severin [101], and, for $\theta > 0$, those of Hocking [Quart. J. Roy. Meteorol. Soc., (363): 44-50 (1959)].

The first case [$\theta = 0$] has recently been investigated in detail by V. I. Timoshenko [116], who regards it as a constituent part of the orthokinetic interaction. The solution obtained by the author may be written in the following form:

$$\frac{\overrightarrow{\Delta x_{12}}}{A_g} = 2\mu_{p1}\left\{3\mu_{p1}\mu_{g1}^2\left(\frac{r_1}{r_2}\right)^2\frac{r_1}{x_{12}} - \mu_{g2}\left[\left(\frac{r_1}{r_2}\right)^2 + \frac{3}{2}\frac{r_2}{x_{12}} - 1\right](\mu_{p1}\mu_{g2} + \mu_{p2}\mu_{g1})\right\} +$$

$$+ \mu_{g1}\left\{\frac{3}{2}\left(\frac{r_1}{r_2}\right)^2\frac{r_1}{x_{12}}\mu_{g1}(\mu_{g1}^2 - \mu_{p1}^2) - \mu_{g2}\left[\left(\frac{r_1}{r_2}\right)^2 + \frac{3}{2}\frac{r_2}{x_{12}} - 1\right](\mu_{g1}\mu_{g2} - \mu_{p1}\mu_{p2})\right\}(1 - e^{-\pi(\mu_{p1}/\mu_{g1})}) \qquad (12.11')$$

where $\overrightarrow{\Delta x_{12}}$ is the change in the distance between the particles during the first half period of the oscillations, x_{12} is the initial distance between the particles, r_1, μ_{p_1}, and μ_{g_1} are the radius, degree of entrainment, and amount of flow around the first particle, and r_2, μ_{p_2}, and μ_{g_2} are the radius, the degree of entrainment, and the amount of flow around the second particle.

During the second half period of the oscillation, where the stream reverses its direction, the change in the distance between the particles $\overleftarrow{\Delta x_{12}}$ may be found from the same formula, if we exchange the subscript numbers on r, μ_p and μ_g. The particles get closer together during a period of the oscillation by the amount $\Delta = \overrightarrow{\Delta x_{12}} - \overleftarrow{\Delta x_{12}}$.

We shall not give the solution for the case of attractional interaction between particles of different sizes in Oseen flow, since it is unusually unwieldy. We note only that the rate of approach of the particles is much higher in this case than in Stokes flow. But to assume that this effect is the only one responsible for acoustic coagulation of aerosols, as done by the author of [116], is, of course, incorrect.

Experimental confirmation of the existence of complex hydrodynamic interaction between oscillation aerosol particles in a sound field, as discussed partially in §§ 10, 11, and 12, is provided by the work of O. K. Éknadiosyants and L. I. Buravov [12], in which an SKS-1 high-speed motion picture camera was used to catch the phenomenon of approach and "opposition" of aerosol particles. The aerosol used was an atomized aluminum paint powder, in which the particle radii lay in the range $1.5-15\mu$. The frequency of the oscillations was $0.7-3.0$ kcps, with the pictures taken at a rate of from 300 to 5000 frames per second. The investigators observed the formation and simultaneous motion over the field of view of space complexes made up of two or three or more separately oscillating particles.

To conclude this section we shall give a brief discussion of the Bernoulli and Bjerkness hydrodynamic forces mentioned at the start. Bernoulli forces is the name given to the forces set up between two bodies as a result of narrowing down the stream flowing between them, so that a certain amount of the static pressure is lost in the narrow space.

If the viscous losses in the medium are insignificant as is the case in vortex-free, potential flow around bodies, then, throughout the length of the stream, we have, as we know, the relation:

$$p + \frac{1}{2}\rho_g u_g^2 = \text{const},\tag{12.12}$$

which is known as Bernoulli's law or integral, and is nothing more or less than a mathematical expression of the law of conservation of energy for an ideal liquid.

Equation (12.12) says that in the space between the particles where the tubes of flow are narrowed down so as to increase the velocity, the pressure in the medium is somewhat lower than the pressure from the outside. The result is that forces are set up between the two particles that tend to bring them together.

Based on Bjerkness' hydrodynamic theory ([146], König derived the following expression for the forces acting in a sonic field between spherical particles along the line joining their centers [215]:

$$F_\rho = \frac{3}{2}\frac{\pi\rho_g r_1^3 r_2^3}{\rho_{12}^4} U_{g\rho}^2 (3\cos 2\theta_{12} + 1),\tag{12.13}$$

where θ_{12} is the angle between the lines joining the centers in the direction of the vibratory velocity.*

This equation found quite good experimental confirmation in the early experiments of Thomas [279], who made a study of the interaction between spheres of radii 2.8-7.8 mm in a very low-frequency sonic field, produced, as in [283] (see §5), by Zernov's method. At the same time, some experiments gave results considerably at variance with the theoretical calculations. Andrade [141], after making an experimental study of the flow around spherical bodies in a sonic field, came to the conclusion that the reason for the difference was that vortices were formed around the bodies, and that this occurred for the condition $u_{g\rho}r > 0.35$. Andrade also pointed out, citing Cook's observation [182], that for short distances between spheres, when the line joining the centers is perpendicular to the direction of the acoustic flux, it is possible to have repulsive forces acting instead of attractive.

Recently, Stashevskii [271] confirmed this idea experimentally, and made it more precise in his experiments on wax and glass spheres 0.34 to 5.45 mm in diameter. The experiments were made in a glass tube 35-40 mm in diameter at frequencies of from 184 to 533 cps, and various sound intensities. Somewhat later, Adamchik and Stashevskii [136] observed a similar phenomenon for spheres arranged one behind the other: there were some small distances in this case at which the repulsion changed to attraction. Dörr [185] showed experimentally that the angular dependence of the attractive force is given by the factor $(6 + 4\sin^2\theta)$, instead of that shown in König's formula (12.13). The experiments were made with hollow glass spheres from 2.75 to 4.95 mm in diameter, suspended on fine threads about 7-10 mm apart. The vibratory velocity reached an amplitude of 40 cm/sec.

In his day, Andrade [141a] resorted to an attempt to use the Bernoulli forces to explain the mechanism of acoustic coagulation of aerosols, but was not successful.

---

*Expressions are given in [215] for the forces Y and X which are the projections on the x and y axes of the resultant of our "radial" force F_ρ and the "tangential" force F_θ perpendicular to it.

As has already been pointed out, the flow around aerosol particles in a sonic field is viscous in nature, and is very far from the ideal conditions for which Eq. (12.13) was derived.

The viscous losses decrease at large Reynolds numbers as occurs for high sound intensity and large-size particles, and it is only under these conditions that the viscous losses may be left out of consideration with a certain amount of reservation. The necessary conditions only occur in very coarsely disperse aerosols, which do not as a rule need any further particle consolidation, or else they are the result of prolonged coagulation of finely disperse aerosols. The Bernoulli attractive forces that show up in this final stage of aerosol coagulation are, however, no longer of any great use, particularly since they are of small magnitude anyhow.

In proof of this, Brandt, Freund, and Hiedemann [167] derived the following formula for the time required for two spherical particles of the same size to come into contact when located in the optimum position with respect to the acoustic flow ($\theta = \pi / 2$) and with complete flow around the particles ($\mu_g = 1$):

$$ t_{\text{app}} \approx \frac{2}{5} \frac{\eta}{\rho_g} \frac{(\rho_{12rr})^5}{U_{g\rho}^2}. \tag{12.14} $$

The authors arrived at this formula by setting the attractive force F_ρ given by Eq. (12.13) equal to the resistance of the medium to motion as given by Stokes law $F_{St} = 6\pi \eta r (\frac{1}{2} \, d\rho/dt)$, and integrating the resulting equation from ρ_{12} at $t = 0$ to $\rho_{12} = 2r$ at $t = t_{\text{app}}$. Strictly speaking, this is not right: since for Re > 1, the resistive force is not a linear function of the radius, as given by Stokes law, but is a quadratic function or something close to it.

Let us see however what results Eq. (12.14) leads to, assuming that Re is not too large. The mean reduced distance between the particles in aerosols lies in the range $S_m = 35\text{-}160$, so that for a sound intensity of J = 0.1 W/cm^2 (U $\simeq$ 220 cm/sec) we find, for unit particle density in air:

$$ t_{\text{app}} = 138 - 2.76 \cdot 10^5 \text{ sec.} $$

Thus we see that, even for a high particle concentration (of the order of k = 100 g/m^3), the time required to bring the particles into contact is more than 2 minutes, while at low concentrations (k = 1 g/m^3 or less) the time required is many days. Hence, the conclusion is forced upon us that the Bernoulli forces acting on aerosols undergoing coagulation in a sonic field may be completely neglected even in the final stage of the process.

Bjerkness forces is the name given to the forces of attraction (or repulsion) set up between two bodies vibrating or pulsating under the influence of an external force. Kelvin has also pointed out that the vibratory velocity of the particles in the medium behind a body in a sonic field is always somewhat less than the velocity ahead of the body. This is due to scattering of part of the energy by the surface of the body facing the stream, and is only true in the case of an ideal medium. We find from Bernoulli's principle that the pressure behind the body is somewhat higher than ahead of it, so that in this case there is a certain force acting on the body tending to bring it closer to the vibrating object. The vibrating object may be another body that is vibrating or pulsating, or both simultaneously. In the latter case, forces of either attraction or repulsion may be set up between the bodies, depending on the phase of the vibrations.

The ponderomotive interaction forces just described which are set up in vibratory or pulsational motion of bodies was investigated theoretically by Bjerkness [146]. P. N. Lebedev [64] made an experimental study of the ponderomotive forces set up in electromagnetic, hydrodynamic, and acoustic vibrations, and came to the conclusion that all these forces act according to identical laws, i.e., the laws are independent of the nature of the wave field.

A. B. Severnyi [109] in studying the interaction occurring in a sonic field between two water drops, suggested, on the basis of Olivier's observations [242] that the drops are executing virtual pulsations: each of the drops is converted from an ellipsoid extended along two axes to an ellipsoid compressed and symmetric along the same axes. In the opinion of this author, the pulsating drops interact with one another, with the result that attraction or repulsion occurs between the drops.

Based on the equation derived by Bjerkness for the force of interaction between two radially pulsating spheres:

$$F = \frac{1}{\rho_g} \frac{\Omega_1 \Omega_2}{4\pi\rho_{12}} \qquad (12.15)$$

(Ω_1 dnd Ω_2 are the mean square rates of change in volume of the first and second sphere respectively), and modifying the equation for the case of virtual pulsations, A. B. Severnyi after complicated derivations, derived the following expression for the interaction force between drops of the same size in the plane of the sound wave (θ = 90°):

$$F = - K \frac{u_g^2}{\rho_{12}^2}, \qquad (12.16)$$

where

$$K = - 6.19 \cdot 10^3 \frac{r^4}{\rho_p} c_g \frac{6 + (kr)^2}{12 + (kr)^2} \approx - (3.1 - 6.2) \, 10^3 c_g r^4.$$

Here, k = $2\pi/T_p$, where T_p is the period of the ellipsoidal and symmetric pulsations, determined by Olivier [242] from the expression:

$$T_p = \sqrt{\frac{3\pi m}{8\sigma}} \qquad (12.17)$$

(m_p is the mass of the drops, σ is the surface tension which, for water at 20° C, is σ = 73 dynes/cm).

Using Eq. (12.16), and neglecting the resistance of the medium, A. M. Severnyi derived the following equation for the time required to bring the drops into contact:

$$t_{app} = \frac{\rho_{12}}{u_{gp}} \sqrt{\frac{(1 + \rho_{12})(2 + \rho_{12}) m_p}{2K\rho_{12}}} \approx \frac{1}{U_{gp}} \sqrt{\frac{\rho_{12} m_p}{2K}}. \qquad (12.18)$$

For droplets of radius r = 10μ, we have the ratio $m_p/K \approx 0.01$, from which, for a distance between the droplets of the order of ρ_{12} = 1 mm and a sound intensity of J = 0.1 W/cm^2 ($u_{gp} \approx$ 150 cm/sec) we have t_{app} = 0.0014 sec, which corresponds to a mean rate of approach of V_{app} = 70 cm/sec.

Thus, we see that the results are more than favorable. However, they were obtained by using equations which do not apply to actual aerosols in a sound field, where viscous flow occurs around the particles. More than this, the equations derived also fail to hold in the final stage of prolonged aerosol coagulation, where viscous flow is replaced by potential flow.

If Eq. (12.17) is used to calculate the inherent frequency of the pulsations of the drops in an actual water fog, it may be seen that the frequency is enormous as compared with the frequencies of the sound fields used in practice. Under these far from resonant conditions, it is impossible to "excite" a drop and force it to execute virtual pulsations.

The inadequacy of the theory is shown by a simple experimental fact: solid aerosol particles, which are not capable of virtual pulsations, coagulate just as easily as liquid particles (unless they are too large, and thus do not stick together well).

It follows from everything that has been presented that Bjerkness and Bernoulli forces may be neglected in aerosols undergoing coagulation in a sound field, and left completely out of consideration when considering the mechanism of acoustic coagulation of aerosols. The same may also be said of the new interaction forces investigated by Embleton in [318] which are related to particle radiation drift forces.

§13. Pulsational Interaction between Aerosol Particles

It was shown in §7 that as long as aerosol particles are not too large they take some part or other in the turbulent pulsations of the vibrating medium. As a result, it becomes possible for them to come together at some finite velocity.

In the theory of turbulent coagulation of colloids, developed by Levich [67, 68, 69], two mechanisms are indicated by which, colloid particles come together:

1) The diffusional mechanism, by which the particles come together in a purely diffusional way, namely, by taking part in the pulsations that occur in different directions of the medium, and

2) The orthokinetic mechanism, occurring between particles of different sizes, as a result of both sets of particles taking part in pulsations on a scale not exceeding the internal scale of the turbulence.

Let us now consider both mechanisms as they apply to the conditions found in a turbulent acoustic field.

The Diffusional Mechanism. This is a way in which particles of both the same and different sizes may be brought together. The way particles of the same size come together in a turbulent acoustic field does not differ in any practical respects from the particle approach in an ordinary turbulent stream as investigated by Levich in [67], since all the particles take exactly the same part in the vibrations of the medium.

Let an aerosol particle of radius r be placed at the origin of a spherical coordinate system, and consider the diffusion set up at the particle in a turbulent acoustic field.

The equation for the steady state diffusion to the surface of an absorbing sphere of radius a = R surrounding a particle of radius r ≪ R is of the form:

$$j = D_{\mathfrak{s}}\left(\frac{\partial n}{\partial a}\right)_{a=R} \quad \left[\frac{1}{cm^2 \cdot sec}\right], \tag{13.1}$$

where $D_{\mathfrak{s}}$ is the effective diffusion coefficient of the particles, equal to the sum of the two coefficients: $D_{\mathfrak{s}} = D_{turb} + D_{Br}$.

The boundary conditions are:

$$\begin{aligned} n &= n_0 \quad \text{as} \quad a \to \infty, \\ n &= 0 \quad \text{as} \quad a \to R. \end{aligned} \tag{13.2}$$

Turbulent diffusion of the particles is the predominant factor as long as the radius of the sphere satisfies the inequality [69]:

$$R > \left(\frac{D_{Br}}{\sigma_2} \sqrt{\frac{2\nu}{\varepsilon}} \right)^{1/2}. \tag{13.3}$$

For aerosol particles, this leads to the condition: $r > 0.1\mu$, from which it follows that the Brownian diffusion coefficient of the particle D_{Br} may practically always be neglected in comparison with the turbulent diffusion coefficient, so that we may set $D_{\mathfrak{A}} \approx D_{turb}$. Here, the turbulent diffusion coefficient of the aerosol particles may be set equal to the turbulent diffusion coefficient of the particles in the medium. This is self-evident if the aerosol particles are completely carried along by the turbulent pulsations. It is not so obvious however if the particles are only partly carried along in the turbulent pulsations, although Chen [278] has shown convincingly that the aerosol particles and the particles in the medium have the same turbulent diffusion coefficient in this case as well [122].

From the general expression $D \approx l^2/t \approx v_l l$ (l is the "step" length, and t is the time spent per step) the turbulent diffusion coefficient for pulsations of scale l may be written, from Eqs. (1.36) and (1.37), as:

$$D_{turb} \sim v_l l \sim \begin{cases} \dfrac{1}{4} \left(\dfrac{\varepsilon}{b/\rho_g} \right)^{1/2} l^2 \quad \text{for} \quad l < l_0, & (13.4) \\[3mm] (\varepsilon l)^{1/2} l \quad \text{for} \quad l > l_0. & (13.5) \end{cases}$$

Thus we see that the rate at which two particles come together by diffusion decreases rapidly as the distance between them becomes less.

The theory gives the following simple expressions [121, 69] for the concentration gradient $(\partial n / \partial a)_{a=R}$ at the surface of an absorbing sphere with the condition $t_D \gg R^2/D_{turb}$:

$$\left(\frac{\partial n}{\partial a} \right)_{a=R} = \frac{3n}{R}, \tag{13.6}$$

where n is the aerosol count concentration, taken as being equal to the mean concentration of particles per cm^3. Substituting this expression, as well as Eq. (13.4) in Eq. (13.1) and making use of the fact that $l = R + r \simeq R$, we obtain the following equation for the specific flux of aerosol particles to the sphere:

$$j \approx \frac{3}{4} \left(\frac{\varepsilon}{b/\rho_g} \right)^{1/2} Rn. \tag{13.7}$$

The total particle flux to the surface of the sphere, if we consider Eqs. (1.32) and (9.1) is equal to:

$$N = 4\pi R^2 j = \frac{9}{4} \left(\frac{R}{p} \right)^3 \frac{k}{\rho_p} \frac{\xi^{1/2} J^{3/4} f^{1/2}}{b^{1/2} \rho_g^{1/4} c_g^{5/4}} \cdot 10^{-6}. \tag{13.8}$$

If the concentration by weight of the diffusing particles is k = 10 g/m^3, and we have the normal acoustic parameters (J = 0.1 W/cm^2 and f = 1 - 10 kcps) the flux of particles of density ρ_p = 1, alighting on a particle of the same radius (R = 2r), turns out to be equal to

$$N \approx 0.10 - 0.31 \ sec^{-1}.$$

Thus we see that the flux is very small and may practically always be neglected.

Diffusional interaction between particles of different sizes in a turbulent acoustic field is much more important.

Each large particle is able to come in contact with all the small particles which get into the aggregation volume as shown dotted in Fig. 42a, i.e., a cylinder of altitude $2A_{12}$ with rounded ends, and a cross section equal to $\vartheta \pi r_1^2$, where A_{12} is the maximum value of the relative motion of the particles, and ϑ is the capture coefficient of the small particles.

Over the greater part of the length of the cylinder, the capture coefficient has the value given by Eq. (10.20'). Accordingly, neglecting a certain amount of bulging in the middle and the rounding at the ends, the discussion of the particle diffusion flux may be limited to an ordinary cylinder of altitude $2A_{12}$ with permeable walls of radius $R_a = \sqrt{\vartheta}\, r_1$. To make things clearer, it is best to think of diffusional interaction as consisting of a large particle vibrating with the amplitude A_{12}, with the small particles diffusing about in the aggregation cylinder. Then, the small particles diffusing in the aggregation cylinder are being continuously "cleaned out" by the large particle which it surrounds.

Diffusion of the small particles into the aggregation cylinder occurs in short acts, the duration t_D of which depends on the ordinate x of the diffusing particle, and varies from 0 to T, where T is the period of the vibrations, equal to $1/f$.

It is not difficult to see by examining the graph of $x = F(t)$ that the mean duration of a diffusion act is given by:

$$(t_D)_m = \frac{1}{2}\, T = \frac{1}{2f}.$$

The differential equation for the diffusion of the small particles in cylindrical coordinates is of the form:

$$\frac{\partial n}{\partial t} = D_{turb}\left(\frac{\partial^2 n}{\partial a^2} + \frac{1}{a}\frac{\partial n}{\partial a}\right). \tag{13.9}$$

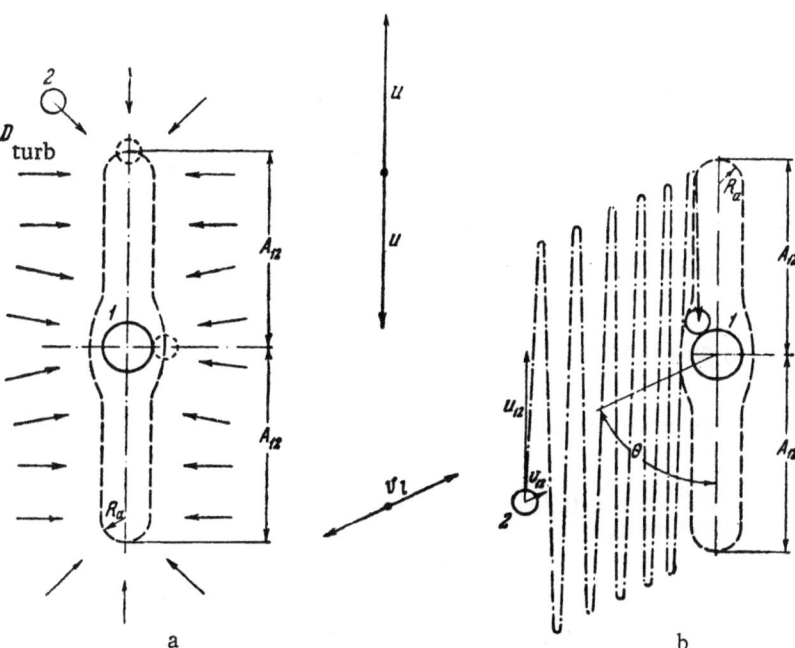

Fig. 42. Pulsational interaction between aerosol particles in a sound field. a) Diffusion mechanism; b) orthokinetic mechanism.

The initial and boundary conditions are:

$$n(a, 0) = 0 \quad \text{and} \quad \frac{\partial n}{\partial a}(0, t) = 0 \quad \text{for} \quad a < R_a,$$
$$n(a, 0) = n_2 \quad \text{and} \quad \frac{\partial n}{\partial a}(\infty, t) = 0 \quad \text{for} \quad a > R_a.$$
(13.10)

From the theory of heat conduction [70], we find the following solution for an infinite cylinder at $a < R_a$:

$$n = n_2 \left[1 - \frac{4}{\pi^2} \int_0^\infty B_\mu J_0 \left(\mu \frac{a}{R_a} \right) J_1(\mu) e^{-\mu^2 \text{Fo}} \, d\mu \right],$$
(13.11)

where

$$B_\mu = \frac{1}{\mu^2 [J_1(\mu) Y_0(\mu) - J_0(\mu) Y_1^2(\mu)]} ;$$

$J_0(\mu)$ and $J_1(\mu)$ are zero and first order Bessel functions of the first kind, $Y_0(\mu)$ and $Y_1(\mu)$ are zero and first order Bessel functions of the second kind, μ is the variable in the characteristic equation $J_0(\mu) = 0$, and Fo is Fourier's criterion, $D_{\text{turb}} t_D / R_a^2$.

The resulting rigorous, but unwieldy equation, containing nonelementary functions, is little suited to practical calculations, so we shall find an approximate solution.

An analysis of Eq. (13.11) shows that with very little error, the integration may be restricted to limits of from 0 to $\mu_n = 2.4$ (which is the first root of the characteristic equation). Further, the quantity B_μ, which is only slightly dependent on the value of μ may be taken to be $B_\mu = \pi^2/4$, while the functions $J_0(\mu a/R_a)$, $J_1(\mu)$ and $e^{-\mu_n^2 \text{Fo}}$ may be expanded in the power series:

$$J_0 \left(\mu \frac{a}{R_a} \right) = 1 - \frac{\mu^2}{2^2} \left(\frac{a}{R_a} \right)^2 + \frac{\mu^4}{2^2 \cdot 4^2} \left(\frac{a}{R_a} \right)^4 - \frac{\mu^6}{2^2 \cdot 4^2 \cdot 6^2} \left(\frac{a}{R_a} \right)^6,$$
(a)

$$J_1(\mu) = \frac{\mu}{2} - \frac{\mu^3}{2^2 \cdot 4} + \frac{\mu^5}{2^2 \cdot 4^2 \cdot 6} - \frac{\mu^7}{2^2 \cdot 4^2 \cdot 6^2 \cdot 8},$$
(b)

$$e^{-\mu_n^2 \text{Fo}} = 1 - \mu_n^2 \text{Fo} + \frac{\mu_n^4 \text{Fo}^2}{1 \cdot 2} - \frac{\mu_n^6 \text{Fo}^3}{1 \cdot 2 \cdot 3} + \frac{\mu_n^8 \text{Fo}^4}{1 \cdot 2 \cdot 3 \cdot 4}.$$
(c)

Substituting (a), (b), and (c) in (13.11) and limiting ourselves to the first four or five terms in each series, we find:

$$n = (0.50 + 0.78 \text{Fo} - 0.99 \text{Fo}^2 + 1.03 \text{Fo}^3 - 0.99 \text{Fo}^4 + \ldots) n_2.$$
(13.12)

The concentration gradient at the wall of the cylinder is given by:

$$\left(\frac{\partial n}{\partial a} \right)_{a = R_a} = (0.78 - 2.52 \text{Fo} + 4.86 \text{Fo}^2 + \ldots) \frac{n_2}{R_a}.$$
(13.13)

If the sound intensity is not too high ($J \leq 0.1$ W/cm^2), and the frequency is not too low ($f > 1 - 2$kcps), we can, to a first approximation, limit ourselves to the first term in the parentheses. The average value of Fo is:

$$(\text{Fo})_m = \frac{D_{\text{turb}} (t_D)_m}{R_a^2} = \frac{1}{8f} \left(\frac{\varepsilon}{b/\rho_g} \right)^{1/2} = \frac{1}{8} \frac{\xi^{1/2} J^{3/4}}{b^{1/4} \rho_g^{1/4} c_g^{5/4} f^{1/2}},$$

which, for J = 0.1 W/cm², and air as the medium, gives:

$$(Fo)_m = \frac{1.8}{\sqrt{f}}.$$

For the frequency range f = 1 - 10 kcps, $(Fo)_m$ = 0.06-0.02, and, hence, the second term is less than 18-5.7% of the first, and the third term is less than 2.0-0.2%.

Thus, as a first rough approximation:

$$\left(\frac{\partial n}{\partial a}\right)_{a=R_a} \approx 0.78 \frac{n_2}{R_a}. \tag{13.14}$$

If, however, we are limiting ourselves to the range f = 1-10 kcps, a better approximation (5-10%) is given by the formula:

$$\left(\frac{\partial n}{\partial a}\right)_{a=R_a} = \frac{2}{3}\frac{n_2}{R_a}, \tag{13.14'}$$

which is the one we shall use from now on.

The particle diffusion flux to 1 cm² of the surface of the cylinder per sec (assuming that the diffusion time is, on the average, 1/2 of the total sonic treatment time) is equal to:

$$i_a = \frac{1}{2} D_{turb} \left(\frac{\partial n}{\partial a}\right)_{a=R_a} = \frac{1}{12}\left(\frac{\varepsilon}{b/\rho_g}\right)^{1/3} R_a n_2, \tag{13.15}$$

The total particle flux to the surface of the cylinder usings Eqs. (1.32) and (9.1), is equal to:

$$N' = 4\pi R_a A_{12} i_a = \frac{10^{-6}}{4\pi \sqrt{2}} \frac{\mu_{12} k_2}{\rho_p r_2} \left(\frac{R}{r_2}\right)^2 \frac{\xi^{1/2}}{b^{1/2} \rho_g^{3/4} c_g^{7/4}} \frac{J^{5/4}}{f^{1/2}}. \tag{13.16}$$

The ratio between this flux and the flux to the sphere, as given by Eq. (13.8) and using (10.20'), is equal to

$$\frac{N'}{N} \simeq 0.02 \frac{A_{12}}{r_2}, \tag{13.17}$$

Usually, $A_{12}/r_2 > 50$, and, hence $N'/N > 1$.

The absolute value of the flux of small particles diffusing into the aggregation volume of the large particle is, however, not large. Thus, under optimum conditions, where f is given by Eq. (10.5), μ_{12} is given by (10.10), and ϑ is found from Eq. (10.20'), we have, for a particle of radius r_1 = 3.5μ in the normal sound intensity (J = 0.1 W/cm²):

$$\text{for } r_{2rr} = 0.2 \ (f_{opt} = 5.4 \text{ kcps}; \ \mu_{12} = 0.92; \ \vartheta_{min} = 0.06) \ N' = 0.38,$$
$$\text{for } r_{2rr} = 0.5 \ (f_{opt} = 2.2 \text{ kcps}; \ \mu_{12} = 0.60; \ \vartheta_{min} = 0.33) \ N' = 0.15.$$

This flux can only partly fill the aggregation volume with small particles in the length of time required for one diffusion act, with the result that the mean particle concentration inside the volume is always much lower than the mean particle concentration in the surrounding volume. For the aggregation volume to be completely filled with small particles, we need a much larger diffusion flux, namely:

$$N_r' = 2 \vartheta_{\min} \pi r_1^2 A_{12} f n_2 \approx \frac{\sqrt{2 \cdot 10^{-6}}}{\pi} \frac{\mu_{12} k_2}{\rho_p'^2} \frac{J^{1/2}}{(\rho_g c_g)^{1/2}}. \tag{13.18}$$

From this formula, we have:

for $r_{2rr} = 0.2$, $N_r' = 9.8$, and for $r_{2rr} = 0.5$, $N_r' = 1.4$,

which is approximately an order of magnitude greater than the corresponding values of N'.

It may however be seen from Eq. (13.16) that the particle diffusion flux rises rapidly with increase in radius of the cylinder being cleaned out. Let us find what radius R_{dif} will allow the aggregation cylinder to be completely filled by diffusion of small particles. Equating Eqs. (13.16) in (13.18), we have:

$$\frac{R_{dif}}{r_1} = \sqrt{6}\, \vartheta^{1/2} \left(\frac{b/\rho_g}{\varepsilon}\right)^{1/4} f^{1/2} = \sqrt{6} \left(\frac{1.5 + r_{2rr}}{1 + r_{2rr}}\right)^{1/2} r_{2rr} \frac{b^{1/4} \rho_g^{1/8} c_g^{5/8}}{\xi^{1/4} f^{1/4} J^{3/8}}. \tag{13.19}$$

For the previous conditions, we have:

for $r_{2rr} = 0.2$, $R_{dif}/r_1 = 1.20$ or $R_{dif}/(r_1 + r_2) = 1.00$;
for $r_{2rr} = 0.5$, $R_{dif}/r_1 = 2.30$ or $R_{dif}/(r_1 + r_2) = 1.53$,

i.e., usually, $R_{dif} \geq r_1 + r_2$.

In our calculations, we have completely neglected Brownian diffusion of the particles (it need not be included unless $r_2 \lesssim 0.1$).

The Orthokinetic Mechanism. Particles at a distance apart less than the internal scale of the turbulence ($l < l_0$) have only the pulsations flowing around them, and if the particles are of different sizes, they move at different velocities, so that it is possible for them to come together (while if the motion is in the opposite direction, they move apart).

The relative velocity in the direction of pulsation between two particles of radii r_1 and r_2 is, from (7.11):

$$v_{12} = (\mu_{g1} - \mu_{g2}) v_l = a_l(\tau_1 - \tau_2) = \frac{2}{135} \frac{\rho_p}{\eta} \frac{\varepsilon^{3/4}}{(b/\rho_g)^{1/4}} (r_1^2 - r_2^2) \tag{13.20}$$

Since the particles are, at the same time, being carried along to different degrees in the vibrations of the medium, the frequency being much higher than the frequency of the pulsations, the particles come together along a sinusoidal path, as shown in Fig. 42b. The "period" of the sinusoid is usually much less than the radius of a small particle, thus: $v_{12}/4f \ll r_2$. It may accordingly be assumed that collision with the large particle in a time of 1 second is possible for all the small particles contained in a rounded parallelepiped of altitude $2A_{12}$, length $v_{12} \sin \theta$ [where θ is the angle between the directions of the vibrations and the pulsation in question $(\sin \theta)_m = 2/\pi$] and thickness $2 \vartheta_{\min}^{1/2} r_1$. Thus, the flux of small particles alighting on the large particle is, for optimum conditions:

$$N'' = \frac{8}{\pi} A_{12} v_{12} \vartheta_{\min}^{1/2} r_1 n_2 \simeq 2 \cdot 10^{-9} \frac{\xi^{3/4} k_2}{b^{1/4} \rho_g^{11/8} c_g^{19/8} \eta} \frac{1 - r_{2rr}^2}{r_{2rr}^2} \left(\frac{1.5 + r_{2rr}}{1 + r_{2rr}}\right)^{1/2} \mu_{12} \frac{J^{13/8}}{f_{opt}^{1/4}}. \tag{13.21}$$

For air, we have:

$$N'' \simeq 1.4 \cdot 10^{-12} k_2 \frac{1 - r_{2rr}^2}{r_{2rr}^2} \left(\frac{1.5 + r_{2rr}}{1 + r_{2rr}}\right)^{1/2} \mu_{12} \frac{J^{13/8}}{f_{opt}^{1/4}}. \tag{13.21'}$$

The ratio between this flux and the flux to a sphere in an ordinary turbulent field is given by:

$$\frac{N''}{N} = \frac{8/\pi A_{12} v_{12} \vartheta_{min}^{1/2} r_1 n_2}{\pi r_1^2 v_{12} n_2} \simeq \frac{A_{12}}{r_1} \, r_{2rr} . \tag{13.22}$$

Usually, A_{12}/r_1 is greater than ten, so that $N''/N > 20$.

The absolute value of the flux of small particles entering the aggregation volume of the large particle by the orthokinetic mechanism is also small. Thus, for a particle of radius $r_1 = 3.5\mu$, and normal sound intensity, we have, from (13.21'):

for $r_{2rr} = 0.2$, $N'' = 2.37$;
for $r_{2rr} = 0.5$, $N'' = 0.23$.

However, having an orthokinetic flux present makes an appreciable reduction in the radius R_{dif} at which there is a sufficient particle diffusion flux to fill the aggregation volume of radius R_a completely during each diffusion act.

For $r_{2rr} = 0.2$, which corresponds to $R_a = 0.20\,(r_1 + r_2)$, we have $R_{dif} \simeq 0.37\,(r_1 + r_2)$, while for $r_{2rr} = 0.5$, which corresponds to $R_a = 0.39\,(r_1 + r_2)$, $R_{dif} \simeq 0.96\,(r_1 + r_2)$.

Thus we see that in both cases $R_{dif} > R_a$. Hence it follows that for normal sound intensity the path of the particles to the aggregation volume is blocked by some "barrier" of thickness $\Delta R \simeq R_{dif} - R_a$, which the majority of the particles are not able to overcome by the pulsation mechanism. The particles overcome the "barrier" by means of the particle self-centering phenomenon, which we discussed in §11. At higher sound intensity, the need to employ this phenomenon naturally ceases, since, as a result of the rapid increase in the orthokinetic flux [see Eq. (13.21)], a condition is reached where $R_{dif} < R_a$.

CHAPTER 4

MECHANISM AND GENERAL LAWS GOVERNING
ACOUSTIC COAGULATION OF AEROSOLS

§14. How Acoustic Coagulation of Aerosols Works

It is clear from what has been said in the last two chapters that aerosol particles behave in a substantially different way in an acoustic field than in an unperturbed medium or a turbulent stream. Because of this, there is something quite specific about the coagulation process. This is evident even when the process is simply observed with the naked eye.

As soon as the sound source is turned on, the aerosol first goes into a sort of "stressed" state, which is difficult to describe in words, but is easily grasped if it is recalled that this is the instant at which the aerosol particles go into vibration, and in addition drift and move forward under the influence of the acoustic wind. A peculiar, one may say, "orientation" of the aerosols occurs. Here, the details of the behavior of the individual particles are, of course, not clear, since the primary particles are so small that they cannot be distinguished by the naked eye (the human eye does not begin to distinguish individual objects until they are of the order of 100 μ in size).

Then the aerosol begins to clear up, and immediately afterward we see particle formations moving about at random, in addition to drift and the circulation of the medium. Liquid particles form drops, while dry solid particles form flocculent or filamentary structures, which are more tightly stuck together than in natural (Brownian) coagulation. This is illustrated in Fig. 43, which shows the carbon black aerosol deposited on a microscope slide before and after sonic treatment [272].

Local phenomena begin to show up in a standing sound wave as soon as clarification starts. Clarification is accompanied by the formation of regularly alternating transverse bands, which gradually get wider, and finally fill up the whole space. The particle aggregates formed in the process collect into transverse "discs," or, better, "rings" at the vibrating loops, and sometimes into longitudinal "collars" [277], from which they are then carried into the vibration nodes at the walls of the vessel, where they are deposited as transverse ridges around the perimeter. The ridges are closer together, the higher the frequency of the vibrations. Sometimes it is possible to distinguish intermediate ridges at the walls, corresponding to the harmonic components in the sound wave.

In a traveling wave, where there are no local phenomenon, the particle aggregates formed are deposited on the bottom of the treating chamber by the force of gravity, and to some extent on the walls. After the particle aggregates have been precipitated, the aerosol seems, for practical purposes, to have been cleaned out of the chamber.

This is a typical picture of coagulation of highly disperse aerosols (like ammonium chloride, magnesium oxide, titanium tetrachloride, gas black, etc.), when treated with moderate sound intensities in a stationary condition. As an illustration, Fig. 44 gives photographs of four successive stages in the coagulation of an ammonium chloride smoke in a standing sound wave field at a frequency of 10 kcps [179]. The first photograph shows the aerosol before the treatment started, the next two show the aerosol during treatment, and the last shows the coagulated and precipitated aerosol after the sound source has been turned off.

Coagulating and subsequently precipitating the coagulated particles requires 10 or 20 or more seconds at moderate sound intensities. At very high sound intensities, the coagulation is over in several seconds, but no large flakes are formed because of the instability of the sound field. Rotating foglike clusters of smoke parti-

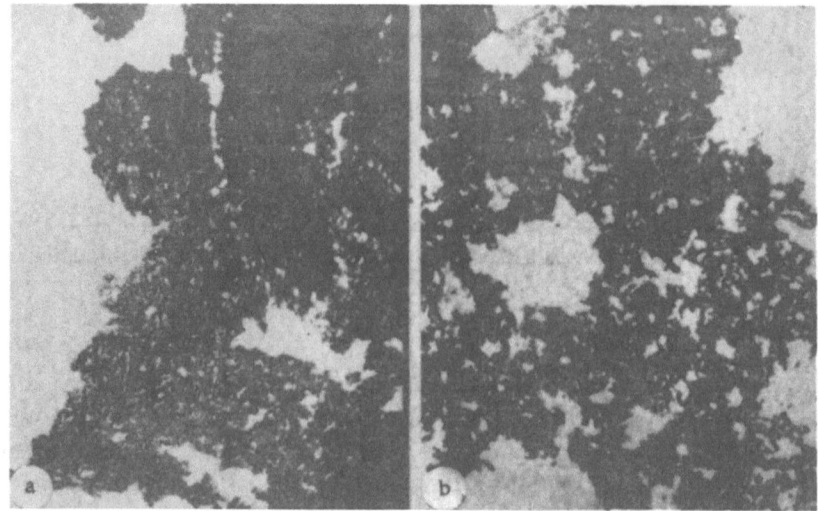

Fig. 43. Gas black aerosol before sonic treatment (a), and after 4 sec of sonic treatment (b). × 100. [Chem. Eng. Prog., 46 (8): 423-432 (1950).]

cles are formed at definite intervals along the chamber, and ridges are formed and disappear along the walls.*

If the aerosol is pumped through the sound chamber so that it is in a state of flow, the above picture of how the aerosol clears up and the particle aggregates are formed and move about at random unfolds in space rather than time, i.e., it takes place as the aerosol moves through the sound chamber. At the input to the sound chamber, we see the primary aerosol, and at the output we see the coagulated, clarified aerosol. Here, none of the local phenomena described above are present in either a traveling or a standing wave. This is due, first, to the fact that the time required for the aerosol to move from a node to a loop is very small, and, second, to the fact that the velocity vector of the particle drift and the acoustic flow vector alternately change sign as they move from one quarter wave of the field to another.

When coagulation of an aerosol in a sound field is observed with the ultramicroscope, it is possible to see somewhat more in detail how the particles behave. It may be seen that they take part in the vibrations of the medium, although, let us note, even this fact is difficult to see, since the particles are being rapidly removed from the field of view. This difficulty can be avoided to some extent, by examining the aerosol at a vibration loop, where the drift velocity of the particles approaches zero. However, it is not possible even in this case to make a direct observation of the elementary act in which the particles come together and form an aggregate, because of the extreme rapidity and complexity of the motion of the particles in the sound field, which the human eye cannot follow.

Great possibilities are opened up in this respect by taking moving pictures of the process. A study of this type has actually been made by Brandt, Freund, and Hiedemann [171, 170]. The pictures were taken at a rate of 25 frames per second. Figure 45 shows eight successive frames from this paper, taken by dark field micro-photography of acoustic coagulation of tobacco smoke, as selected by the authors from the whole series of pictures. The first frame (a) shows the aerosol before the sonic treatment was started. The second frame (b) was taken immediately after turning on the sound source, which was a magnetostriction radiator, driven by a vacuum tube oscillator operating at 10 kcps. It may be seen that the particles have gone into vibration. The next four frames (c, d, e, and f) show the successive stages in acoustic coagulation of the aerosol. It may be clearly seen that the particles are taking part in the circulation of the medium, and, in addition, are executing some sort of motion, the details of which are not clear (as shown by the blurring of the picture). The particles be-

*It is not difficult to "flush" the precipitated ridges off the walls by changing the frequency.

Fig. 44. Ammonium
chloride aerosol in dif-
ferent stages of coagu-
lation in a standing
sound wave (f = 10
kcps). [Ind. Eng. Chem.,
41 (11): 2434-2438 (1949).]

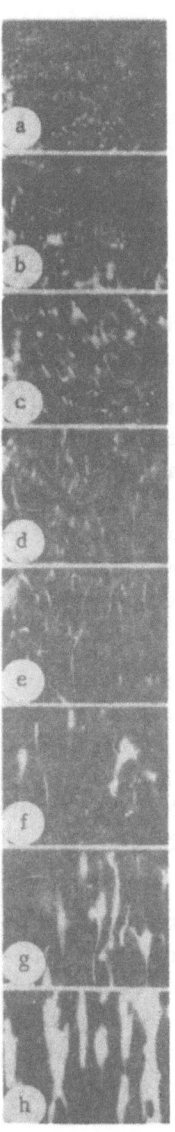

Fig. 45. Micromotion pictures of the successive stages in
acoustic coagulation of smoke (exposure time 0.04 sec).
a) Before treatment; b) at the instant the sound is turned on;
c, d, e, f) successive phases of the particle enlargement;
g, h) settling of the enlarged particles after turning off the
sound. [Kolloid-Z., 75 (2): 129-135 (1936); Trans. Faraday
Soc., 32 (184): 1101-1110 (1936).]

come larger and larger from picture to picture, and at the same time move over a larger portion of the field
of view. The last two pictures (g and h) were taken after the sound source had been turned off. They show how
the coagulated particles are precipitated by the force of gravity.

On the basis of their studies, the authors of the above paper divide acoustic coagulation of aerosols into
two stages. In the first stage, the particles vibrate under the influence of the sound, and take part in the general
circulation of the gas, increasing in size by colliding with one another. In the second stage, where the particles
have reached such a size that they vibrate with an amplitude that is only a small fraction of the amplitude of

the vibrations in the gas, they suddenly stop vibrating altogether and begin to move along irregular, often greatly bent, zig-zag (in the case of spherical particles) or spiral trajectories (in the case of irregularly shaped particles). At this stage of the process (if it gets that far) the aerosol is being coagulated as a result of particles that are not vibrating coming together, as well as by collisions between the particles that are not vibrating and those that are still vibrating.

The authors of the paper claim that their studies have enabled them to determine the elementary processes by which aerosols are coagulated in a sound field. It is difficult to agree with this, since each frame embraces about 400 cycles of the vibration, which, naturally, made it impossible to follow the trajectories of the interacting particles.* Nevertheless, by using the information on the elementary interactions between aerosol particles in a sound field obtained in the previous chapter, it is possible to work out a quite satisfactory scheme of how acoustic coagulation of aerosols works.

It may be concluded first of all from the information obtained that if the aerosol particles were all of the same size, sound treatment would have a very small effect. Actually, there are only two types of interaction in this case: attractive and diffusional. However, the rate at which particles are brought together when they are in the immediate vicinity of one another ($\theta > 0$) is equal to zero, and, hence, cannot provide any reason for the particles coming into contact, i.e., making the particles form an aggregate. Moreover, the rate of diffusional interaction between particles of the same size in a sound field is of the same order of magnitude as the rate of diffusional interaction between the particles in ordinary turbulent flow, i.e., it is insignificant.

It has nevertheless been shown by experiment that coagulation of aerosol particles goes incomparably faster in a sound field than in turbulent flow (for the same turbulence constants). This shows that the effect which sound has in intensifying aerosol coagulation is to a large extent due to the fact that all the aerosols are polydisperse, so that the particles are of different sizes, and this makes them vibrate at different velocities. Here we note the following: no matter how small the difference in size is between two particles, when they are treated with sound, they usually vibrate at sensibly different velocities (as long as the particles take sufficiently active part in the vibrations of the medium). Let us give a concrete example of this.

Of all the aerosols that have been used to test the coagulating effect of sound, the one in which the particles are most nearly of the same size seems to be the highly disperse dioctylphthalate fog described in [94, 95]. The droplet radii lay in the range $0.16-0.48\mu$, and the mean radius was $0.28\,\mu$. The frequency of the vibrations was 13 kcps. Under these conditions, the particles were carried along to a high degree, such that $\mu_{p_1} = 1.0$, $\mu_{p_2} = 0.997$, and $\mu_{p_3} = 0.975$ for the largest, the mean, and the smallest dimensions respectively, with the result that the arithmetic difference between the amplitudes of vibrations of the particles was not greater than $\mu_{13} = 2.5\%$. This gave the author of the paper [93] reason to claim that in this aerosol there was practically no difference between the rates of vibratory motion of the particles, which accordingly eliminated any orthokinetic interaction between them. Nevertheless, calculating the relative motion between the particles from Eq. (10.3) which takes account of the difference in phase shift between the vibrations of the particles, gives different results, namely; $\mu_{12} = 7.7\%$, $\mu_{23} = 15\%$, and $\mu_{13} = 22.4\%$ of the particle velocity in the gas. These are very large values, particularly if it is kept in mind that the frequency used was extremely far from the optimum values of the frequency given by Eq. (10.10) (269, 99, and 17 kcps).

Polydisperse aerosols show all the forms of interaction between aerosol particles in a sound field that we have discussed, and each of them plays a specific role. To get a better understanding of this, let us note that for the primary particles to form an aggregate with a radius of the order of $r = 10 - 20\,\mu$, the particles must cover a distance of the order of $500 - 1000\,\mu$ [this follows from Eq. (9.5)]. Thus we see that the distance is very large, and, at the same time, much greater than the mean distance between the primary particles as well as the amplitude of the particle motion in the medium. Particles this far from a coagulation center can only be brought together by the diffusional interaction resulting from turbulence in the vibrating medium. However,

---

*An attempt was made recently in the Acoustics Institute of the Academy of Sciences of the USSR to take high speed micromotion pictures of acoustic coagulation of aerosols at a rate of up to 5000 frames per second. However, the first experiments only succeeded in catching the formation of particle complexes in space, as has already been mentioned in §12.

as the distance between the particles decreases, we know that the rate at which they are brought together by diffusion drops rapidly and becomes infinitesimally small when the particles get really close to the aggregation volume of a large particle. What appears on the scene here is self-centering of the small particles at the large particle, so that the rate at which the small particles approach the aggregation volume increases sharply (with the exception of the middle part of the aggregation volume, where the particles are repelled and are then brought into the extreme parts of the volume by acoustic streaming and diffusion). The self-centering rate of small particles is such that they reach the aggregation volume in small fractions of a second, especially since the process is aided by the orthokinetic mechanism of pulsational interaction.

When the small particle enters the aggregation volume of the large particle, its motion is instantaneously (during a period of the vibrations or less) stopped by orthokinetic collision with the large particle. Thus we see that the aggregation volume is being filled continuously, and cleaned out periodically.

The above scheme of how acoustic coagulation of aerosols works, as applied to an aerosol containing particles of two different sizes, is shown in Fig. 46. Here, the number 1 designates the large particle, which is the coagulation center, while the other numbers represent particles all of the same size, located at different characteristic points in the surrounding space, all vibrating with an amplitude A_{12} with respect to the large particle. The dotted line shows the outline of the aggregation volume of the large particle, while the dashed line shows the temporary outline of the preaggregation volume, in which self-centering of the particles occurs (R_{dif} is the averaged radius of the volume). The zig-zag arrows marked V_{sc} indicate the flow of small particles into the aggregation volume by self-centering, while the similar arrows marked V_{dc} indicate self-decentering of the particles. The straight arrows marked V_{attr} designate small particles being brought in by attraction as well as by acoustic streaming, while the arrows marked V_{ort} designate particles brought in by the orthokinetic pulsational interaction mechanism. The arrows marked D_{turb} designate small particles brought into the preaggregation volume by diffusion. This is the way rapid coagulation of aerosols works, as observed in the optimum frequency range, where an appreciable difference occurs between the vibratory velocities of the particles.*

If this difference is absent, as is inevitable in sonic treatment of coarsely disperse and coagulated finely disperse aerosols, aggregation of the particles follows a different scheme. In this case, the only definite difference maintained is that between the drift velocities of the particles and the particles form aggregates by the orthokinetic mechanism, at the same time settling under their own weight. Also, in a standing wave, local particle accumulations are built up in the vibration nodes at the walls. This is due to the fact that these regions form a "dead" zone between the two oppositely directed acoustic streams, and the large particles moving with them fall into the dead zone as a result of the centrifugal force when they are turning around.

Since the drift rate of the particles is small in comparison with the vibratory velocity, the above rate of orthokinetic aerosol coagulation is very small. Accordingly, to this type of coagulation in a sound field we shall henceforth give the name slow coagulation of aerosols. We use the same term for the coagulation of particles that are all the same size, where the tempo of the aggregation is characteristically slow.

§15. Kinetic Equation of the Process

If we assume that the interaction between particles of different sizes is the basic factor in acoustic coagulation of aerosols, we immediately see that the rate at which coagulation occurs is a linear function of the particle count concentration. Let us illustrate this for the case of an aerosol containing particles of two different sizes.

---

*Recently, A. I. Gulyaev and V. M. Kuznetsov [31] established the fact that coagulation of aerosols may be brought about by the effect of periodic shock waves (a single shock wave produces no appreciable effect, as has been shown by E. Richardson [257]. The aerosol coagulation mechanism in this case is evidently similar to that described above. We come to this conclusion from the fact that the amount of turbulence for the pressure amplitude used by the authors (0.3 atm) was of approximately the same value as in the acoustic field (4-6%) and, hence, the amount of coagulation occurring by the purely turbulent mechanism described by V. G. Levich [68, 69] was not sufficient to account for the good results obtained. There does not seem to be any basis for assuming that any particular importance attaches to having had oblique shock waves present [322].

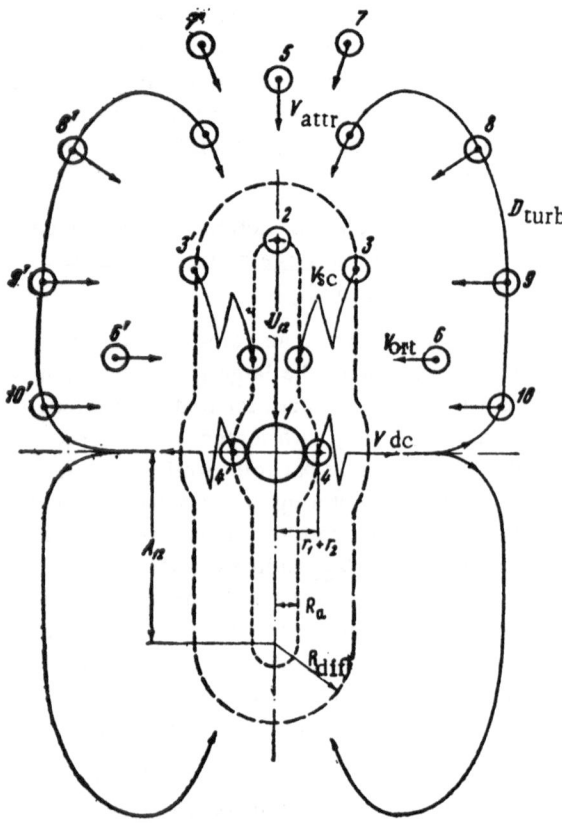

Fig. 46. Diagram of acoustic coagulation of
aerosols.

A model of this sort is of course not completely equivalent to a polydisperse system but it does contain the principal distinguishing feature — the difference in particle sizes — and any polydisperse aerosol can, generally speaking, be thought of as a combination of systems of particles of two different sizes.

Let our aerosol at the start contain n_{10} large particles and n_{20} small particles per unit volume. It is here assumed that $n_{20} \gg n_{10}$, because otherwise it is impossible to get any appreciable particle consolidation (see §9).

It is assumed in accordance with what has been said in the preceding section that particles of the same size do not aggregate with one another, and that the reduction in particle count concentration that occurs during coagulation results solely from small particles sticking fast to large particles.

In setting up the kinetic equation for acoustic coagulation of our aerosol we need only turn to the formal kinetics of homogeneous chemical reactions, which states as follows [43]: the rate of a reaction is proportional to the product of the concentrations of the reacting substances, with each of the concentrations participating to an extent which, in the simplest cases, is equal to the coefficient standing in front of the formula of the particular substance in the equation of the reaction. As we know, absolutely nothing is specified about the mechanism by which the substances react. This makes it possible to extend the above rule to the coagulation of our aerosol with two different size particles, which, by the way, is formally very similar to the case of a reaction between two types of gas molecules. The specific feature of our case is that the concentration of one of the "substances," namely that of the large particles, remains constant during the process: $n_1 = n_{10} = \text{const}$. Bearing this in mind, as well as the fact that the "coefficients standing in front of the formula of each substance" are equal to unity in our case, so that the expression for the acoustic coagulation rate of the aerosol will be written as

$$\frac{dn}{dt} = - K_a n, \qquad (15.1)$$

where n is the concentration of the particles (remembering that $n_2 \gg n_1$, it may be assumed that the total number of particles n is the same as the number of small particles n_2), t is the time during which the treatment occurs, and K_a is the acoustic coagulation coefficient of the aerosol, which is a function of the physical properties of the aerosol and the constants of the sound field. Thus, we see that the equation for acoustic coagulation of aerosols is of the same form as the equation of a monomolecular chemical reaction.

Note that if acoustic coagulation of aerosols depended upon interaction between particles of the same size, the rate of the process would not be linear, but would be a quadratic function of the particle concentration at any instant. The kinetic equation in this case would be the same as the equation of a bimolecular chemical reaction, such as is found for Brownian coagulation of aerosols [see Eq. (9.2)]. This would be at variance with all the experimental data on the kinetics of acoustic coagulation of aerosols, which we shall now consider. But

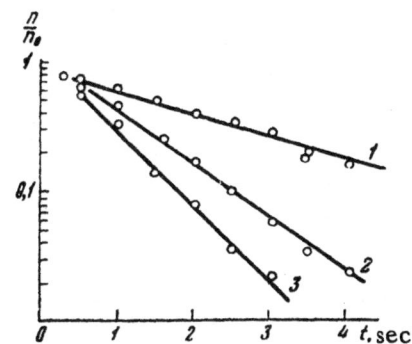

Fig. 47. Acoustic coagulation rate of a paraffin fog as a function of particle count concentration (f = 10 kcps). 1) For J = 0.0066 W/cm^2; 2) for J = 0.06 W/cm^2; 3) for J = 0.11 W/cm^2.

first let us integrate Eq. (15.1), assuming that at the initial time t = 0, the particle count concentration is n = n_0:

$$n = n_0 e^{-K_a t_0}. \qquad (15.2)$$

The exponential relation between the particle count concentration and the coagulation coefficient and the treatment time defined by this equation is in good agreement with the experimental data on acoustic coagulation of aerosols.

The relation (15.2) was first demonstrated experimentally by Brandt [161] in experiments on acoustic coagulation of a paraffin oil fog, made at a frequency of 10 kcps. The radii of the fog droplets lay in the range 0.2-1.9μ (predominantly 0.8-0.9μ), and the concentration of the droplets by weight was 15-20 g/m^3. The results of these experiments are shown in Fig. 47. The curves shown give the following values for the coagulation coefficient:

for J = 0.0067 W/cm^2, K_a = 0.43,
for J = 0.06   W/cm^2, K_a = 0.92,
for J = 0.11   W/cm^2, K_a = 1.28.

So as to be able to make a comparison between the coagulation coefficients of different aerosols, we shall in future refer them to the normal sound intensity J = 0.1 W/cm^2, and call this the "normal" coagulation coefficient of the aerosol. In the present case, the normal coagulation coefficient is $K_a \simeq 1.25$.

Inoue [37] also gives in support of Eq. (15.2) the results of St. Clair's experiments [179, 181], made on ammonium chloride smoke at a frequency of 10-20 kcps. It does not however seem to us that this is entirely justified, since the experiments did not make a direct measurement of the size of the particles undergoing coagulation, but only of the change in intensity of the light scattered by the particles, which is by no means the same thing in this case.

A very convincing demonstration of Eq. (15.2) is provided by the experiments on acoustic coagulation of a dioctylphthalate fog made recently by B. F. Podoshevnikov [94, 96]. The dioctylphthalate fog was produced in a Lamar aerosol generator. The radii of the fog droplets lay in the range 0.16-0.48 μ (predominantly 0.28 μ). The concentration by weight was 1.8-2.1 g/m^3, and the frequency was 13 kcps (generated by a St. Clair electrodynamic radiator).

As a result of his experiments, this author found the following relation between the droplet count concentration and the sound exposure pt_0 (p is the sound pressure in kilobars):

$$\frac{n}{n_0} = e^{-0.08 p t_0 + 0.0002 (p t_0)^2}. \qquad (15.3)$$

The second, quadratic term in the exponent is extremely small in comparison with the first term for normal or even high sound intensity (J = 0.1-1.0 W/cm^2), and moderate treatment times (t $\leq$ 15-20 sec). Thus the second term may be neglected for practical purposes, giving a relation of the form (15.2). The normal coagulation coefficient in this case is found to be K_a = 0.08, p = 0.8·6.4 $\approx$ 0.5.

The change in dispersion composition occurring during sonic treatment is shown in Fig. 48 by curves giving the distribution of the particles in radii. The figure shows that the maximum shifts comparatively little during coagulation, in spite of the fact that the large particle fraction has increased considerably.*

---

*It was concluded in [300] that the distribution curves are of two-modulus type, but this was the result of an error in the method of measuring the dimensions of the water droplets.

That the equation giving the kinetics of acoustic aerosol coagulation is exponential is also shown by the results of semi-industrial scale experiments on sonic-inertial precipitation of various industrial aerosols, made by Oyama, Inoue, Savahata, and Okada. We give information on these experiments in §20 (see Fig. 68 and Table 18).

The most detailed study made by these authors was that on the acoustic coagulability of a cracking gas fog. The particle radii in this aerosol lay in the range $0.5\text{-}5.0\mu$ (predominantly $3.0\text{-}3.5\mu$), and the concentration by weight varied from 6 to 15 g/m^3. The optimum frequency was 4 kcps. The author calculates [259] that the normal coagulation coefficient of this aerosol in their industrial setup was $K_a = 0.35\text{-}0.37$.

Let us briefly consider the physical content of the acoustic aerosol coagulation coefficient K_a. Formal kinetics makes it possible to establish only one thing: the coefficient is proportional to the count concentration n_{10} of the large particles, acting as coagulation centers:

$$K_a = K_{a1}n_{10}. \tag{15.4}$$

However, if we consider the way the process goes as described in the previous section, we can expand this idea although it must be pointed out that the motion of the small particles is so complicated that it is still very difficult to give a complete analytical solution of the problem.

We know that each of the large particles has deposited on it all the small particles getting into the aggregation volume of the large particle as shown by the dotted line in Fig. 46. This volume may be thought of approximately as an ordinary circular cylinder, with a cross-sectional area of $\vartheta\pi r_1^2$, and altitude $2A_{12}$, so that the volume is $Q_a = 2\,\vartheta\pi r_1^2 A_{12}$.

The concentration n_a of small particles filling the aggregation volume is directly proportional to the mean particle concentration in the surrounding space: $n_a = \beta n$, where β is the filling coefficient which cannot yet be determined analytically ($\beta < 1$). The total number Δn of small particles captured by the large particles in the time Δt is equal to

$$\Delta n = -2Q_a\beta nn_{10}f\Delta t = -2\vartheta n_{10}r_1^2\mu_{12}\beta U_g n\Delta t. \tag{15.5}$$

Hence it follows that the rate of acoustic coagulation of an aerosol may be expressed by Eq. (15.1), if the coefficient K_a is taken to be:

$$K_a = 2\vartheta\beta n_{10}r_1^2\mu_{12}U_g. \tag{15.6}$$

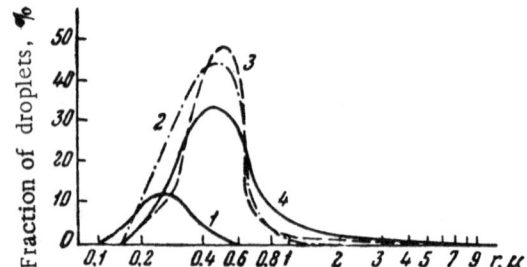

Fig. 48. Change in dispersion composition of a dioctylphthalate fog during sonic treatment ($f = 13$ kcps, p = 8600 bar). 1) Initial distribution of droplet sizes (k = 1.82 g/m^3); 2) after treatment for $t_0 = 2.3$ sec; 3) the same, $t_0 = 8.75$ sec; 4) the same, $t_0 = 14.8$ sec.

It follows from everything that has been said that the acoustic coagulation coefficient of an aerosol with particles of two different sizes is simply the fraction of the small particles captured by all the large particles per unit time.

Slow coagulation of aerosols due to a difference in the drift velocities is also described by Eq. (15.1), but in this case the acoustic coagulation coefficient is given by

$$K_a = \vartheta\pi r_1^2(V_1 - V_2)\,n_{10}, \tag{15.7}$$

where V_1 and V_2 are respectively the drift velocities of the large and the small particles. It is not difficult to arrive at this equation if it is assumed that as each of the large particles is drifting it captures all the small particles in a cylinder of cross-sectional area $\vartheta\pi r_1^2$, and altitude equal to the difference $V_1 - V_2$.

Let us consider the experimental data in existence on what effect the physical properties of the aerosol and the constants of the sound field have on the coagulation kinetics, in the light of the various theoretical ideas bearing on the question.

State of Aggregation, Density, and Structure of the Aerosol Particles. Solid particles consolidate somewhat more rapidly than liquid particles of the same degree of dispersion, density, and concentration. This is due to the fact that solid particles tend to join up into structures that are less compact than droplets, forming loose flakes, chains, etc., more or less at random. The particle aggregates formed have more tendency to settle than droplets of the same weight although their apparent density is considerably less. This follows directly from the expression for the relaxation time of the particles (4.4), in which the particle size enters as the square, while the density appears only to the first power.

However, dry solid particle aggregates are less stable in a turbulent state, so that they may be partly broken up when they finally get into a cyclone or other type of inertial precipitator [206], where the turbulence is very high ($\varepsilon = 10^9 - 10^{10}$). This applies particularly to aerosol particles having a low degree of dispersion, which, as shown by the theoretical studies of B. V. Deryagin, have much less tendency to stick together than highly disperse particles [Kolloid- Z. 69 (2):155-164 (1934)].

If the sound intensity is very high ($J \geqslant 1.0$ W/cm^2), the dry particle aggregates may even be partially broken up right in the sound field, but this is only true of very large conglomerates, where the sound pressure or the velocity of the turbulent pulsations may be appreciably different at the two ends. This seams to have very little effect on the results of subsequent precipitation, since when the aggregate breaks up the "fragments" are still so large that they have no trouble settling out. This is shown by the fact that the precipitation efficiency of the coagulated aerosols increases continuously, rather than dropping off, as the sound intensity is raised (compare, for example, the results of sonic-inertial precipitation of gas black at an intensity of 0.5 W/cm^2, as given below in §20).

The density of the primary particles does not seem to play any essential role, although this is not supported by any direct experimental evidence. This is probably due to the fact that changing the density results in phenomena that directly oppose one another. On the one hand, increasing the density, from (11.13), raises the inertial self-centering rate of the particles, and thus increases the coagulation coefficient, and further, the optimum frequencies shift toward lower values, at which the sound absorption of the medium is less. On the other hand, increasing the density of the particles means, from (9.1), that there is a reduction in the particle count concentration, which enters directly into the kinetic equation of the process, and indirectly, as a factor in the expression for the coagulation coefficient.

Nor is the form of the primary particles found to have any specific effect on the rate of the process. It is about equally easy to coagulate particles in a sound field whether they are spherical (fog droplets, carbon black), cubical (magnesium oxide), or needle-shaped (zinc oxide) etc. It is found on the whole that the physical properties of the aerosol particles have comparatively little effect on the kinetics of the acoustic aerosol coagulation process.

The Dispersion Composition and Concentration by Weight of the Aerosol Particles. Highly disperse aerosols are much easier to coagulate than aerosols having a moderate, or particularly, a low degree of dispersion. This follows directly from the kinetic equation (15.1) considered from the standpoint of the data on the acoustic coagulation coefficient given in the previous section, and from Eq. (9.1) for the particle count concentraton.

The acoustic coagulation coefficient changes comparatively little as the particle size is decreased, but the particle count concentration rises rapidly, which keeps the process from going any faster. This may be accounted for physically in the following way: the total cross-sectional area of the particles rises rapidly as the particles become more highly disperse (as is shown experimentally by the fact that the aerosol becomes much less transparent), and at the same time there is a large increase in the volume "combed" by the vibrating particles with the result that there is a higher probability of the particles colliding with one another.

However, bringing the particles of highly disperse aerosols up to a size where they can be readily precipitated by gravitational or inertial means requires an enormous number of aggregation acts. For example, to bring particles of radius $r_0 = 0.1\mu$ up to a radius of $r = 10\mu$ requires, from (9.8), $(10/0.1)^3$ acts. It takes a long sonic treatment, and hence a considerable expenditure of energy to bring this about. If the acoustic coagulation coefficient is known, the time required may be found on the basis of (15.2) from the following formulas:

For fogs

$$t_0 = \frac{3}{K_a} \ln \left(\frac{r}{r_0} \right) , \tag{16.1}$$

For smokes and dusts (which require corrections for the reduction in density of the particle aggregates):

$$t_0 = \frac{3}{K_a} \ln \left[\left(\frac{\rho_p}{\rho'_{p0}} \right)^{1/3} \frac{r}{r_0} \right] . \tag{16.2}$$

It may be seen from these equations that the time required for sonic treatment rises rapidly as the particles become more highly disperse. For example, to bring the droplets of a highly disperse dioctylphthalate fog ($r_0 = 0.28\mu$) up to a radius of $r = 5 - 6\mu$, where they can be trapped in cyclones, using the normal sound intensity $J = 0.1$ W/cm^2, with $K_a = 0.50$ takes, from (16.1), a time $t_0 \simeq 18 - 20$ sec.

The time required for the treatment may be reduced by increasing the sound intensity. Thus, if the sound intensity is increased to $J = 1$ W/cm^2, Eq. (15.6) shows that the coagulation coefficient rises to $K_a = 1.6$, so that the treatment time drops to $t_0 \simeq 6$ sec. This length of time is more or less usable in practice, but it involves an expenditure of more than three times as much energy per unit volume of aerosol [see Eq. (20.8)].

It is clear from what has been said that the best aerosols for industrial coagulation are those with a moderate degree of dispersion, in particular those having a particle radius of the order of $r = 2 - 4\mu$. Aerosols that contain no particles with radii less than $5 - 7\mu$ are very difficult to coagulate, and this is particularly true of solid phase aerosols where the particles do not stick together very well. Good examples are fly ash, mineral dusts, artificial fogs produced by mechanical atomization, etc., as well as powder suspensions ("aggregated" aerosols).

The acoustic coagulation rate of aerosols is also greatly affected by the concentration by weight of the particles. The higher the concentration by weight of the particles, the better the aerosol coagulates, as follows from Eq. (15.1) in view of (9.1). Physically, this is due to the fact that the higher the concentration, the smaller the volume of aerosol from which each of the aggregates is formed, i.e., the particles have less distance to go through to get to the coagulation center.

It has been found that the efficiency of the process drops off greatly at concentrations below $2 - 5$ g/m^3. Good results are obtained in such cases by squirting atomized water into the low concentration aerosol, which is called watering the aerosol. This greatly increases the efficiency of coagulation and subsequent precipitation of the particles, as may be seen from Fig. 49, which shows the results of sonic-inertial precipitation of a gas black aerosol in the natural, as compared with the watered from [273].

The improvement produced by watering the aerosol is due primarily to the fact that it puts more large coagulation centers into the aerosol, which are completely trapped in the precipitator, and only secondarily to the fact that it wets the dry particle aggregates (if there are any). Very high particle concentrations (above 100 g/m^3) are undesirable, since this gives an exceedingly large drop off in sound intensity with distance, which greatly reduces the acoustic coagulation rate in the aerosol.

Viscosity, Temperature, and Pressure of the Gas. The higher the viscosity of the gas, the higher the optimum frequency required [see Eq. (10.5)] and the lower the inertial self-centering rate of the particles [see Eq. (11.13)]. Hence it follows that any increase in the viscosity of the gas has a bad effect on acoustic coagulation of aerosols.

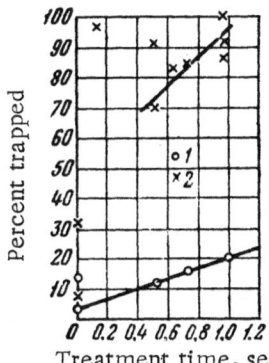

Fig. 49. Acoustic coagulation efficiency of gas black (p_c = 0.35 atm, f = 2.1 kcps) as affected by adding a water fog. 1) In dry form; 2) after introducing the water fog.

Increasing the temperature of the gas means [see Eq.(b) on p. 46] that the viscosity of the gass increases, with all the attendant consequencies, i.e., the acoustic coagulation rate of the aerosol is definitely reduced. The process goes normally otherwise, so that the high temperature does not prevent the process from being used to clean hot gases.

Cases are known where aerosols have been successfully coagulated at temperatures of 300 - 500°C and higher. However, when this is done, serious thought must be given to getting all of the radiated acoustic energy into the aerosol, since a large amount of reflection and scattering of the sound waves occurs at the point where the cold air from the siren meets the hot aerosol.

Increasing the pressure in the gas means increasing the density, and hence the acoustic resistance of the medium. This reduces the particle velocity in the medium [see Eq. (1.9)] which, as will be shown below, is directly proportional to the acoustic coagulation coefficient. The value of the coefficient is greatly reduced, which in turn lowers the rate of the process. If the coagulation coefficient is to be maintained at its former level, the sound intensity has to be raised by approximately the same factor by which the pressure in the medium differs from normal pressure. Acoustic coagulation of aerosols has been tried out experimentally at high pressures of the order of 10 atm gage [86] and 50 atm gage [80].

The viscosity, temperature and pressure of the gas are generally about the same in most aerosols and approximate atmospheric conditions, so that these factors are not as a rule what determines the differences observed in the acoustic coagulation rates of aerosols.

Sound Frequency. It has been shown experimentally that the frequency of the sound used has a very substantial effect on acoustic coagulation of aerosols. This is shown by laboratory studies of the process, as well as by the large scale tests described in the next chapter on acoustic fog dissipation, and the sonic-inertial method of precipitating industrial dusts, smokes, and fogs.

As an illustration, Fig. 50 shows the results found in the laboratory experiments of Horsley and Sivi (Ultrasonic Corporation, USA [156]) for the frequency dependence of the sound level required for 50% clarification of an artificial water fog, while Fig. 51 shows the frequency dependency of the percentage of various commercial aerosols precipitated by the sonic-inertial method, as found by Inoue, working with Oyama, Sawahata and Okada [38].

It may be seen from the graph shown that each aerosol has an optimum frequency at which acoustic coagulation goes in the most efficient way. Even small departures from the optimum frequency have a large effect on the efficiency of the process. Thus, in the first case (Fig. 50), shifting the frequency 2 kcps above the optimum value (3.0 - 3.5 kcps) means that the sound level has to be raised 4 db, or else the treatment time has to be doubled. In the second case (Fig. 51) the same frequency shift means that one and a half to two times as much material is left in the aerosol.

The conclusion may be drawn from Fig. 50 that the optimum frequency is not a function of either the sound intensity or the treatment time, but is a function solely of the properties of the aerosol. Here, we immediately have to stipulate that the optimum frequency is likewise unaffected by the concentration by weight of the aerosol particles. This has been shown by Kawamura [210] who conducted a fairly extensive study to find how acoustic coagulation of tobacco smoke and ammonium chloride smoke is

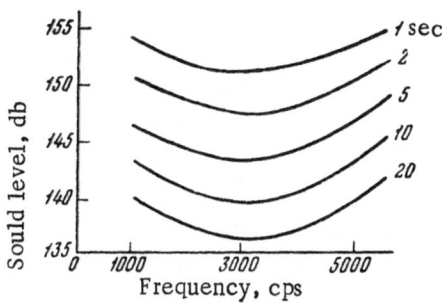

Fig. 50. Sound level required for 50% clarification of an artificial water fog for different times and frequencies.

TABLE 13

Aerosol	Particle radius* r, μ	Optimum frequency† f_{opt}, kcps	Author
I. Laboratory studies			
Tobacco smoke	$\dfrac{0.2 - 2.5}{0.8}$	7−8	Kawamura [210]
Ammonium chloride smoke	$\dfrac{0.3 - 2.6}{1.2}$	5−6	
Artificial water fog	−	5−6	N. P. Tverskoi [115]
" " "	2.0	3−3.5	Horsley and Sivi [156]
II. Industrial tests			
Furnace gas black	0.03−0.07	3.5−4.0	Stokes [272]
Aggregated carbon black	0.5−15.0	3.0	Inoue et al. [38, 246]
Zinc oxide sublimate	$\dfrac{0.5 - 5.0}{2.5}$	3.0−3.5	
Coke gas fog	$\dfrac{0.5 - 5.0}{2.5}$	3.5− 4.0	
Cracking gas fog	$\dfrac{0.5 - 5.0}{3.0}$	3.5 − 4.0	
Dilute sulfuric acid	2.5−50	1.0−2.0	

* The numerator gives the maximum radii, while the denominator gives the predominant radius.

†The aerosol coagulation efficiency was determined in the laboratory studies from the light scattered by the particles, while in the industrial tests it was determined from the percentage of the particles precipitated inertially in cyclones.

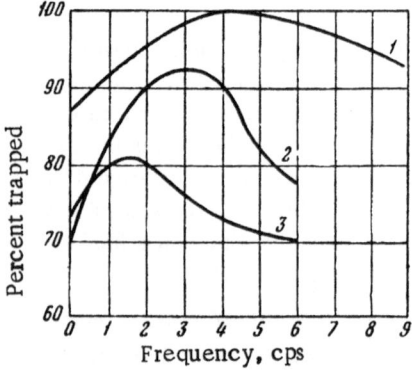

Fig. 51. Sonic-inertial precipitation of various commercial aerosols as a function of frequency. 1) Coke gas tar (r = 0.5 - 5μ), 2) aggregated carbon black (r = 0.5 - 15μ); 3) dilute sulfuric acid fog (r = 2.5 - 50μ).

affected by the acoustic constants. Unfortunately, in these studies, the frequency dependence of the process was determined from the light scattered by the aerosol particles, while making a check of the theory requires explicit knowledge of the coagulation rate, dn/dt.

Table 13 gives a compilation of the gas data on the optimum frequencies required for acoustic coagulation of different aerosols. Examination of these data leads to an important conclusion: the lower the degree of dispersion of the aerosol, the lower the optimum frequency required.

This conclusion suggests the one about the extent to which aerosol particles are carried along in the vibrations of the medium, which caused Hueter and Bolt [205] to suggest the following formula for finding the optimum frequency in air:

$$f_{\text{opt}} = \frac{22.4}{\rho_p r_m^2} \text{ kcps,}$$

TABLE 14

Type of fog and place of test	Prominant drop radius, r, μ	Frequency used, f, kcps	Evaluation of test results	Entrainment factor, μ_p, %	Flow-around factor, μ_g, %
Artificial stationary fog (vertical tube 150 mm diameter × 1000 mm long)	4.0	0.5	Successful	85.5	52.0
Artificial moving fog (horizontal tube 75 mm diameter × 3600 mm long)	4.0	0.5	"	85.5	52.0
Artificial stationary fog (rectangular chamber 7400 cm³)	2.0	3.5	"	68.8	72.9
The same (tunnel 1.2 × 2.1 × 30 m)	4.5	0.6	"	73.6	67.8
Artificial fog (Palme's experiments)	7.5	8.5	Failure	2.8	99.9
Artificial stationary fog (swimming pool 5600 m³)	1.0	0.7	"	99.8	5.3
Artificial moving fog (12.8 × 14 × 18 m chamber)	0.5	33	Successful	84.7	52.9
The same	4.0	33	Failure	2.7	99.9
The same	0.5	9.5	"	98.4	17.9
The same, in a restricted part of the chamber (400 m³)	4.0	9.5	Slow clarification	8.7	99.6
Artificial stationary fog (1000 m³ reservoir chamber)	5.0	0.3	Successful	87.1	49.2
The same	5.0	0.4	"	80.0	60.3
The same	5.0	13.0	Failure	4.1	99.9
Slowly moving natural continental fog (Lunken airport, USA)	6.0	0.44	Successful	64.1	76.7
Natural continental fog (Arcata and Breezy Grove, USA)	15	3.5	Failure	1.7	99.98
Natural moving sea fog (Sandberg, USA)	5.0	0.44	Successful	77.0	64.0

where r_m is the predominant radius in μ. The two authors derived this equation from the expression (5.19) for the particle entrainment by setting $\mu_p = 0.50$, without any serious reasons whatever for doing so.

To show that this was really the case, consider the data on the degree entrainment, and at the same time, the amount of flow around the particles in a vibrating gas for different aerosols coagulated in a sonic field.

Table 14 gives information on the degree of entrainment and the amount of flow around the droplets in natural and artificial fogs on which acoustic dissipation was tried, as discussed in §18. It may be seen from the table that in the successful experiments, degree of entrainment was usually much higher than $\mu_p = 0.50$, having the value $\mu_p = 0.65-0.85$. (In [156], Boucher interpreted this fact as a weighty proof in favor of the idea that orthokinetic interaction is the basic process in acoustic coagulation of aerosols).

The sonic-inertial precipitation experiments on industrial fogs, discussed in §20, give different values for the entrainment factors, and hence for the flow-around factors of the droplets (Table 15).

Thus we see that at the optimum frequency of these experiments the degree of entrainment was much less than $\mu_p = 0.5$, having the value $\mu_p = 0.15 - 0.27$.

It may be seen from what has been presented above that the original assumption made in deriving the formula to be used in calculating the optimum frequency for acoustic coagulation of aerosols was simply a guess, and it is no wonder that the formula gave results widely different from those found experimentally.

TABLE 15

Aerosol	Predominant drop radius, r, μ	Drop density, μ_p, g/cm^3	Gas viscosity, η, g·cm^{-1}·sec^{-1}	Optimum frequency f_{opt}, kcps	Theoretical entrainment factor, μ_p,%	Theoretical flow-around factor, μ_g, %
Sulfuric acid fog	7.5	1.7	$1.8 \cdot 10^{-4}$	1.0	15	99.0
Cracking gas hydrocarbon fog	3	1.1	$1.0 \cdot 10^{-4}$	4.0	18	98.0
Coke gas tar fog	2.5	1.2	$0.9 \cdot 10^{-4}$	3.5	27	96.5

Even greater disagreement with experiment is found when using Vyzhikovskii's formula $f_{opt} = 7.64/\rho_p r^2_m$, which was derived on the basis of an excessively simplified conception of acoustic aerosol coagulation [295].

In both cases, what we have in mind is principally disagreement with results of laboratory studies, since in commercial scale installations, the optimum frequency is affected, as we shall see below, by both the degree of dispersion of the aerosol and by a factor that is geometrical in nature.

Consider Eq. (15.6) for the acoustic coagulation coefficient of aerosols having two different size particles. Of the quantities making up this equation, the only ones that are frequency dependent are the degree of relative motion μ_{12} of the particles, and, possibly, the filling coefficient β of the aggregation volume. If it is assumed that β is only slightly dependent on the frequency, the optimum frequency may be determined by the use of Eq. (10.5)

$$ f_{opt} = \frac{9\eta}{4\pi\rho_p r^2_2} r_2 rr , \qquad (16.3) $$

derived for the condition that μ_{12} is a maximum. For air, this equation is of the form:

$$ f_{opt} = \frac{13.2}{\rho_p r^2_2 \mu} r_2 \, rr \, kcps. \qquad (16.3') $$

Serious difficulties are, however, encountered in the practical use of Eq. (16.3) due primarily to the fact that actual aerosols are polydisperse. Even if we have a curve giving the distribution of the aerosol particles in dimensions, it is difficult to decide what numbers to put into the formula for r_2 and r_{2rr} (the only thing that is clear is that $r_2 < r_m$, and $r_1 < r_{max}$). It must also be kept in mind that the dimensions of the particles increase during coagulation, and, from (16.3), this means that the optimum frequency is becoming increasingly lower. Hence it follows that the optimum frequency depends on both the initial and final size of the particles.

The optimum frequency observed experimentally is some sort of a mean between the instantaneous values of the optimum frequency at the beginning and end of the process. We should add to what has already been said that in commercial scale installations the optimum value of the frequency begins to be seriously affected by a geometric factor, namely, the length of the coagulation chamber. This is especially important in coagulating highly disperse aerosols, carbon black in particular.

The theoretical value for the optimum frequency to be used in the initial stage of consolidation of the particles in such aerosols, as given by Eq. (16.3), turns out to be tens and hundreds of kilocycles. Frequencies this high, however, attenuate so rapidly with distance from the source in gases that the aerosol flowing through the chamber has practically no sound in it for the greater part of the time. It is therefore better in practice to use lower frequencies of the order of 3 - 4 kcps and below which suffer comparatively little attenuation. The primary particles, which require higher frequencies, are then coagulated by the harmonics that are produced during propagation of the sound wave, and are to some extent already present in the radiation spectrum of the sound sources generally used. This idea is supported by the fact noted by Boucher [150, 151] and other investigators that "adding" high-frequency vibrations improve the action of a coagulator.

The geometric factor also has an important effect in experiments on acoustic dissipation of natural fogs, where the irradiated zone is of particularly large extent. The optimum frequency is here, as a rule, even lower than in industrial coagulators. Bringing all these factors together into some well defined function so as to form a single unified whole is extremely difficult. Thus, for the present, the only reliable way of finding the optimum frequency to be used in acoustic coagulation of aerosols is to make a direct experiment on the natural aerosol under operating conditions.

It is stated in [33] that the rate at which acoustic coagulation of aerosols occurs is completely independent of the frequency used, and it is therefore recommended to do the work at the lowest possible frequencies, which have the least attenuation [89]. This is however a misunderstanding, which arose from the fact that what was used in the experiments was not a natural zinc oxide aerosol, but atomized zinc white powder. Aerosols prepared in this way contain primary particle aggregates that are stuck together and coagulated, and since they are so coarsely disperse, the particle aggregation occurs by slow coagulation (§14), i.e., by orthokinetic collisions between particles of the same size, brought about by differences in drift velocity. This is shown by the relation $p^2 t_0$ = const obtained by the authors. For any type of drift, the particle velocity is $V \sim p^2$ (see Table 5 in §6), from which it follows that $p^2 t_0 \sim (V_1 - V_2) t_0 \simeq L_1$ = const and for $\mu_g \approx 1$, neither $p^2 t_0$ nor V_1 depends on the frequency.

Sound Intensity. It has been found that the acoustic coagulation coefficient is proportional to some power of the sound intensity. If the sound intensities and treatment times are not too great, the proportionality is as follows:

$$K_a \sim J^{1/2}. \tag{16.4}$$

This important relation was first pointed out by Inoue [37], on the basis of the experimental data of Brandt and Freund [161, 163] and of Neumann and Norton [239].

From Eqs. (1.9) and (1.10), we may also write in place of (16.4):

$$K_a \sim p_g \sim u_g. \tag{16.4'}$$

Figure 52 shows the particle count concentration of tobacco smoke as a function of the product $A_g t_0$, which is proportional to $J^{1/2} t_0$ and $U_g t_0$, as taken from the experiments of Brandt and Freund, while Fig. 53 shows the degree of consolidation of titanium chloride particles as a function of $J^{1/2}$ as found in Neumann and Norton's experiments. Since the values of the function are plotted to a logarithmic scale on the ordinate axes of both figures, there is a linear relation between the argument of the exponential containing the coagulation coefficient and the values of the quantities plotted as abscissas.

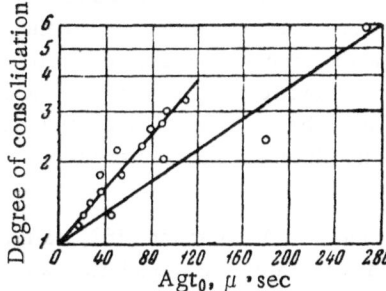

Fig. 52. Degree of consolidation of tobacco smoke particles as a function of the product $A_g t_0$ (f = 10 kcps).

That these relations hold is also shown by B. F. Podoshevnikov's experiments on acoustic coagulation of a dioctylphthalate fog, which has already been mentioned above [Eq. (15.4)]. From Eq. (15.4), if the sound exposure $p t_0$ is increased above 400 - 500 kilobarsec, the acoustic coagulation coefficient rises more and more slowly. Here, as we know, (see §1), the sound absorption in the medium is increasing rapidly at the same time. For these reasons, it is not a good idea economically to use very high sound intensities in industrial aerosol coagulation. Most often, the sound intensity used is of the order of 0.1 W/cm^2, or, what is the same thing, a sound pressure of the order of 6400 bar.

125

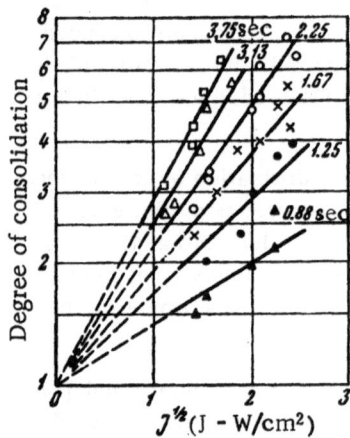

Fig. 53. Degree of consolidation of titanium tetrachloride particles as a function of the quantity $J^{1/2}$ (f = 1.6 kcps).

Structure of the Sound Field. Aerosol particles are unquestionably consolidated somewhat more rapidly in a standing sound wave field than in a traveling wave field. This is due to the fact that the vibratory velocity is of higher amplitude (for the same acoustic power radiated), and some, though perhaps small (see §17), increase in the particle count concentration occurs. Further, it is possible to get a high degree of particle consolidation in a standing wave field, but this is not really required in practice. All that has been said naturally applies only to the case of acoustic coagulation of stationary aerosols, since, as we know (see §14), the local phenomena do not occur in a moving aerosol.

It may be stated that if the sound chamber is quite long, better results are achieved when the aerosol is moving toward the sound source, than when it is moving away from the source, in the forward direction. This follows from the idea that when the aerosol is moving backward, it is subjected at the start to the action of the harmonic components of the sound wave, i.e., to the higher frequencies. There is as yet no experimental confirmation of the idea. An attempt was made to solve the problem in [94], but there was no difference between the results whether the aerosol was moving "forward" or "backward," which was evidently due to the fact that the sound chamber was not very long.

The effect that the geometric dimensions of the sound chamber, and thus of the sound wave, have on the acoustic coagulation rate of aerosols is not limited to what happens when the direction of motion is reversed. The longer the sound chamber, the higher the harmonic content in the sound wave, and the greater the attenuation of the sound sent into the chamber, so that the mean sound intensity in the chamber will be less than the nominal intensity which is, as a rule, measured at the output of the source. This means, from (16.4), that, other conditions remaining the same, the acoustic coagulation coefficient drops off as the sound chamber is made longer. The data on the acoustic coagulation coefficient of aerosols given in §15 must also be regarded from this angle.

It follows from the experiments of B. F. Podoshevnikov et al. [30] that the acoustic coagulation coefficient also depends on the cross-sectional area of the sound chamber. In these experiments, the sound chamber had longitudinal partitions in it (d = 1 - 2 cm), and optical methods showed that this tended to reduce the rate of the process (see Fig. 57). However, we are inclined to doubt that this would still be true for sound chambers of large cross-sectional area.

§17. Some Older Hypotheses in the Acoustic Coagulation Field

It may be seen from the general review of the problem of acoustic coagulation of aerosols, given in §3, that repeated attempts have been made in the past to show how the process works and even to construct a mathematical theory.

The first two attempts to show how acoustic coagulation of aerosols operates, made by Andrade [141a] and A. B. Severnyi [109] may be omitted from the discussion completely, since it was shown in §12 that these authors based their theories on fictitious effects, so that their schemes of how the process goes are completely worthless. Let us note simply that if, as suggested by some workers even now, acoustic coagulation of aerosols were dependent upon some type of attractive force, not requiring the particles to be of different sizes, the rate of the process would be a quadratic function of the particle count concentration, which is contradictory to experience.

The third attempt to show how the process works, made by Brandt, Freund, and Hiedemann [167] started from the right assumptions, and the only reason that they didn't bring the matter to a correct conclusion was that there was not enough theoretical knowledge in existance at that time on how aerosol particles behave in a sonic field.

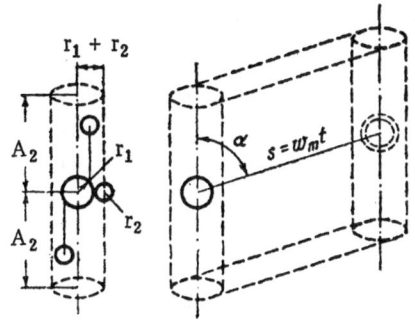

Fig. 54. Diagram used by Brandt, Freund, and Hiedemann in calculating the orthokinetic interaction between aerosol particles in a sonic field.

The scheme was based on orthokinetic interaction between aerosol particles in conjunction with a sort of ordered motion that the large particles execute with respect to the small particles. The diagram used in the calculations is shown in Fig. 54. The dotted lines in the left-hand part of the figure show the outline of the aggregation volume around a large particle, which is for practical purposes not vibrating. We see that it was considered to be a cylinder of radius $r_1 + r_2$, and altitude $2A_2$. The factor w_m in the diagram is the transverse velocity component of the random motion of the larger particle. The total aggregation volume swept out in the motion is a rounded parallelpiped with an altitude equal to twice the amplitude of the vibrations of the small particles, and a length equal to the product $w_m t$. The basic idea of the authors of the scheme, that acoustic coagulation of aerosols relies upon interaction between particles of different sizes, was a realistic one, and, as may be seen from §14, was the one we used in constructing the general scheme of how the process goes.

An even better thing about the theory is that orthokinetic particle interaction is used in conjunction with the relative motion of the particles in the transverse direction. If we did not have this relative motion between the large and small particles ($w_m = 0$) the aggregation volume would be simply the cylinder (shown dotted on the left-hand side of Fig. 54), and it would be denuded of small particles as soon as the first orthokinetic approach cycle was over.

However, the scheme shown in Fig. 54 is really somewhat primitive, and only serves to visualize the possibilities for aggregation inherent in orthokinetic interaction between vibrating particles in conjunction with relative transverse motion. The attempt made by the authors of the theory to introduce the random motion of the large particles into the scheme is not justified theoretically, and their reference to visual observation of this type of motion is not very convincing, since there is no proof that the large particles are executing the motion alone, rather than in conjunction with the small particles.

The elongated tracks of consolidated particles, visible in the pictures taken by the authors of the theory (see Fig. 45), and due to the increase in drift and gravitational forces, are distorted by turbulent pulsations, which have almost no effect on particle approach at short distances, and are of more importance to the small particles.

The author of this book once [73, 74] made an attempt to invoke Brownian diffusion to account for the random relative motion of aerosol particles. In a subsequent paper [76], throughly convinced that the aggregation volume around the coagulation centers could not be filled in this way unless $r < 0.1\mu$, turbulent diffusion of the particles due to entrainment in the turbulent pulsations of the medium was brought into the picture instead. However, a paper recently published by B. F. Podoshevnikov [309] gives a belated criticism of the earlier hypothesis and in a quite primitive way at that. There is no attempt to make a diffusional approach to the problem of acoustic coagulation of aerosols, and it is therefore erroneously stated that the condition for orthokinetic particle aggregation to occur is to have $A_{12}/S_m > 1$ (by the way, the same assertion is made in a new paper by Vyzhikovskii [330]).

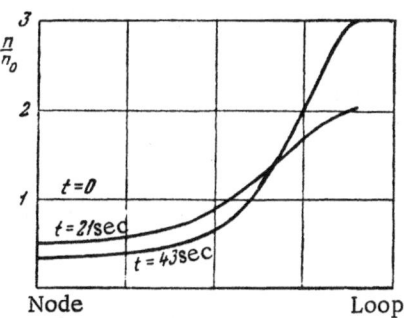

Fig. 55. Distribution of the concentration of particles of radius $r = 1\mu$ ($\rho_p = 1$ g/cm^2) between a node and a loop, as given by St. Clair ($\overline{E} = 300$ ergs/cm^3, $f = 10$ kcps).

* * *

A number of investigators have considered acoustic coagulation of aerosols to come wholly or in part from the particle drift in a standing sound wave.

St. Clair [169, 181], for example attached a large amount of importance to the fact that radiation drift (no other types of drift were known at that time) causes the particle concentration to increase in the direction of a vibration loop, where the particle velocity in the medium is also higher. Using Eq. (6.8), St. Clair illustrated his idea by plotting curves showing how the concentration of particles of radius $r = 1\mu$ were distributed between the nodes and loops of a sound wave after being treated for different lengths of time at a frequency of 10 kcps (Fig. 55). He pointed out further that the harmonics present in the wave would make the actual particle concentration higher than that shown in the figure.

However, we showed in §6 that it is completely wrong to use Eq. (6.8) to calculate the drift of very small aerosol particles. Further, everything that St. Clair had to say was restricted to the case of a standing wave, and, moreover, one in a stationary aerosol. More than that, it may be seen from his graph that the role played by the effect in question is small even under these conditions. The graph shows that in 21 seconds, which is an intolerably long time, the particle concentration at a loop has no more than doubled, and tripled in 42 seconds, and this isn't much of a rate when it comes to coagulating highly disperse aerosols. If, in addition, we consider the drift due to asymmetric vibrations in the standing wave, which is in the opposite direction, the increase in concentration turns out to be even less than that shown on the graph.

Jahn [206] tried to use the local phenomena accompanying particle drift in a standing wave to show the advantages of using audio frequencies, arguing as follows: "In an ultrasonic field at a frequency of 22 kcps, the nodes where the dust collects are 0.87 cm apart. If the sound chamber has a volume of 1 m^3 and is 1 m high, 128 nodes are formed, having a total area of 128 m^2. This is made up of the areas where the dust collects and is coagulated. If an aerosol stream with a concentration of 8 g/m^3 is passing through the chamber at a rate of about 3 m^3/sec, 24 grams of dust gets distributed over 128 m^2 of surface. Under these conditions, the resulting conglomerations are of very small size.

If, however, using the same chamber, with the same amount of dust in the gas, the sound vibrations are at a frequency of 1.5 kcps, the distance between the nodes is about 12 cm. Then the 24 grams of dust is distributed among 8 nodal surfaces having a total area of 8 m^2. The result is that the conglomerations of dust formed are much larger in size."

This explanation is beneath criticism, since lower frequencies are also better in a traveling wave, where there are no local phenomena.

A. D. Bagrinovskii [3] took, as the cornerstone of his theory, the orthokinetic particle interaction occurring during the drift resulting from asymmetric vibration of the medium in a standing sound wave. To demonstrate the fallacy of this point of view, let us find the maximum number of small particles captured during drift of any one large particle.

The maximum length of the aggregation cylinder in a standing wave is equal to the distance between a node and a loop, i.e., $\lambda/4$. Assume that the particles undergoing capture are so small that any motion in the same direction may be neglected, so that it may be further assumed that the concentration of the particles is, on the average, constant everywhere along the drift path of the large particle.

From Eqs. (15.1) and (15.7), we find the following expression for the maximum number of small particles captured by any large particle, using Eqs. (10.20) and (9.1):

$$N_{\max} = \vartheta \pi r_1^2 \frac{\lambda}{4} n_2 = \frac{(2.3 - 2.8) c_g k}{\rho_p r_2 f} \cdot 10^{-7}. \qquad (17.1)$$

The shortest time required for a large particle to cover the distance between a node and a loop may be calculated from the formula:

$$t_{\min} = \frac{\lambda}{4 V_d} = \frac{c_g}{4 f V_d}, \qquad (17.2)$$

where V_d is the resultant drift velocity of the large particle.

By using these formulas and the graph in Fig. 23, we obtain the following values at a frequency of $f=5000$ cps for $\rho_p = 1$ and $k = 10$ g/m^3:

$$\text{for } r_1 = 0.1\ \mu,\ N_{max} = \quad 1.6-1.9 \quad \text{in } t_{min} \to \infty;$$
$$\text{for } r_1 = \ \ 1\ \ \mu,\ N_{max} = \quad 0.16-0.19 \quad \text{in } t_{min} = 2 \text{ min;}$$
$$\text{for } r_1 = 10\ \ \mu,\ N_{max} = 0.016-0.019 \text{ in } t_{min} = 6.7 \text{ min.}$$

Thus we see that even in the present case the large particle does not capture as much as a single small particle in any short length of time. It is true that if we take account of the fact that turbulent diffusion of the particles will make the capture coefficient ϑ much greater than ϑ_{min}, the figures turn out to be about an order of magnitude higher. But even this fails to give a satisfactory explanation for the intense aerosol coagulation observed in a sonic field.

* * *

Some investigators, particularly those who have made experiments on aerosol coagulation in high intensity sound fields, have been inclined to give first importance to the turbulence set up in the vibrating gas.

The most sweeping pronouncement was made by Matula, who wrote in his dissertation [232]: "It is beyond doubt that it is the turbulence of a sonic field which plays the fundamental role in aerosol coagulation." The reason for this conclusion was provided by the experimental fact that rapid aerosol coagulation is not observed until the sound intensity has become high enough for the turbulence in the gas to start showing up clearly too.

This fact has also been noted by Boucher [156], who further calls attention to the great similarity found between the results of experimental studies of aerosol coagulation made earlier by E. Richardson [257] in turbulent and acoustic fields. These studies were made in a chamber with a volume of 1 m^3, filled with ammonium chloride smoke ($r \approx 1\mu$). The turbulence was produced by a fan, and the sound vibrations were produced by a loudspeaker. The amount of coagulation that had been achieved was determined from the change in absorption of a light beam passing through the aerosol. The results of the experiments made in the turbulent field are shown in Fig. 56a, which gives the change in light absorption with time for different rates of pulsation in the gas (concentration by weight of the smoke, 0.25 g/m^3). Results of the experiments in the acoustic field are shown in Fig. 56b, where similar curves are given for different frequencies (concentration by weight of the smoke, 0.50 g/m^3, $n = 9.2 \cdot 10^4$).

The experiments made by the State Scientific Research Institute of Sanitary and Industrial Gas Purification showed even more similarity between the results of aerosol coagulation in turbulent and acoustic fields. A study was made in these experiments of how the aerosol coagulation rate varied with Reynolds number in a turbulent gas washer (Venturi scrubber) and in an acoustic coagulator. In the first case, the Reynolds number used was the one for a flowing stream, and in the second, for a vibrating stream. It was found in both cases that the coagulation rate is a linear function of the Reynolds number, and thus of the velocity of the gas stream.

The above similarities of course give no reason to assume that it is the turbulence in the vibrating medium which is the primary process in acoustic coagulation of aerosols. They only go to show that particle aggregation follows a common orthokinetic mechanism in both cases. The only difference is that in a turbulent field, as has been shown by V. G Levich [68, 69] and other investigators [122], the orthokinetic particle collisions result from the particles being carried along to different degrees in the turbulent pulsations of the medium, while in an acoustic field, they collide because they are carried along to different degrees in the vibrations of the medium (which, to use the colorful expression of E. Richardson, is a type of "monochromatic" turbulence in the medium).

However, the turbulence of the vibrating medium plays no small role in acoustic coagulation of aerosols, since it is the turbulence that brings distant particles into the aggregation zone. Anything that tends to suppress the turbulence in the vibrating medium artificially will reduce the coagulating effect of the sound waves. This is illustrated by the experiments of B. F. Podoshevnikov et al. [30], in which it was shown that mounting

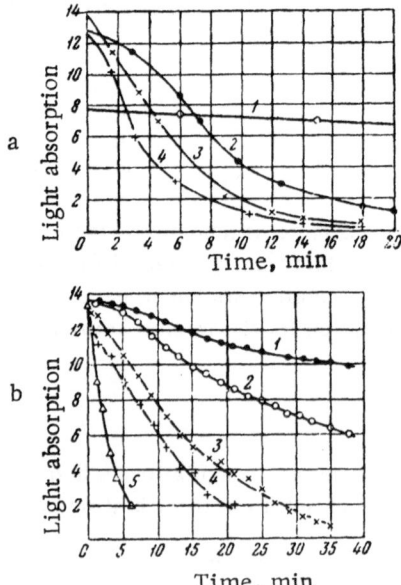

a

b

Fig. 56. Coagulation of an ammonium chloride aerosol (from E. Richardson); a) in a turbulent field, for different values of the pulsation veloc- ity u', 1) for u' = 0, 2)for u' = 6cm/sec, 3) for u' = 8 cm/sec, 4) for u' = 12 cm/sec; b) in an acoustic field, 1) no sound, 2) for f = 0.5 kcps and u_g = 0.5 cm/sec, 3) for f = 2 kcps and u_g = 2.0 cm/sec, 4) for f = 7.0 kcps and u_g = 2.0 cm/sec, 5) for f = 0.5 kcps in a standing wave).

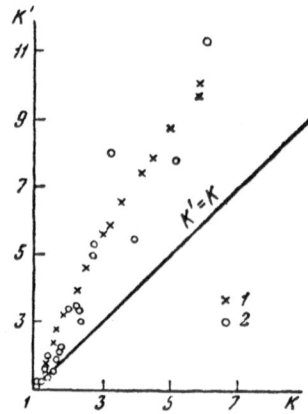

Fig. 57. Acoustic coagulation of a dioc- tylphthalate fog with longitudinal parti- tions, from B. F. Podoshevnikov et al. K) Light intensity ratio in tube with partitions; K') the same, in tube with no partitions; 1) for k = 1.8 g/m^3; 2) for k = 2.5 g/m^3.

longitudinal partitions close together in the chamber, so as to reduce the scale of the vortices, produces a substantial reduction (by a factor of 1.8) in the coagu- lation of an aerosol (dioctylphthalate fog). The results of these experiments are shown in Fig. 57, where the parameter K is the ratio of the light intensity scattered by the aerosol before and after coagulation. It appears to us that the reason why such striking results were obtained was that the space between the partitions was less than the scale λ of the primary vortices being propagated from the immediate   field of the radiator.

Some authors (White [291] and Müller [238]) have expressed the opinion that electrical forces have to be invoked. However, having the aerosol particles in a sound field does not result in forming charges or dipoles on the particles, so that there is no point in talking about them.

So far, no investigator has ever found that the electrical properties of the particles have any effect on the ease with which they are coagulated in a sonic field. This is not to be wondered at, since acoustic coagulation of aerosols is, beyond any doubt, a purely hydrodynamic process.

CHAPTER 5

PRACTICAL ACOUSTIC COAGULATION
AND PRECIPITATION OF AEROSOLS

§18. Acoustic Dissipation of Natural and Artificial Fogs

It is well-known that the natural fogs formed by spontaneous cooling of moist air at the earth's surface greatly reduce the transparency of the atmosphere. This interferes with or completely eliminates human vision and orientation, outdoor work, and transportation. Air transport experiences special difficulties. Landing present-day airplanes at airports in foggy weather, in spite of radar equipment, even now involves a certain amount of risk, so that civilian airports often forbid airplanes to land. This has stimulated scientists to get interested in finding ways for dissipating fogs artificially. Studies have been conducted, and a certain amount of use has been made of the following methods of dissipating supercooled fogs artificially:

1) Heating the layer of air at the ground to the point where the fog droplets evaporate. This is the so-called thermal dissipation method, as is used, for example, in the FIDO system with J-33, J-47, etc. nozzles.

2) Hygroscopic materials (calcium chloride, aluminum sulfate) are blown into the fog to absorb the moisture in the air and thus make the droplets evaporate. This system, proposed by Langdon, has been used, for example, at the San Diego Airport (California, USA).

3) Highly supercooled crystals (solid carbon dioxide, propane) are blown into the fog, which form new nuclei around them for the condensation of the moisture and subsequent crystallization of the water.

4) Special smokes (silver iodide, lead iodide) are put into the fog, constituting ready made nuclei for condensation of the moisture and crystallization of the water.

The last three methods are versions of the physicochemical type of fog dissipation that has been tried out on clouds [120] and has been used to some extent in various countries.

In the first two methods, the atmosphere is made more transparent by getting rid of the droplets, while in the last two, the drops are made larger,* by condensing and crystallizing the moisture.

The atmosphere becomes more transparent as the droplets become larger because less light is scattered by the system. In natural fogs, the droplets are usually much larger than the wave length of visible light (λ_l = 0.40 - 0.76μ), so that the light is principally scattered according to the laws of geometrical optics. The theory in this case gives the following expression for the light scattering factor [16]:

$$\alpha_l = \pi r^2 n = \frac{0.75 \cdot 10^{-6} k}{\rho_p r} . \tag{18.1}$$

It follows from the formula that more light is scattered by the fog, the higher the concentration by weight and the smaller the radii of the droplets.

---

* For this reason, calling the artificial methods of dissipating fogs and clouds drop removal methods, as has been done by many authors (see for example BSÉ, Vol. 30, p. 314) is not quite right. As a matter of fact the purpose of artificial cloud dissipation is not to remove the droplets as such, but only to reduce the scattering power, which can be done either by removing the drops or by making them larger.

In more finely disperse fogs, where the geometric scattering first gives way to diffuse scattering and then to so-called Rayleigh scattering, Eq. (18.1) acquires a factor which depends on the droplet radius and the wave length of the light. In the limiting case, where $r \ll \lambda_l$ the light scattering factor turns out to be proportional to the product kr^3/λ_l^4, i.e., the light scattering depends in exactly the opposite way on the droplet size.

The intensity of the light passing through the fog decreases with distance in the same way as the intensity of sound, i.e., according to the exponential law:

$$J_l = J_{l_0}\, e^{-k_l x}, \qquad\qquad (18.2)$$

where k_l is the attenuation factor of the light, $k_l = \alpha_l + \beta_l \approx \alpha_l$ (β_l is the absorption factor of the light, which may be neglected in fogs).

The increase in atmosphereic visibility from dissipating a fog as measured experimentally with a photocell is given by the percentage reduction $\Delta \alpha_l / \alpha_l$ in the light scattering factor, which is the same thing as $\Delta x / x \cdot 100\%$, the percentage increase in the distance at which the light intensity is the same as before the fog was dispersed.

It has been shown in practice that the existing methods of fog dissipation have substantial disadvantages which make them of extremely limited application. Thus, the thermal method requires extremely large amounts of heat, largely due to the fact that heating the layer of air at the earth produces strong convection currents, which pull cold air into the fog. Very large amounts of hygroscopic materials are needed when this method of dissipation is used. Thus, calcium chloride takes about 25 g per 1 m^3 of fog, and overdosing does the wront thing, — it makes the atmosphere less transparent. The other methods of dissipating fogs have troubles too.

The discovery that sound makes aerosols coagulate and drops evaporate faster stirred up new hope of solving the problem of fog dissipation. It was first intended that the process would be limited to simply treating natural fogs with sound to coagulate the droplets, which, as in condensation, would make them larger, thus reducing the amount of light scattered by the fog. This method was given the name acoustic fog dissipation. It was first proposed by Amy as early as 1931, and was protected by US patent No. 1980171 in 1934. Amy's idea was to dissipate the fogs by treating them with sound from an enormous generator which could be moved over the airport or other area and, so Amy thought, would immediately coagulate and precipitate all the fog droplets that got into the sound beam. The generator described in Amy's patent consisted of a set of Hartman ultrasonic whistles, all mounted on the same chassis, so that they could be turned in different directions like an army search light.

This project was however never carried out in the USA (apparently because no laboratory work had been done in support of the principle). But in Germany, as reported recently by Brandt [156] in a private conversation, similar experiments were set up in 1940 on dissipating a natural fog with Hartman ultrasonic whistles provided with a central rod (Sevori whistle). Appreciable clarification could be observed for a radius of about 10 m around the source.

In 1943 - 1944, Lamer and Sinclair [156]* in the USA made more extensive tests of acoustic fog dissipation. Some preliminary laboratory experiments were first made at Columbia University on dissipating artificial fogs produced by sprayers. The mean radius of the droplets was 4μ, and the concentration by weight was 14 g/m^3, which is much higher than the droplet concentration in natural fogs ($0.2 - 1$ g/m^3). The experiments, which were made with a loud speaker operating at 0.5 kcps in a vertical tube 150 mm in diameter and about 1 m long, showed that at a mean sound intensity of 150 db, the volume was cleaned out by a standing wave in less than 15 sec. Experiments made in a long horizontal tube 75 mm in diameter and 3.6 m long with the same sound source, showed that good results were also obtained when the fog was flowing. Thus, for a rate of flow of the order 5 cm/sec (which corresponded to a sound treatment lasting 70 sec) the visibility through the fog increased 30%. Similar laboratory experiments were also made subsequently by the Ultrasonic Corporation in the USA, Taraba in Czechoslovakia, etc.

* The content of this paper was later repeated with some additions in the review by the same author [316].

The Ultrasonic Corporation experiments in the USA (1948) were made in a rectangular glass vessel with a volume of about 7400 cm^3, with a U-1 dynamic siren working at from 1 to 6 kcps mounted below it. The siren was separated from the vessel by a thin rubber diaphragm about 25μ thick. The mean radius of the droplets in the fog was 2μ, and the concentration by weight was about 4.5 g/m^3. As in all experiments on fog dissipation, the measurements were made from the change in intensity of a narrow light beam passing through the aerosol and caught by a photo cell. The results of the experiments are shown in Fig. 50. It may be seen from the figure that the optimum frequency was 3.5 kcps (but, as Boucher [156] has pointed out, no account was taken of the fact that the power radiated by the siren drops off at high frequencies). From 1 to 20 seconds were required for 50% clarification of the fog, depending on the sound intensity (152 - 137 db).

Taraba [156, 274] made experiments on dissipation of an artificial fog in a horizontal tube about 400 mm in diameter and of the order of 4.5 m long, provided with a dynamic siren giving a maximum power of about 11 kW. Two cyclones in parallel were mounted at the end of the tube to catch the coagulated droplets. The concentration by weight of the droplets in the cloud was 5 - 10 g/m^3 (no check was made on the droplet size). The fog was pumped through at a rate of up to 0.9 m/sec. The frequency varied from 4 to 17 kcps. It was possible to dissipate and catch 99% of the coagulated drops in a few seconds.

Lamer and Sinclair did not limit themselves to experiments on a laboratory scale, but worked on dissipating large volumes of artificial fogs — in a tunnel, and at the Columbia University swimming pool [156, 266]. The tunnel had a cross section of 1.2 × 2.1 m and was about 30 m long. The cloud was produced by a battery of 12 sprayers. The mean droplet radius was 4.5μ, with a concentration of from 3 to 6 g/m^3. The light source was placed in the middle of the tunnel, 0.6 m above the floor. The observations were made from outside the tunnel through glass windows in the door at one end. An HOR type siren, radiating 120 W of acoustic power at a frequency of 0.6 - 0.7 kcps, was placed halfway between the observer and the light source. For a sound intensity of the order of 137 db at the siren, 75% improvement was observed in one case, and 50% improvement in another. The experiments in the swimming pool, which had a volume of more than 5600 m^3, gave no results. The dynamic siren used in the experiments was made by the Federal Electric Company USA and had a nominal power of 2.4 kW. At a frequency of 0.7 kcps, there were no signs of dissipation of the fog, which must have been due to the high degree of dispersion ($r_{mean} \simeq 1\mu$), since, for the frequency used, all the droplets were simply carried along with the vibrations of the medium instead of colliding with one another (see §16).

Experiments on the same scale were made by Boucher in France (Chatillon, 1956) [156]. The experiments were made in a 12.8 × 14 × 18 m chamber. The source used was a static siren ("multiwhistle") as built by Boucher, suspended from the ceiling of the chamber. Two types of fog were worked on: a coursely disperse fog, having nearly the same characteristics as a natural fog (radius r = 2 - 10μ, concentration 1 - 2 g/m^3), and a finely disperse fog (radius r_{mean} = 0.5μ, concentration 1 - 2 g/m^3). The siren operated at two frequencies: 9.5 and 32 - 33 kcps. The coarsely disperse fog was easily dissipated (2 minutes) at the low frequency (9.5 kcps), but at the high frequency (32 - 33 kcps) there were no appreciable results even though the power was much higher (600 W). The finely disperse fog, however, was easily dissipated at the high frequency (32 - 33 kcps), but gave negative results at the low frequency (9.5 kcps). This is again in complete agreement with the conclusions as to how the degree of dispersion affects the optimum frequency, arrived at in §16.

In the same year, 1943, Lamer and Sinclair, under contract with the U.S. Air Force, made some tests on acoustic dissipation of fogs under natural conditions [156, 266]. The best known tests were those at Lunken Airport (Cincinnati, Ohio), made in March 1943. The natural fog consisted of droplets of radii 4 − 16μ (predominantly 6μ) at a concentration of 1 g/m^3. There was absolutely no wind. Four "Victory" dynamic sirens were used, built by the Chrysler Bell Corporation, giving 35 kW each. The frequency was 0.44 kcps. A diagram of the tests is shown in Fig. 58. The sirens irradiated a space over 120 m long and of the order of 23 m wide to a height of about 15 m. It was found in the tests that the fog cleared up in one minute, and that the atmospheric visibility increased in the process from 65 to 130 m.

In December 1943, Lamer, Sinclair, and Brecci made some acoustic fog dissipation tests on the open sea at Sandberg (California). The radius of the fog droplets was 5μ. They used eight Chrysler Bell Sirens with a power of 35 kW each, arranged every 30 m in a line 210 m long, at an angle of 10 - 50° to the direction of the prevailing wind. The wind velocity got as high as 5 - 6 m/sec. Although the conditions were not so favorable,

TABLE 16

Test location	Average drop radius r, μ	Concentration by weight g/cm³	Characteristics of space being cleaned	Type of source and power	Frequency kcps	Specific power, W/m³ of gas	Dissipation time	Investigators, year
Laboratory tests*								
Vertical tube 150 mm in diameter × 1000 mm long, Columbia University, USA	4	14	Stationary mass, standing waves	Loudspeaker (150 db)	0.5		15 sec	Lamer and Sinclair 1943 [156, 266]
Horizontal tube 75 mm in diameter ×3600 mm long, Columbia University, USA	4	14	Continuous flow at a rate of 5 cm/sec	The same	0.5	—	15 sec	Lamer and Sinclair 1943 [156]
Rectangular chamber 7400 cm³, Ultrasonic Corporation, USA	2	4.5	Stationary mass, standing waves	Dynamic siren (152 - 137 db)	3.5	Several kW/m³	1 - 20 sec (see Fig. 50)	Horsley and Sivi, 1948 [156]
Horizontal tube 400 mm in diameter × 4500 mm long (with cyclones). Czechoslovakia	—	5-10	Continuous flow, 0.9 m/sec	Dynamic siren (11 kW)	4-17	—	Several sec (99%)	Taraba, 1956-1957 [156, 274]
Chamber tests*								
1.2 × 2.1 × 30 m tunnel, Columbia University, USA	4.5	3-6	94 m³, continuous flow, standing waves	Dynamic siren (120 kW)	0.6-0.7	1.2	1 min (50% clarification)	Lamer and Sinclair 1943 [156, 266]
Swimming pool, Columbia University, USA	1	—	5600 m³, stationary mass	Dynamic siren (2.4 kW)	0.7	—	No results	The same
12.8 × 14 × 18 m experimental chamber, Chatillon. France	2-10 Predominantly 4	1-2	400 m³ continuous flow, standing waves	Static siren (60-100 W)	9.5	0.15	2 min	Boucher, 1956-1957 [156]
The same	0.5	1-2	100 m³	Static siren (60-100 W)	32-33	4	2 min	The same
" "	2-10* Predominantly 4	1-2	2600 m³, stationary mass, no standing waves	Static siren (60 W)	9.5	0.02	15 min	The same
" "	0.5	1-2	2600 m³	Static siren (400 W)	32-33	0.15	15 min	The same
Outdoor tests								
Reservoir chamber Bellahøj, Denmark	5	1	1000 m³	Dynamic siren (100 W)	0.425	0.1	3-15 min	Rasmussen, Rallis, and Ridel 1956-60 [316]
The same	5	1	1000 m³; no standing wave	Electric dynamic (membrane) siren (200 W)	0.300	0.2	3-18 min	The same
Lunken Airport, Cincinnati, Ohio, USA	4-16 Predominantly 6	1-2	5100 m³, no wind, traveling waves	Four dynamic sirens (35 kW each)	0.44	2.35	1 min	Lamer and Sinclair 1943 [156, 266]
Open sea, Sandberg, California, USA	5	1	100,000 m³, wind 5-6 m/sec traveling waves	Eight dynamic sirens (35 kW each)	0.44		Slow clarification up to 50%	Lamer, Sinclair and Breccia 1943-44 [156]
Open locality near Arcata and Breezy Grove, USA	15	1	Traveling and standing waves	Dynamic siren	3.5-4.0		No results	Ultrasonic Corporation USA 1946 [156]
Open locality near the head of a mine shaft, Czechoslovakia	5	1	No wind traveling waves	Dynamic siren (11 kW)	4-17		Unknown	Taraba ("Komsomol'skaya Pravda" May 8, 1957)
El'bruss All-Around Mountain Climbing Expedition, Academy of Sciences, USSR, Baksan Ravine. Cacasus (see §19)	—	—	Rain cloud, traveling waves	Dynamic sirens (25 kW each)	< 0.3			Geophys, Institute, Academy of Sciences of the USSR, 1960 [32]

*All the artificial fogs were produced by atomizing water in nozzles.

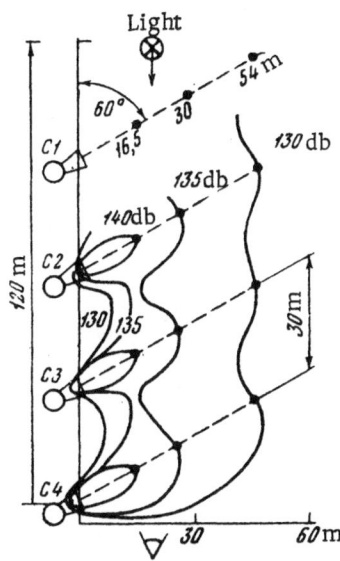

Fig. 58. Diagram of acoustic fog dissipation tests made at Lunken Airport (USA).

they got almost 50% clarification of the fog, but it was felt that the acoustic power was not enough for the wind conditions, and that the method was scarcely suitable.

In 1946, the attempt to dissipate natural fogs was repeated by the Ultrasonic Corporation USA after they had succeeded in producing powerful dynamic sirens of type U2 etc. The tests were first made at an open locality near Arcata, then at Breezy Grove. However, both attempts failed: the fog was very coarsely disperse (mean radius 15 μ), and would not coagulate at the frequency used (3.5 - 4 kcps). Recently experiments on acoustic fog dissipation have been repeated in Denmark by Rasmussen, Rallis, and Ridal [316].

A compilation of the data on all types of tests made on acoustic fog dissipation are given in Table 16. The general conclusions are:

1. Coagulation, followed by clarification of artificial and natural fogs does not occur instantaneously, but requires a certain length of time. Even in small areas where a high sound level can be produced, the time required for the treatment is several seconds at best, and in large spaces the time required may be 1 minute or more.

2. It is very important to choose the proper frequency if acoustic fog dissipation is going to work. Coarsely disperse fogs require low frequencies, while finely disperse fogs require high frequencies, not generally exceeding 0.5 - 0.7 kcps for natural fogs.

3. Since the sound attenuates greatly in an open space, the effective dissipation range for natural fogs is not more than 25 - 30 m (in the direction of the sound beam). Accordingly, a number of sirens have to be set up when treating large spaces.

4. In view of this last fact, the amount of energy used in acoustic fog dissipation is quite high, although it does not for example, exceed that required for thermal fog dissipation.

The unpleasant effect of sound on the human ear is no obstacle to the use of the method, since outside the region where the dissipation is going on, the noise level quickly drops to the values usual around airports.

The above disadvantages of acoustic fog dissipation have made it difficult to use under airport conditions, and have led to attempts at solving the problem by speeding up the evaporation of the drops (see Appendix I).

§ 19. Sonic-Gravitational Precipitation of Industrial Dusts, Smokes, and Fogs

Some industrial dusts and fogs are so coarsely disperse that when they are precipitated (either to extract and recover the suspended material or simply to clean the gas), use is made of a natural property of suspended particles — that of settling out of the gas under their own weight. On the other hand, some finely disperse industrial smokes and fogs are at such a high temperature and pressure, or are so explosive, sticky, or reactive, that it becomes impossible to use highly efficient precipitators such as electric and cloth filters or even cyclones, and the only way left to precipitate the aerosol particles is to make use of the force of gravity.

The rate at which spherical particles settle out under the force of gravity, also known as the hovering rate of the particles, is given by the familiar formula [121]:

$$V_g = \tau g = \frac{2}{9} g \frac{\rho_p}{\eta} r^2,\qquad(19.1)$$

which is easily derived by setting the force of gravity acting on the particle equal to the resistive force of the medium, as given by Stokes' formula. (For Re > 1, use is made of the general expression $F = \psi(\rho_g V_g/2) \pi r^2$, where ψ is the coefficient of resistance, so that Eq. (19.1) no longer holds).

135

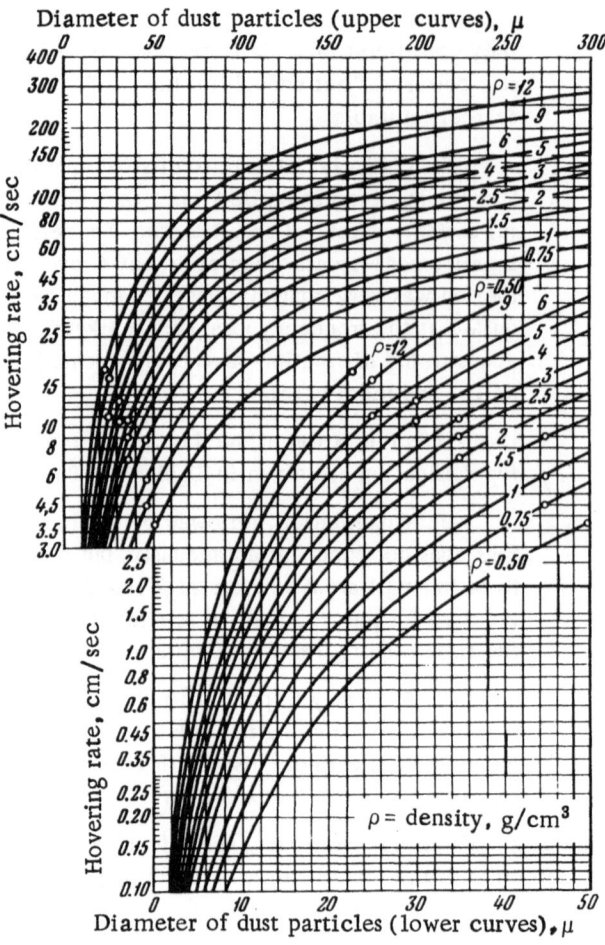

Fig. 59. Gravitational settling (hovering) rate of suspended spherical particles.

Figure 59 gives values of the gravitational settling rate calculated for air as a function of particle radius for different densities [119]. It may be concluded from the graph that the absolute value of the gravitational settling rate of the particles is not very high unless the radii are above 25 - 50 μ.

Particles smaller than this, which are present to some extent in all industrial aerosols, settle out extremely slowly. This fact has led investigators to the idea of using sound in the settling chambers to coagulate the finely disperse fractions and thus increase the gravitational precipitation rate (which, when sound is used, must be corrected for the particle drift in acoustic wind velocities).

The first experiments on sonic-gravitational precipitation of industrial dusts were made in 1950 by Tarnoczy and Greguss (275), who used sound in the gas ducts of cement kilns to get better precipitation of the cement dust. This was a very coarsely disperse aerosol, with the particle radii ranging from 5 to 100 μ or more (the predominant radius was 15 - 25 μ). The source used in these experiments was an ordinary Hartmann whistle built into a parabolic reflector. The results of the experiments are shown in Table 17. It may be seen from the table that the use of sound made it possible to precipitate out 1.6 - 7.1 times as much dust in the ducts as with ordinary gravitational settling. This is certainly a positive result, but there is a simpler and more economical way of doing it, namely, by putting ordinary cyclones at the ends of the gas ducts, which in this case give an even lower residual dust concentration in the exhaust gases.

Extensive experiments have been made in the Soviet Union on sonic-inertial precipitation of drilling dust in mines. These were the type of experiments made by R. Sh. Shkol'nikova [130, 131, 132] at the "Gipronikel'" Institute (Leningrad). Laboratory experiments on sonic-inertial precipitation of drilling dust under static con-

TABLE 17

Place precipitated	Frequency	Point dust collected	Amount of dust collected		Increase in the amount of dust collected
			Without sound, kg	With sound, kg	
First gas duct	4.6	Door No. 3	4	28.4	7.1
Second gas duct	1.2	Lower door	43	70.3	1.6
Second gas duct	3.0	" "	43	145.0	3.4
First gas duct	3.0	Door No. 1	2.00	5.75	
		" No. 2	2.75	5.00	
		" No. 3	3.50	2.40	
			8.25	13.15	1.6
" " "	3.0	" No. 1	2.00	7.50	
		" No. 2	2.75	12.00	
		" No. 3	3.50	2.30	
			8.25	21.80	2.7
" " "	4.6 Generator pointed obliquely downward	" No. 1	4.20	18.00	
		" No. 2	5.60	12.00	
		" No. 3	16.50	137.00	
			26.30	167.00	6.3
" " "	5.5	" No. 1	3.00	7.85	
		" No. 2	3.80	2.75	
		" No. 3	0.80	10.75	
			7.60	21.35	2.8
" " "	3.9	" No. 1	3.00	4.20	
		" No. 2	3.80	2.90	
		" No. 3	0.80	4.90	
			7.60	12.00	1.6
" " "	4.0 Generator pointed obliquely downward	" No. 1	3.00	10.30	
		" No. 2	3.80	4.80	
		" No. 3	0.80	4.40	
			7.60	19.50	2.6

ditions were made in a 0.45 m^3 dust chamber. The drilling dust, produced at the Chalcopyrite mines in the Urals, contained up to 40% free silicon dioxide, and the particle radii were distributed as follows: $r < 2.5\mu$, 56.8% $r = 2.5$ to 5.0 μ, 19.8%; and $r = 5$ to 26μ, 33.4%. The experiments lasted up to 60 minutes. The count concentration of the microscopic dust fraction was found with an SN-2 counter, while the submicroscopic fractions were determined with a counter designed by E. A. Vigdorchik. The sound intensity, generated by a Hartman whistle, was about 0.1 W/cm^2. It was found from the experiments that using sound reduced the dust particle count concentration by a factor of 2 or 3. The best frequency turned out to be 7 kcps (the other frequencies, 10 and 13.8 kcps, gave poorer results).

Laboratory experiments on sonic-gravitational precipitation of drilling dust under dynamic conditions have been made using a dust with the following composition: $r = 0.5$ to 2.5μ, 46.9%; $r = 2.5$ to 26μ, 10.5%; and $r = 26$ to 150μ, 42.7%. The concentration by weight of the dust was enormous, and varied from 66 to 1189 g/m^3. The air flow varied from 0.004 to 0.016 m^3/sec. Sonic treatment gave the following results:

$$\text{for } k_{in} = 66 \text{ g/m}^3, k_{out} = 39.1 \text{ mg/m}^3, \eta_{sg} = 99.29\%;$$
$$\text{for } k_{in} = 453 \text{ g/m}^3, k_{out} = 41.3 \text{ mg/m}^3, \eta_{sg} = 99.82\%;$$
$$\text{for } k_{in} = 753 \text{ g/m}^3, k_{out} = 21.3 \text{ mg/m}^3, \eta_{sg} = 99.93\%;$$

It may be seen from the values given that the amount of precipitation was very high, but the residual concentration, although about a fifth of what was before the use of sound, was much greater than the maximum save concentration for dust in air (10 mg/m^3). Studies made at the Third International Mine showed that 99.8% of the dust was precipitated, but the residual concentration was still $k_{out} = 115.4 \text{ mg/m}^3$ which was much higher than the allowable value.

These experiments have led investigators to the conclusion that sonic-inertial precipitation of drilling and other types of mineral dust cannot be used unless followed by a gas filter. After installing a glass mat filter 190 mm in diameter and 50 mm high with 40 μ diameter fibers (hydraulic resistance 40 - 50 mm of water), the residual concentration could be reduced to $2 - 6 \text{ mg/m}^3$.

The dust load on the filters turned out to be less in this case, so that the filtration rate could be increased, thus making up for the energy expended in the sound treatment. A combination of this sort is a transition stage of the sonic-inertial aerosol precipitation described in the next section. This is the method used in the work now being done by "Gipronikel'" on precipitating drilling dust [310].

The Institute has built compound type UPZ dust precipitators with four-layer capron filters mounted at the output, using a modified Hartmann whistle, which allows the filter to operate for a long time without clogging [310]. Recently, the Institute has been testing a compound dust precipitator with several tiers of Hartmann whistles, designed for extracting a mercury aerosol under mining conditions [311].

Extensive experiments were made in Poland in 1960 on trapping a phthalic anhydride $C_8H_4O_3$ aerosol, using a purely sonic-gravitational scheme, which had to be resorted to in order to avoid catastrophic gumming-up of the multicyclones [88, 306, 325]. The coagulating and precipitating chamber was 0.6 m in diameter, and 10 m high. Gas was pumped through at a rate of $1000 - 1300 \text{ m}^3/\text{h}$, and the amount of dust in the gas varied from 1.5 to 4.7 g/m^3. The sound was generated by a special type of dynamic siren giving a concentrated acoustic field, and operated by compressed nitrogen. The frequency was from 1.0 to 3.8 kcps. The acoustic power was only 200 W, since the efficiency of the siren was extremely low ($\sim 5\%$), so that the sound intensity in the chamber was not more than 0.07 W/cm^2.

In spite of this, results deserving attention were obtained. On the average, about 90% of the dust was trapped, instead of 60% without the use of sound. The best results were obtained at a frequency of 1.5 kcps, for a treatment time in excess of 8 sec. The residual dust concentration k_{out} was $0.2 - 0.8 \text{ g/m}^3$, so that cloth filters had to be mounted at the output in this case as well.

The experiments just described led to the conclusion that purely sonic-inertial precipitation of industrial dusts, smokes, and fogs is feasible, and gives promise of application in cases where the gas volumes to be cleaned are not too large (several hundred cubic meters per hour or less), or when the precipitates have special value, and other methods cannot be used. Such cases occur in modern industry, which exhibits an enormous variety of conditions and requirements.

As long as the gas volumes are small, the absolute amount of energy required for precipitation is insignificant, even when the pneumatic sound generators used are operating at low acoustic efficiency, and have to be separated from the gas by a diaphragm to prevent dilution by air from the siren.

Neither high temperature and pressure in the gas, nor an explosive or highly reactive disperse phase present any obstacle in this case to the use of sonic-gravitational aerosol precipitation. This is a rare and valuable advantage, not previously encountered in dust and drop collecting work.

In our opinion, interesting possibilities are opened up for sonic-gravitational and sonic-inertial methods of aerosol precipitation in separating the condensate from oil well gases, and particularly from natural gases. These gases have a high pressure head (100 - 200 atm) [112], part of which could be used without upsetting the economy of the operation to generate sound waves. so that the question of the energy used up is of no great importance.

What we encounter here in the gaseous state are both light hydrocarbons such as methane and ethane, and heavy, high boiling hydrocarbons with boiling points up to 300 - 400° C. The amount of such hydrocarbons is quite considerable (4 - 5% or more).

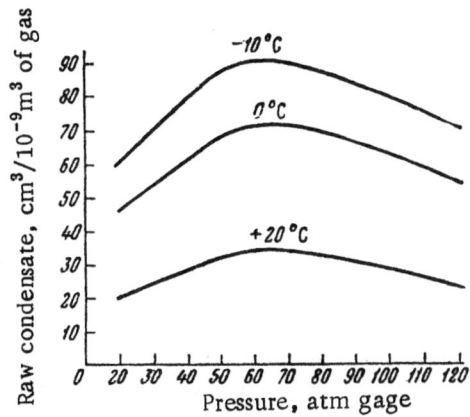

Fig. 60. Amount of condensate in natural gas as a function of pressure for different throttling temperatures (Leningrad deposit, Krasnodar region).

Since the temperature and pressure decrease as the gas moves up the bore hole, it contains a considerable amount of condensed heavy hydrocarbons, as well as moisture, so-called "film" condensate. It is not particularly difficult to extract the condensate. But to prevent the condensate and the gas hydrates from being precipitated out as they go through the pipe lines, the gas is given an additional throttling at the well. This greatly reduces the temperature of the gas (Joule—Thomson effect), and further condenses the hydrocarbons and moisture, which are converted into a fog that precipitates out on the spot under the force of gravity in settling chambers called "volume separators."

The isotherms for the condensation of natural gases (which is called reverse or retrograde condensation) are of the form shown in Fig. 60. The pressure at which the maximum amount of hydrocarbon goes over into the condensate is called the maximum condensation pressure, and it usually lies between 55 and 70 atm

gage. Since the supersaturation is high at this pressure, as much as 100 - 200 g per 10^{-9} m^3 of gas condenses into the fog in some cases, which, when calculated for an actual cubic meter at a pressure of 55 - 70 atm gage gives a value of the order 5.5 - 14 kg/m^3.

Under these conditions, condensation, isothermal distillation, and coagulation of the hydrocarbons go very rapidly (see appendix I), but the gas still has to remain in the separator for a considerable length of time (not less than 15 sec), to bring the drops up to a size (r > 55 - 60 μ) where they can be successfully precipitated by gravitational means.

In order to speed up the condensation, distillation, and coagulation of the hydrocarbons and moisture that condense out when the gas is throttled, and thus increase the capacity and trapping power of the separating units, we made the proposal of using sound waves in [80].

Unlike the method used at present, in which the natural gas is throttled through a calibrated cylindrical fitting ("nipple"), mounted ahead of the separator, it is suggested in [79] to throttle the gas inside the separator using a special built in whistle-nipple (Fig. 61a).

Since there is an enormous pressure drop in the gas, and the density is high, the whistle-nipple may be made to furnish any desired amount of acoustic power (10 kW or more). This is very much to the point in the present case, since the compressed gases have a very high value for the acoustic resistance $\rho_g c_g$ (due mostly to the increase in density ρ_g of the gas), which reduces the particle velocity u_g in the gas [see Eq. (1.9)]. The particle velocity can only be kept at its usual level by making an appropriate increase in the sound intensity (as compared with that used under atmospheric conditions). Considering the small size of the space to be irradiated, and the high concentration of the drops in the gas separators, the process going on can be successfully speeded up by using sound intensities of the order of 0.5 - 1.0 W/cm^2, or even less. Under these conditions, the sound level at the wall of the separator reaches 125 - 130 db but it drops to acceptable levels* in a distance of 5 - 10 m.

---

* The permissible noise level depends on the frequency of the highest component f_0 of the spectrum of the sound, and according to the accepted standards [110] has the following values:

Frequency f_0, cps	Permissible sound level L, db	Frequency f_0, cps	Permissible sound level L, db
350	90	3 000—4 000	70
800	85	5 000	75
1 600	80	6 000	80
2000	75	10 000	85

In another version of the sonic gas separator (Fig. 61b), the gas is throttled in the usual way, while the self-irradiation is done separately by means of a static siren built into the output of the separator, so that the separated gas goes through the horn on the way out. It may be shown that when the gas goes through the siren backwards, sound waves are radiated in the usual amount and in the same direction i.e., in the direction the horn is pointing (the radiating element of the siren is the pulsating gas stream, which constitutes an acoustic dipole which radiates sound mainly in the direction the horn is pointing).

Experience has shown that treating the gas with sound lowers the residual concentration of droplets in the condensate several fold. However, a large amount of turbulence is developed in the gas, which prevents the drops from precipitating out, so that it is a good idea to do the precipitation in a separate settling chamber or a straight-through cyclone, (at the same time lowering the oscillation frequency to a minimum).

Another version of the sound equipped gas separator has been tried out at the Korobkov deposite (Volgograd region) [86]. The source used in this case was a turbodynamic siren built in between the flanges in the input fitting of the separator. The frequency, as stated by the investigators, was 6 kcps (from our calculations this figure is ten times too high!). The sound intensity was not measured; all we know is that the pressure drop expended in rotating the siren, generating the sound, and hydrodynamic losses was 1.5 - 2.0 atm.

Tests have been made on two separators, for oil-well and natural gases, at a pressure of 10 atm gage in both cases. In the first case, the amounts of moisture and condensate at the output of the separator were 0.2 and 0.1 cm^3/10^{-9} m^3 respectively. The effect of the sound was to cut the residual moisture content in two, and reduce the residual condensate by a factor of 17. In the second case, the amount of condensate trapped by the separator increased from 19.5 to 25.6 cm^3/10^{-9} m^3, i.e., by 30%.

Since moisture is present in the gas, gas hydrate crystallites are formed inside the separator in addition to the condensate droplets, and massive gas hydrate deposits are formed on the walls, which interfere with the normal operation of the separator. In order to prevent the hydrates from being formed on the walls and to pre-stabilize and heat the extracted condensate, a design has been proposed for a self-heating sound equipped gas

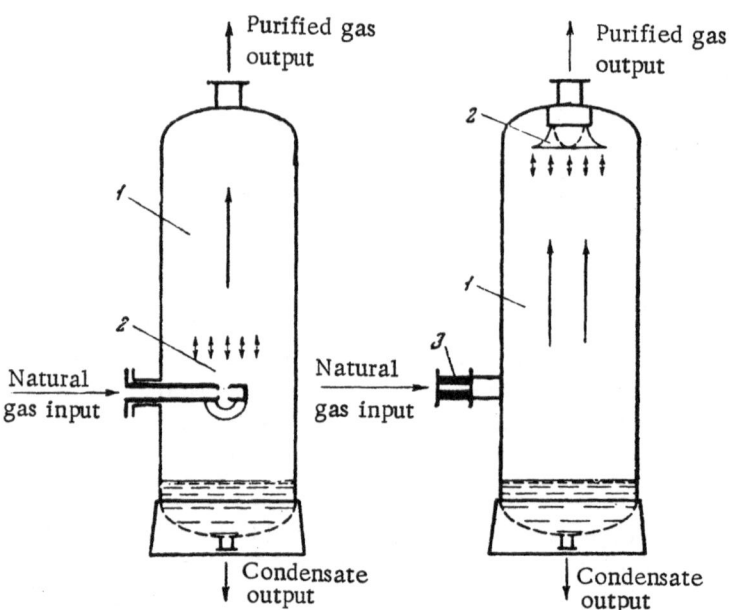

Fig. 61. Sonic-inertial natural gas separators. a) Separator with whistle-nipple, 1) main body of separator, 2) whistle-nipple; b) separator with reverse feed sound siren, 1) main body of separators, 2) reverse speed siren, 3) nipple.

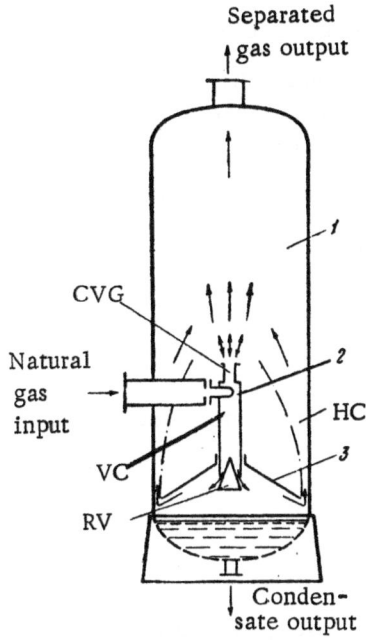

Fig. 62. Self-heated natural gas separator. 1) Body of separator; 2) vortex whistle tube; 3) shield; VC) vortex chamber of whistle tube; CVG) cold vibrating gas output; RV) hot gas reducing valve; HC) heat curtain.

Separated gas output

Natural gas input

Conden-sate output

separator [84], which gets rid of the above difficulties in separator equipment (Fig. 62). The vortex whistle tube 2 differs from the vortex whistle described in §2 in that the inner chamber IC is somewhat larger, and provided at the bottom with an additional annular outlet — the reducing valve RV, like a Rank tube. As a result, the gas vortex acts simultaneously to excite sound waves in the gas and to separate the gas into a cold and a hot stream. The cold vibrating stream goes out through the upper opening CVG, while the hot gas stream, which is 10 - 20% of the total, goes out of the lower end of the chamber through the reducing valve RV, passes under the hood, heating the hood and the space above it, and passes out through the annular space between the hood and the wall to form the heat curtain HC, which heats up the wall so that no gas hydrate deposits are formed on it. As it rises, the hot gas, containing, as already pointed out, the greater part of the condensed hydrocarbons, mixes with the vibrating cold stream coming out of the whistle. The condensate droplets condensed in the process, as well as the gas hydrate crystallites, are deposited on the hot shield, where the crystallites melt, while the lighter hydrocarbons dissolved in the condensate evaporate, and go out of the separator with the gas.

With a vertical gas separator designed in this way, there is no longer any need for a boiler, heating coils, or thermal insulation. It is not impossible however that the turbulence in the vibrating gas will slow up the precipitation of the drops even in this case, and it will then be necessary to find another design using the, in principle, correct idea of self-heating.

Ingenious experiments on sonic precipitation of aerosols have been made recently in Czechoslovakia by Slavik and Geid [24]. These workers set themselves the task of using the coagulating effect of sound in the struggle with dangerous gas contaiminates, for which purpose they proposed to put appropriate gaseous reagents into the gas, which, combining chemically with the dangerous components of the gases, would form suspended solid or liquid particles. If, for example, we are talking about purifying atmospheric air of sulphur dioxide, SO_2, the reagent to use is ammonia NH_3. With moisture present in the air, the sulphur dioxide will react with the ammonia according to the equation

$$SO_2 + H_2O + 2NH_3 = (NH_4)_2SO_3$$

to form a suspension of solid ammonium sulfate.

This method of removing sulphur dioxide was tried out in a foundry, where castings were being made from the light alloy electron. Once the casting was finished, a cover was put on the mold, having mounted on it a row of four Hartmann whistles, operating at 8 - 11 kcps. Under the whistles were small vessels containing ammonia. In a few minutes, the choking gas was all gone from the mold, and was no longer there to poison the atmosphere in the shop.

In conclusion, let us mention the experiments on using the coagulating effect of sound for artificial precipitation of clouds to produce rainfall, which is of definite interest to meterologists and agricultural workers.

The radii of the water drops in clouds vary over a wide range, from 1-2 to 70 - 100μ, with mean radii of 10 - 20 μ [120].

Experiments on producing artificial rainfall with sound were made by the Él'bruss Mountain Climbing Expedition of the Academy of Sciences of the USSR [32]. Powerful low-frequency sound sirens were set up on the slope of the mountains in the Baksan Ravine. Each siren radiated about 25 kW and was provided with a horn with an output cross-section of up to 9 m^2. The sirens were pointed at the rain cloud hanging above the ravine, and the effect of the sound was to make the droplets in the cloud coalesce, after which rain fell.

Sonic-inertial precipitation of aerosols differs from the sonic-gravitational method discussed in the previous section in that precipitation of the coagulated particles is carried out in a separate inertial type precipitator, usually a cyclone, which is immeasureably more efficient than a settling chamber.

The precipitation rate of spherical particles under the inertial forces developed in a cyclone with internal radius of curvature R is given by the formula [121]:

$$V_c = \frac{w_t^2 \tau}{R} = \frac{2}{9} \frac{\rho_p}{\eta} \frac{w_t^2}{R} r^2,$$ (20.1)

where w_t is the tangential velocity of the aerosol. The ratio of the inertial precipitation rate to the gravitational precipitation rate, as given by Eq. (19.1), is:

$$\frac{V_c}{V_g} = \frac{w_t^2}{gR}.$$ (20.2)

Usually, w_t = 15 - 25 m/sec, and R = 0.1 - 1.0 m, from which we find that the inertial precipitation rate of the particles is a factor of 25 - 600 greater than the gravitational precipitation rate.

A typical diagram of the equipment used in sonic-inertial precipitation of industrial dust, smokes, or fogs is shown in Fig. 63. The dust laden gas (aerosol) first enters the coagulation chamber 1. As it passes through the chamber, the gas is subjected to the action of the sound waves radiated by the siren 2, which is fed with compressed air from the compressor 5. This serves to consolidate and precipitate some of the suspended particles. Then, the gas passes to the inertial precipitator 3, which removes the consolidated particles from the gas. The purified gas is discharged to the atmosphere by the fan 4, or is used for engineering purposes. The trapped dust goes to the dust bin.

If the temperature of the gas has to be lowered, the cooler 6 is mounted ahead of the coagulation chamber, while if the gas has to be sprinkled, the chamber is provided with the liquid spray jets 7, or stream nozzles. If the siren is propelled by gas instead of air, the filter 8 is mounted ahead of the compressor.

A Coagulation Chamber, or simply coagulator, consists of a vertical cylindrical tower, covered on the outside with sound insulating material (glass wool, etc. [110]). The siren is usually mounted at the top of the chamber. The incident sound wave at the lower part of the chamber is reflected by a flat bottom or a cone

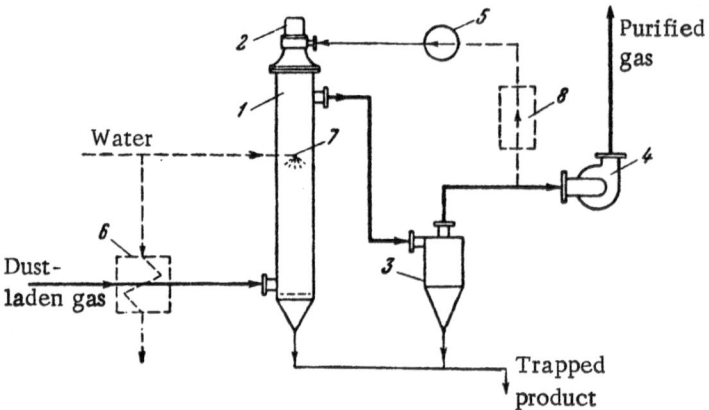

Fig. 63. Schematic diagram of sonic-inertial dust trapping equipment. 1) Coagulation chamber; 2) sound siren; 3) inertial precipitator; 4) fan; 5) compressor; 6) cooler; 7) spray jet; 8) filter.

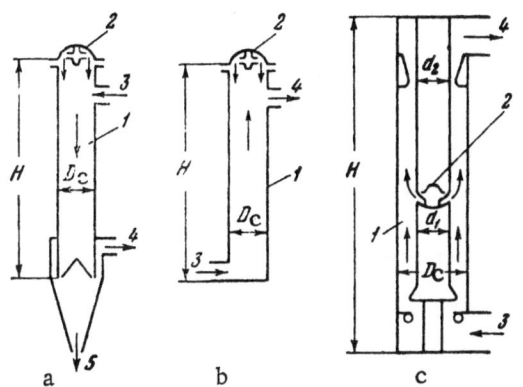

Fig. 64. Types of coagulation chambers.
a) Direct flow; b) reverse flow; c) composite; 1) body, 2) siren, 3) gas input, 4) gas output.

making 45° angles with the axis. The coagulation chamber is usually not more than 2.5 m in diameter. The cylindrical part of the chamber is from 6 to 9 m, and sometimes as much as 11 m high.

The gas velocity w is related to the height H_0 of the part of the chamber where the sound waves are by the elementary equation $w = H_0/t_0$, where t_0 is the aerosol treatment time. For the chamber heights and the treatment times generally used for commercial aerosols, the velocity w turns out to be from 1.5 to 2.0 m/sec. This is considerably higher than the velocities used in electrical filters for trapping fine particles, and is what is mainly responsible for the small size of the coagulaing equipment.

Figure 64a shows the coagulation chamber of the first experimental sonic-inertial installation intended for traping carbon black [272]. The dust laden gas enters the chamber at the top, and, mixing with the air from the siren, goes through the chamber toward the bottom. This may be called the direct flow scheme. A disadvantage of the scheme is that the aerosol is diluted with air from the siren as it enters the chamber. In commercial installations, 7 - 10% of the air comes from the siren, while in laboratory equipment the amount of air coming from the siren may be greater than the aerosol.

The reverse flow scheme is more sensible (Fig. 64b). Here, the aerosol is not diluted with air from the siren until the particle coagulation is over. This is the scheme usually used in practice. Getting rid of the air from the siren before it mixes with the gas [173, 260, 225] greatly reduces the dilution of the gas. It is also possible to have a composite scheme, in which a radial siren is placed inside the chamber, as shown in Fig. 64c. The dimensions of one chamber used are as follows: D_C = 2.4 m, d_1 = 1.17 m, d_2 = 1.3 m, and H_0 = 9.0 m [269].

The extent to which the gas is purified in a sonic-inertial installation depends, on the one hand, on the degree of particle consolidation achieved in the coagulator, and, on the other hand, on the efficiency with which the consolidated particles are precipitated in the inertial precipitator.

The particle precipitation efficiency, as we know, [119], is measured by the percent of trapped (purification) η, or directly by the residual particle concentration by weight k_{out} (g/m^3), which are related to one another as follows:

$$\eta = (1 - \frac{k_{out}}{k_{in}})\,100\ \%\,.$$

(20.3)

(k_{in} is the input particle concentration, g/m^3).

Various types of precipitators have been tried out in sonic-inertial installations: simple cyclones, multicyclones, disintegrators, rotoclons, bubble troughs, wet wire filters, cloth filters, etc. Figure 65 shows the layout of a coagulation chamber using muiticyclones, as designed by "Promenergo" in a sonic-inertial installation for trapping the zinc oxide in the exhaust gases of a bronze and brass factory [308].

Figure 66 gives the efficiencies for different fractions of some inertial precipitators for. ρ_p = 1. It may be seen from the graph that to get high degrees of sonic-inertial purification of industrial gases, the particles have to be brought up to a size of r = 5 - 7 μ, when using multicyclones, and not less than r = 10 - 15 μ when using simple cyclones.

The results achieved in sonic-inertial precipitation of industrial smokes, dusts, and fogs have been published as original papers, as well as in a number of review articles by Soviet and foreign authors [7, 58, 78, 127,

143

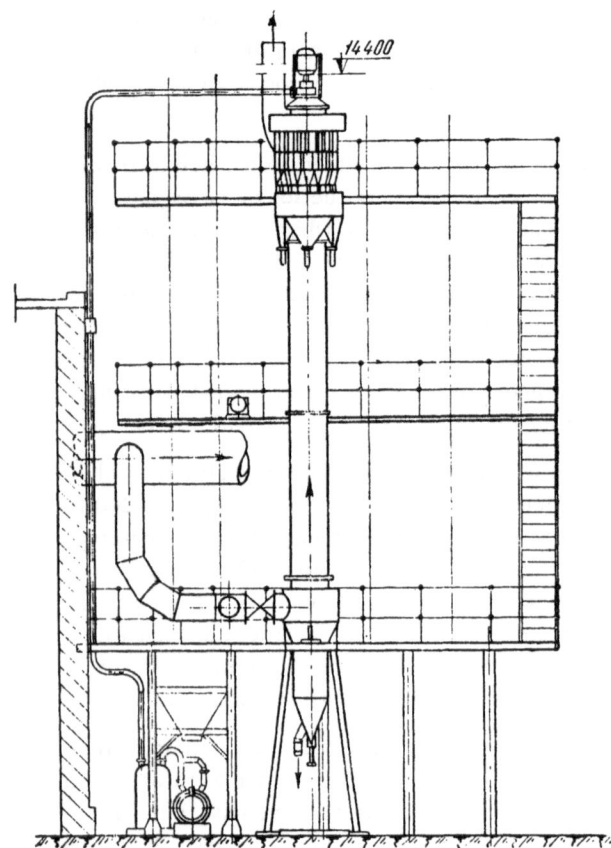

Fig. 65. Layout of a coagulation chamber using multicyclones as designed by "Proménergo."

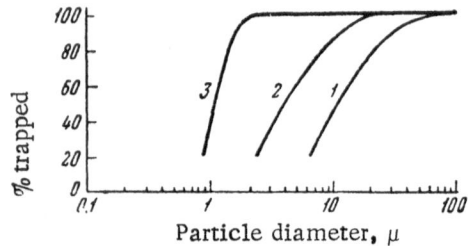

Fig. 66. Efficiencies for different fractions of some inertial precipitators. 1) Large diameter cyclones; 2) small diameter cyclones; 3) laboratory precipitator of shock jet type.

150, 151, 157, 183, 184, 240, 241, 248, 269, 292, 307]. The most important of the foreign papers are to be found in the collection of translations "Acoustic Coagulation of Aerosols" [1], published recently by the State Chemistry Press.

In view of this, we are limiting ourselves here to a concise presentation of the results of sonic-inertial precipitation of industrial aerosols, referring the reader to the original literature for more detailed information.

Table 18 gives a compilation of the data from tests on sonic-inertial precipitation of industrial aerosols, made in the Soviet Union and abroad.

The table does not include the following materials, since there is insufficient information in the literature on experiments made to precipitate them by sonic-inertial means.

1. Calcined soda dust in the exhaust gas from the utilizer boiler of a paper factory, trapped in an industrial sonic-inertial installation with a capacity of 85,000 m^3/h [184].

2. Molybdenum sulphite, satisfactorily trapped in the dry state in a commercial scale sonic-inertial installation [269].

3. Cement dust from the kiln gases in calcining cement, only successfully trapped by sprinkling with water (which does not cause it to harden in the precipitator) [269].

4. Light ashes from the smoke gases of boilers [186, 193, 216, 254], which showed very little coagulability in the dry state (because of the low degree of dispersion).

5. Sulfur from the exhaust gases of a contact chamber, in which sulfur dioxide and hydrogen sulfide react to form elementary sulfur, up to 93% of the sulfur trapped [183].

6. Iron oxide from converter gases in steel extraction with oxygen draft, as well as cobalt oxide, 90% trapped in an experimental setup with a capacity of 3000 m^3/h at a frequency of 1 - 3 kcps [206].

7. Antimony oxide, showing, from Boucher's report, even better results [150, 151].

8. Lead oxide, 95 - 98% trapped in an industrial installation with a capacity of 10,000 m^3/h (Czechoslovakia).

9. Various "aggregated" aerosols, produced by mechanical atomization of already precipitated (powdered) materials in a gas, giving obviously negative results (aggregated coal dust and ash [73], magnesium oxide and aluminum oxide [262] etc.), zinc white [89, 90].

The table likewise contains no information on materials where the acoustic coagulability was not determined from the amount of inertial precipitation, but from other properties, particularly on a laboratory scale. Such materials are ferromanganese dust in blast furnace gas [171], cyclohexane oxime [87], fluorine compounds [15], etc.

An examination of Table 18, together with the additional information given above, yields the following conclusions.

Highly disperse aerosols like gas and nozzle black do not give sufficient consolidation to be successfully precipitated by inertial means, except at a high sound intensity of the order of 1 W/cm^2 or more (or after long treatment). Complete precipitation can only be achieved by using cloth filters in the final stage, which can operate at a high filtration rate, since the particles are large and there is very little dust.

Aersols that are less highly disperse, like zinc oxide sublimate, molybdenum sulfide, etc., give quite good consolidation at the normal sound intensity (0.1 W/cm^2), with on the order of 90 - 95% of the particles trapped. However, the residual particle concentration (20 - 200 mg/m^3) exceeds the allowable limits for toxic substances, so that cloth filters have to be used, as in the previous case. Such filters are naturally not justified unless the materials being trapped are expensive, or the amount of gas involved is small.

Various polydisperse types of dust (such as from open hearth and blast furnaces, cement kilns, etc.), where the highly disperse fractions are in a low concentration by weight, do not give good results unless the gas is sprinkled with water in the coagulation chamber, and then precipitated in a wet settler (which gives a residual concentration of the order of 100 mg/m^3), or cloth filters are used in the final stage (which gives a residual concentration of 5 - 10 mg/m^3 or less, if they have to pass a large amount of gas).

Various types of natural fogs (coke gas, cracking gas, etc.) can be very successfully precipitated by sonic-inertial means (95 - 99.8%), if they are not in too low concentration or too coarsely disperse. The residual droplet concentration in this case is 30 - 300 mg/m^3.

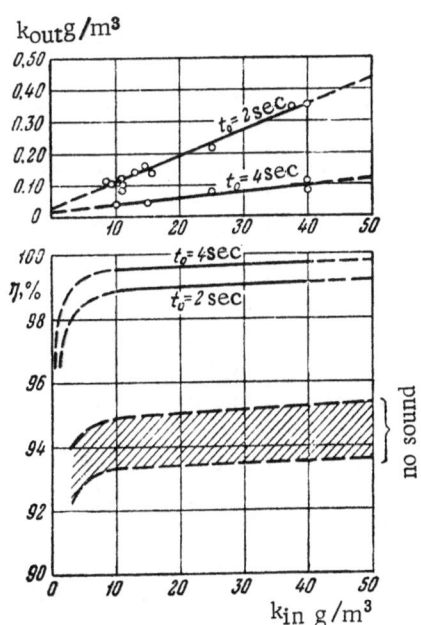

Fig. 67. Amount of sonic-inertial precipitation in an oil fog as a function of the initial concentration by weight (f = 2.4 kcps, J = 0.1 - 0.2 W/cm^2). a) Residual concentration; b) percent trapped.

Some empirical relationships have been discovered in the course of tests on sonic-inertial precipitation of industrial aerosols. It has been found that the residual concentration by weight of the particles is a linear function of the initial concentration by weight of the particles in the gas, as illustrated by Fig. 67a. Here, the percent trapped as a function of the initial concentration gives the typical curve shown in Fig. 67b. It may be concluded from this figure that the percent trapped dropps off sharply at some "critical" concentration of the order of 3 - 5 g/m^3, while there is almost no increase at high concentrations above 10 - 15 g/m^3. This is due to the fact [see Eq. 20.3)] that as k_{in} increases, the ratio k_{out}/k_{in} decreases more and more slowly, as may be seen from Fig. 67.

It has been found that the residual particle concentration in sonic-inertial precipitation is an exponential function of the product of the specific energy consumed by the compressed air in the siren times the treatment time, $\xi' = d_e t_0$ [246], thus:

$$k_{out} = k_{in} e^{-m\xi'}, \qquad (20.4)$$

where m is a constant which depends on the type of aerosol. This is illustrated in Fig. 68, which gives the results of sonic-inertial precipitation of various industrial aerosols as found by Oyama, Inoue, Sawahata, and Okada [246]. For the constant m (related to the constant n given by the above authors by the

TABLE 18

Description	Aerosol				
	Particle radius, r, μ	Concentration by weight k, g/m³	Temperature t, °C	Volume treated, Q, m³/hour	Type and dimensions (D_c × H_c, m)
Gas furnace black	0.03—0.07	1.2—12.6	40	1,700—2,000	Experimental, direct flow, 1.1 dia × 6.6
" " "	0.03—0.07	1.2—2.1	40	1,700—2,000	The same, with sprinkling
Aggregated gas black	0.5—15	0.5—2.5	—	600	Experimental, reverse flow, with sprinkling 0.5 dia × 9
Atomized carbon black	0.1—0.2	26	82	45	Experimental, rising stream, 0.29 dia. × 1.9
Hard coal black	0.5—1.0	0.5—2.4	80—90	90—100	Experimental, reverse, flow, 0.2 dia. × 2.5
Sulfuric acid fog	0.5—5.0	5—40	180	1,700	The same, 0.6 dia. × 6
Natural sulfuric acid fog	0.25—2.5	1	50	40,000	Industrial, composite flow, 2.4 dia. × 10.5 (2 sets)
Dilute sulfuric acid fog	2.5—50, Predominant 7.5	0.5—1.2	20	1,800	Experimental, reverse flow, 0.64 dia. × 11
Oil fog (artificial)	0.5—5.0	10—40	35—40	25	Laboratory, reverse flow, 0.125 dia. × 2.6
Zinc oxide sublimate from roasting zinc ore	0.5—5.0, Predominant 2.5	1—2	40—100	1,600	Experimental, reverse flow, 0.75 dia. × 10
Zinc oxide sublimate from copper smelting	0.5—4.0	0.5—20	50—350	1,300—2,160	The same, 1.0 dia.× 9
Zinc oxide sublimate from brass melting	0.4—0.6	10	400	7000	The same, 0.7 dia. × 10
Coke gas (tar)	0.5—5.0, Predominant 2.5	30—70	40—60	1,300—2,100	The same, 0.5—0.64 dia. × 9
Cracking gas (condensate)	0.5—5.0	5—70	35	1,200	The same, 0.5 dia. × 9
" " "	0.5—5.0, Pred. 3.0—3.5	6—15	40	12,000	Industrial, reverse flow, 1.6 dia. × 11 (2 sets)
Open-hearth furnace smoke	2.5 (55 %)	2	150	5,000	Experimental, reverse flow, with sprinkling
Carbide furnace smoke	0.5—15, Predominant 0.5	0.25—2.8	120	500	Experimental, reverse flow
" " "	The same	0.25—2.8	120	500	The same, with sprinkling (5 g/m³)

*Result without cloth filter, in parentheses.
†Result from sprinkling aerosol, in parentheses.
‡Similar results found in [293].

Coagulation chamber				Precipitator			
Type of siren	Frequency f, kcps	Intensity, J, W/cm^2	Length of sonic treatment t_0, sec	Type	Percentage trapped without sound η_τ, %	Percentage trapped with sound η_{si}, %	Place and year of study
Dynamic, radial	4	0.5—1.0	4.5	Two cyclones 1.3 in dia. (in series)	40	83—90	USA, 1947-1949 [272, 273, 269, 183]
The same	2—4	0.5—1.0	1.2	The same	8—32	99	The same
Dynamic, axial	3	0.1	10	One or four cyclones (in parallel)	68—72	95	Japan, 1950-1954 [38, 246]
Static with pump-off	4.6	1.0	7	Two cyclones and a glass cloth filter (in series)	(30)*	99.98(97)*	USSR, State Scientific Research Institute of Sanitary and Industrial Purification of Gases 1959 [54, 57, 304]
Dynamic, axial	3.6	0.10—0.14	3—4	Cyclone 0.15 m dia.	68—74 (81)†	87(97)†	USSR, Institute of Mineral Fuels 1959 [85]
The same	2.15	0.1	3	Multicyclones (in parallel)	84	99.6—99.9	USA, 1949 [218, 241, 248]
Dynamic, radial	2.25	0.1	4	Two cyclones (in parallel)	—	90	USA, New York, 1948, [184]
Dynamic, axial	1—2	0.1	7	Four cyclones (in parallel)	69—72	78—82	Japan, 1950-1954, [38, 246]
The same	2—4	0.1—0.2	2.4	Cyclone 1.5 m dia.	93—95	99.0—99.8	USSR, Moscow Power Institute, 1954-1955 [73, 74]
'' ''	3—3.5	0.1	10	Cyclone	84—87	94—98	Japan, 1950-1954 [38, 246]
Dynamic, radial	3—9	0.13	10	Cyclone 1.35 m dia.	70	90—95	Poland, Szopienice, 1954-1955, [227, 228]‡
Dynamic, axial	0.7	0.6	2.5	Cyclone 0.15-0.3m dia. and filters (in series)	—	99.8	USSR, Promenergo, 1958-1961, [308]
The same	4	0.1	5—8.5	Two cyclones (in parallel)	88	99—99.8	Japan, 1950-1954, [38, 246]
'' ''	4	0.1	5	The same	76—82	97.5—99.3	Japan 1950-1954 [38, 246]
'' ''	3.5	0.1	6	Two Pelouze tar extractors (in paral.)	73	95	Japan, Tokyo, 1954 [259]
Dynamic	2.2	—	—	Wet type W rotoclone	45	90.7	USA, 1951 [281, 269]
Static	7+10 +26	—	4—6	Multicyclones (in parallel)	11	94	France, 1954, [150, 151]
''	10.5	—	4—6	The same	—	86	

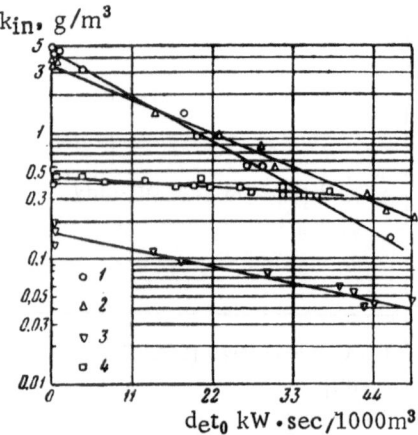

kin, g/m³

deto kW·sec/1000m³

Fig. 68. Residual particle concentration after sonic-inertial precipitation of some industrial aerosols as a function of the product d_{et_0} (after Oyama, Inoue, Sawahata, and Okada). 1) Coke gas tar (r = 0.5 - 5 μ, k_{in} = 30 - 70 g/m³; 2) cracking gas condensate (r = 0.5 - 5 μ, k_{in} 5 - 70 g/m³; 3) aggregated carbon black (r = 0.5 - 15 μ, k_{in} 0.5 - 2.4 g/m³; 4) dilute sulfuric acid fog (r = 2.5 - 50 μ; k_{in} = 0.5 - 1.2 g/m³).

equation: m = n/27.3), we obtain the following values: coke gas, 0.077; cracking gas, 0.059; aggregated gas black, 0.033; and dilute sulfuric acid fog, 0.009.

The specific energy is proportional to the product of the sound intensity by the treatment time, $d_e \sim Jt_0$ [see Eq.(20.8)]. so that $\xi' \sim (\sqrt{J}t_0)^2$. Hence, combining Eq. (20.4) with Eqs.(15.2) and (16.4), we obtain the following relation:

$$\frac{k_{out}}{k_{in}} = \left(\frac{n}{n_0}\right)^2 .$$ (20.5)

It follows from this equation that the concentration by weight of coagulated particles after precipitation in an inertial precipitator decreases considerably more rapidly than the particle count concentration during acoustic coagulation. This is perfectly all right, since the inertial settler precipitates the heaviest of the coagulated particles.

In accordance with (20.4), we get the following expression for the percent trapped:

$$\eta_{si} = 100 - (100 - \eta_i) e^{-m\xi'} \%,$$ (20.6)

where η_i is the efficiency which the inertial settler achieves when cleaning an aerosol with no sound. The equation holds for the condition that the particles have been brought up to a size where they are completely trapped, and are not broken up by the settler, which is only strictly true of fogs.

For gas black, Kidoo [211] used the experimental data of Stokes and Vivian [273] to derive another exponential equation for the percent trapped:

$$\eta_{si} = 100 - e^{\frac{M}{K\sqrt{J}t_0}} \%,$$ (20.7)

where M is a coefficient which depends on the type of carbon black and the efficiency of the coagulating and precipitating equipment.

The problem of the amount of energy used is important in making a correct evaluation of the sonic-inertial method of precipitating aerosols. The energy required consists of that used in coagulation, and that used in precipitating the aerosol. The specific energy used in precipitating aerosols is well-known for all the existing types of precipitators. For example, for cyclones, the average value is 0.2 kWh per 1000 m³ of gas, and for rotoclones it gets up to several kilowatt hours.

If the sound intensity required to irradiate a coagulation chamber of cross-sectional area S_C is J W/cm², and the treatment time is t_0 sec, then, bearing in mind that the total acoustic energy required is $W_{ac} = JS_C$, while the amount of gas worked on is $Q_g = wS_C = (H_0/t_0)S_C$, we get the following expression for the specific energy required to coagulate the aerosol [74]:

$$d_9 = \frac{Jt_0}{0.36 \, \eta_s \eta_c \, \eta_{uf} \, H_0} \quad \frac{kWh}{1000 \, m^3} ,$$ (20.8)

η_s is the acoustic efficiency of the siren, and η_c is the over-all efficiency of the compressor driving the siren, η_{uf} is the utilization factor of the sound vibration in the coagulation chamber, including losses from irregularities in the acoustic field in the chamber, absorption of acoustic energy by the aerosol, leakage through holes in the walls of the chamber, departures from resonance, etc. (as found experimentally) and H_0 is the height of the coagulation chamber receiving the sound, in meters.

A measure of the acoustic energy expended in coagulating aerosols is thus given by the product of the sound intensity by the treatment time Jt_0, which is given the name sonic index.

It may be concluded from Eqs. (15.2) and (20.8) together with (15.6) that increasing J has a less noticeable effect on the efficiency of the process than increasing t_0, while J and t_0 both have the same effect on the specific energy consumed. Hence it follows that the acoustic losses are less for small values of J, while the capital expenditure for equipment is less for small values of t_0 (since the chamber is handling more gas per unit of time when t_0 is smaller). The optimum values of J and t_0 are determined from engineering and economic considerations based on the experimental data.

Neumann, Soderberg, and Fowle (Ultrasonic Corporation USA) give [240] the following limits for the specific energy consumption: d_e = 0.65 - 20 kWh per 1000 m^3 of gas. Other authors give higher values. Thus, in the semi-industrial scale experiments made by Oyama, Inoue, Sawahata, and Okada [246] the following values were obtained: aggregated carbon black and zinc oxide, 4.2 kWh;* dilute sulfuric acid, 5.6 kWh; coke gas, 8.4 kWh, and cracking gas, 7.0 kWh (our calculations, based on η_c = 0.65). In the industrial sonic-inertial cracking gas cleaner designed by these same authors [259] the energy consumption was only 2.5 kWh. The reason for the difference is that the sirens used in the experiments had a low acoustic efficiency of not more than 10 - 15%. For this reason, the experiments on sonic-inertial precipitation of zinc oxide sublimate, made by Central Institute of Industrial Safety (Poland) [227, 228], gave a value of 8 kWh, while in precipitating the smoke from carbide furnaces [150, 151], the values were 3.9 and 7.0 kWh.

Schnitzler (Lugri, West Germany) citing the experiments that he made [262], gave an even higher value: 10kWh, leaving in the dark the fact that the figure was obtained for sonic-inertial precipitation of aggregated materials, i.e., those that coagulate very little.

In summing up the experience accumulated on sonic-inertial precipitation of industrial aerosols, it is seen that the reasons for high specific energy consumption in the process are in general to be found in the following factors:

1) The aerosol is not easily coagulated by sound because the particles are exceedingly large or at a low concentration by weight, etc),

2) The aerosol has large sound absorption (because the particles are of the "critical" size, or are at exceedingly high concentration, etc.),

3) The optimum frequency is not being used (because the generator has a limited range of adjustment, the rpm varies, there are changes in dispersion composition of the aerosol particles, etc.),

4) Low acoustic efficiency in the generator (resulting from poor design or careless construction, wear, etc.),

5) Inefficient operation of the coagulation chamber (resulting from not adjusting the system to resonance, chamber not the right height, high sound leakage through the input and output fittings, variable gas temperature, etc.),

6) Extensive dilution of the aerosol by the exhaust air from the siren (which makes the aerosol harder to coagulate and increases the draft losses),

7) Low efficiency in the compressor (because it is not working under design conditions, throttling of the air, and other factors), and

---

*In [89, 90] the value given for the specific energy consumption in treating zinc oxide is only 0.6 kWh, which, however, is seriously in need of a check.

8) Improper choice of the type of inertial precipitator, or not operating under optimum conditions (decreasing the input velocity means that it is necessary to increase the amount of consolidation of the particles, while increasing the velocity means more breakup of the dry consolidated particle aggregates. From Jahn's data [206], the critical velocity for cyclones comes at 10 - 12 m/sec).

Not all the above sources of high energy losses can be completely removed. Hence the actually attainable value for the total energy required in sonic-inertial cleaning of gases must, for the present, be regarded as 2 - 4 kWh per 1000 m^3 of gas. It is only when the trapped material has to be dried that the specific energy becomes higher (for example, for open hearth gas dust, d_e = 6.5 kWh [269]).

Let us now go over the measures taken to improve the efficiency of sonic-inertial precipitation of industrial aerosols:

1) Putting atomized water droplets or condensing steam [189] into dry gases or those that do not contain a large amount of dust, while in the case of fogs, putting in droplets of the liquid to be trapped in appropriate amounts (recirculation of the fog). Deserving of consideration is the method in which charged droplets of water or other liquid are put into the aerosols,

2) Lowering the temperature of the gas (to increase the actual concentration of the particles, stabilize the condensation temperature of the steam introduced, and reduce the volume of the gas, which increases the capacity of the coagulator) or, conversely, maintaining a high temperature in the gas (to keep the particles in the liquid state),

3) Making the coagulation chamber higher or lower (to get the best sonic treatment conditions for a given aerosol),

4) Using highly efficient sirens (dynamic sirens giving rectangular pressure pulses), as well as sirens with internal air circulation,

5) Using the gas being cleaned to drive the sirens, if excess pressure is available (as is the case with blast furnace gas), or else making use of existing low pressure steam (such as the exhaust from steam engines),

6) Treating the aerosol with a number of frequencies (the good effects of this measure are shown, for example, by the experiments of Boucher [150, 151]),

7) Mounting special acoustic filters at the points where the gas enters and leaves the coagulating chamber, to reflect the acoustic energy back into the chamber [180], and

8) Using more efficient dust precipitators, in particular wet wire filters [184, 239, 240]. Attention should also be given to electrical filters.

Experience in combining turbulent coagulation with an electrical filter when cleaning blast furnace gas [119] has shown that it works exceedingly well: the residual concentration was lowered to 5 - 10 mg/m^3 instead of 20 mg/m^3, while the capacity of the electrical filter was increased by a factor of 1.5-2 in the process.

Even better results are to be expected from combining an acoustic coagulator with an electric filter. The time required for treatment is reduced (since electrical filters can take considerably smaller particles than cyclones), and the capacity of the electrical filters is increased. This reduces the capital expenditure and the energy required for the treatment. An acoustic coagulator has the further important advantage over a turbulent coagulator that the coagulation may be done in the dry state (except for gases containing very little dust), since there is no danger of the aggregates being broken up in the electrical filters (low gas velocity!).

Sonic-inertial dust and drop collecting, like other methods, has its advantages and disadvantages.

The advantages of sonic-inertial dust and drop collecting are:

1) High degree of purification of various industrial gases, primarily fogs, as well as smokes, for which wet trapping is not counter-indicated,

2) No limit on how small the particles of fogs, smokes, and dusts can be,

3) Gas cleaning efficiency independent of the electrical properties of the gases,

4) Usable for corrosive gases, as well as at high temperatures and pressures,

5) No danger from explosion or high voltage in sonic-inertial equipment,

6) Simplicity of the coagulating equipment, particularly when using static sirens and centrifugal compressors, and

7) Smaller equipment and more moderate capital expenditure than when using electrical or cloth filters.

The disadvantages of sonic-inertial dust and drop collecting are:

1) Higher specific energy consumption when cleaning gases, and particularly with smokes and dusts. It is always higher than with electrical filters, but, as a rule, lower than when using disintegrators, turbulent atomizer tubes, and cloth filters,

2) Need to moisten some smokes and dusts, thus lowering the temperature of the gases,

3) Limited residual particle concentration (not lower than 30 mg/m^3 for fogs and 100 mg/m^3 for moistened smokes and dusts) in those cases where cloth filters cannot be used,

4) When using ordinary sound sirens there is some dilution of the gas being cleaned by the air (gas or steam) from the siren, and

5) Need for rotating assemblies in the siren (if it is of dynamic type) and the compressor.

The most important disadvantage is the high specific energy consumption in the process, which shows up to the greatest extent when coagulating highly disperse aerosols (like gas black). Some interest in this connection attaches to our proposals for two new methods for coagulating aerosols in a sound field: step-by-step coagulation at several frequencies [77, 78], and electroacoustic coagulation [76, 78]. We shall stop to consider the physical essence of the methods briefly.

It was pointed out in §16 that every aerosol undergoing coagulation has an optimum frequency at which coagulation occurs most easily. The optimum frequency is lower, the coarser the aerosol, i.e., the larger the particles. This follows from the theoretical studies that were made in §10, 11, and 12 (see Figs. 30 and 41), as well as from extensive experimental studies (see §16, Fig. 51, and Table 13).

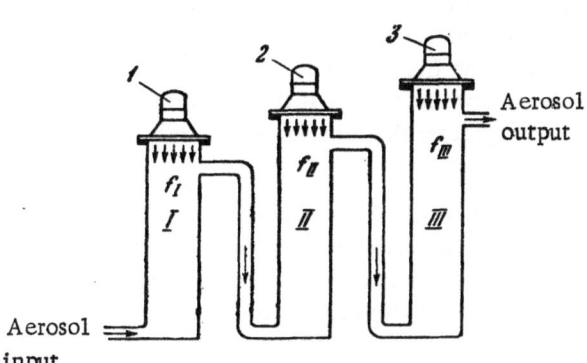

Fig. 69. Step-by-step coagulation equipment. I, II, and III are coagulation chambers and 1, 2, and 3 are sound sirens for the first, second, and third steps ($f_I > f_{II} > f_{III}$).

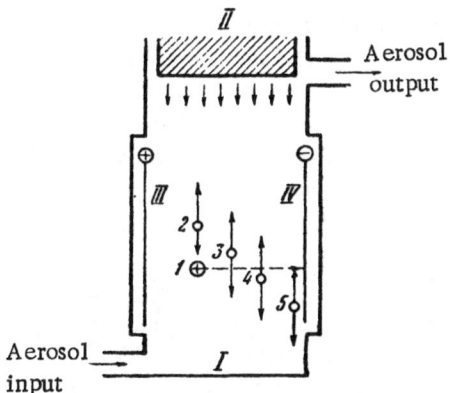

Fig. 70. Electroacoustic method of coagulating and precipitating aerosols.
I) Electroacoustic chamber; II) sound radiator; III and IV) electrodes; 1) fog droplet; 2,3,4, and 5) dust particles.

As coagulation proceeds, the aerosol particles gradually get larger, which means that the frequency should be lower if the process is to go under optimum conditions. This is especially desirable when coagulating highly disperse aerosols, which require an enormous amount of consolidation of the particles. Accordingly, the methods used now for acoustic coagulation of aerosols must be regarded as primitive.

Instead of the present method of acoustic coagulation, we offer the more advanced scheme shown in Fig. 69. Here the aerosol passes through chambers where the frequency decreases to fit the change in size of the particles. This does not mean however, that there is any increase in capital expenditure or in the energy required to drive the air through the sirens, since the rate of flow through the chambers increases by the same number (a factor of 3 for three chambers, etc.).

The essence of the electroacoustic method of aerosol coagulation is (Fig. 70) that the aerosol being treated has charged droplets of water (or other liquid) mixed with it to act as coagulation centers, and the treatment is carried out in an electrical chamber consisting externally of a corona-free electrical filter. Since they are charged, the droplets move toward the precipitating electrode, and while they are moving, are "bombarded" by the vibrating polarized dust particles, which penetrate the droplets and are carried along with them to the precipitating electrode.

Thus, we have coagulation and precipitation of the aerosols combined in a single piece of equipment. However, the coagulation is going according to a new scheme (longitudinal vibration of the particles is produced acoustically, while translational motion in the transverse direction is produced electrically).

If alternating current is used, the dust particles and droplets are simply coagulated, without being precipitated on the surface of the electrodes.

§21. Sonic Separation and Filtration of Aerosols

Sound waves may be used to speed up precipitation of aerosols, not merely by coagulating the aerosol particles, but directly. This may be accomplished primarily by making use of the drift forces which exert an effect on the aerosol particles that prevents them from moving along with the gas, so that they may be separated out of the gas stream. Another possibility is to use the orthokinetic effect, by which the aerosol particles may be deposited on large rapidly settling liquid drops which are then removed from the dust laden gas. Finally, a third possibility is to use the vortex motion in the gas set up in the boundary layer around obstacles (see §1) as a factor in making aerosol particles settle out more rapidly on the obstacles by turbulent diffusion and inertial precipitation.

Let us consider some schemes that have been proposed for stimulating and utilizing the precipitating effect of sound.

A very ingenious but unrealizable, method for sonic separation of aerosols was that advanced by Westervelt and Sieck in [290]. The method is based on Westervelt's theoretical work [286], which we have already quoted in §6, dealing with the drift forces on aerosol particles in a sound field, in which a new type of particle drift was described, due to distortion of the sound wave. It was shown in §6 that if the wave form is greatly distorted, the rate of this type of drift is several orders of magnitude greater than that of all the other types of drift, particularly radiation drift.

In order to speed up separation of the suspended particles from the dispersing medium, Westervelt and Sieck suggested irradiating the medium with sound waves that were artificially distorted (asymmetrically). This may be done in a gas by using a specially designed dynamic siren, with the holes in the rotor made in one of the ways shown in Fig. 71.

The separation equipment consists of a hollow vertical chamber, with the radiator at the bottom, in which a traveling sound wave is set up in some way

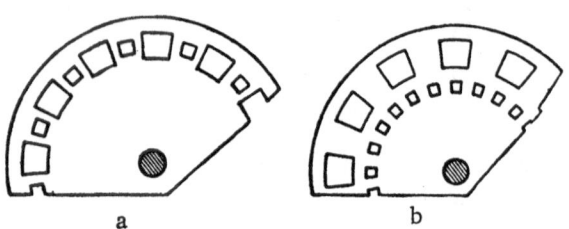

Fig. 71. Shape of the holes in the rotor of a siren to be used for sonic separation of aerosols (after Westervelt and Sieck).

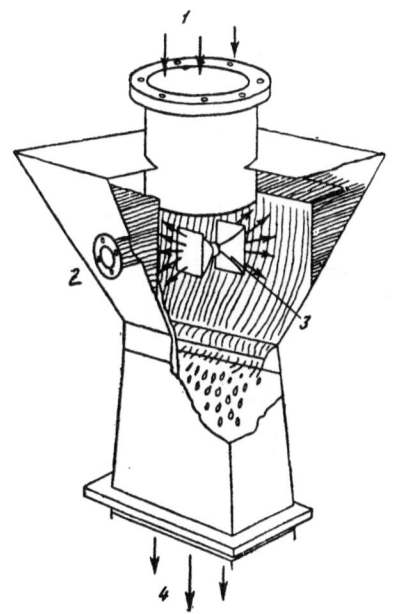

Fig. 72. Sonic-inertial Venturi scrubber (as proposed by Boucher). 1) Gas input; 2) water input; 3) sound radiator; 4) gas output.

or another. The gas to be treated is admitted at the bottom of the chamber and moves upward, while the suspended particles that it contains are held back by the drift forces and then drop to the bottom.

The rate at which the gas is pumped through the separator is determined by the minimum size of the particles to be precipitated. It may be concluded from Fig. 22A that if the very finest particles are to be precipitated, the gas velocity must be held down to a very low value.

It may, however, be assumed that if the particles are not at too low a concentration, they will rapidly form a suspended filtration layer that holds back the finer particles when the gas is pumped through at high velocities. Unfortunately, there are as yet no experimental data in support of this opinion.

The inhomogeneity of the sound field and the acoustic wind must also be taken into account. The inhomogeneity of the sound field over the cross section of the chamber leads to difference in the drift velocities of the aerosol particles, and thus to a difference in the dimensions of the particles being separated. The presence of the acoustic wind, and particularly of acoustic turbulence in the medium, prevents the aerosol particles from being precipitated onto the bottom of the chamber under the action of the drift forces.

It seems to us that this method of separation has some prospects for application, principally in getting the dust out of small closed spaces, where the gas can be given a prolonged treatment. Something like this occurs, for example, during blasting operations when cutting drifts in coal and other mines.

The time lost in airing out the drifts runs to 10 or 20 or more minutes. It has been shown by experience that using sound waves in the ordinary way does not reduce the time required for such mining operations. Irradiating the drifts with special sirens giving distorted pressure pulses, it would seem, should reduce the time required severalfold. The energy expended in the process would be small, since the irradiations would be sporadic and no measures would be required to keep down the sound in the surrounding space (because of the safety requirements on blasting operations, there would be nobody in the irradiated zone).

Boucher [157] has suggested a method for speeding up precipitation of aerosol particles right in existing types of dust and drop collecting equipment, by building in compact gas-jet sound radiators at the proper places. This idea is appealing for the reason that very little capital expenditure is required to carry it out (particularly if there is a compressed air line handy).

Figure 72 shows one of Boucher's ideas for a sonic-inertial Venturi scrubber [149, 157]. Liquid flows down in a continuous film along the slopping walls, and is guided into the mouth of the pipe by deflecting baffles, where it is atomized by the dust laden gas, which is moving at high velocity. A gas-jet whistle mounted inside the pipe irradiates the mixed aerosol formed, and by speeding up orthokinetic interaction and turbulence increases the number of collisons with the water droplets.

Naturally, sonic treatment will not have any appreciable effect unless the mixture stays in the irradiated zone for a reasonable length of time. For this reason, sonic treatment is little suited to the various types of high-speed gas washers, but does work with ordinary sprinkler scrubbers and gas washers, in which the gas is moving comparatively slowly.

This is supported by the results of the first experiments made by Boucher and Weiner [159]. They made a study of the effect of 11 kcps sound waves on trapping a low-concentration triethyleneglycol aerosol (r_m = 2.5 μ, k_{in} = 79 - 136 mg/m^3) in a gas washer made by the "Schmig Industries" with a capacity of 850 m^3/h.

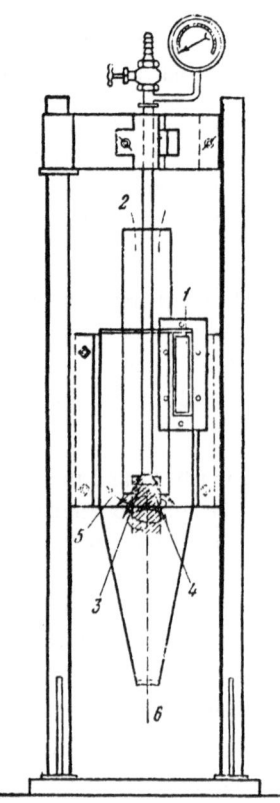

Fig. 73. Sonic-inertial cyclone (as proposed by Boucher). 1) Tangential input fitting; 2) gas output; 3) rod-jet whistle; 4) acoustic field; 5) trajectory of the moving particles; 6) dust output.

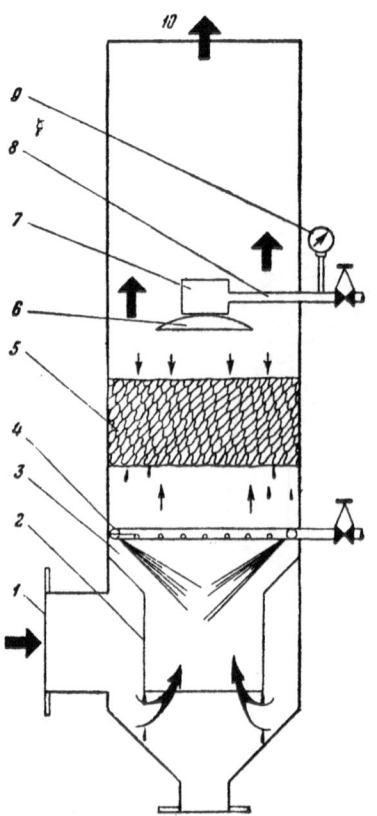

Fig. 74. Acoustic drop collector filter as proposed by Asklof. 1) Tangential input fitting; 2) output fitting of internal cyclone- 3) output to sprinkler; 7) sound generator; 8) compressed air input; 9) manometer; 10) gas output.

The sound level produced by the rod-jet whistles was 150 db. The investigators state on the basis of their experiments that irradiating the water curtain raises the efficiency of gas washers a minimum of 10-15%, even for very low aerosol particle concentrations.

Figure 73 shows Boucher's idea [157] for a sound equipped conical cyclone. The sound radiator (a rod-jet whistle) is mounted in the rarefaction zone occurring under the output fitting of the cyclone, to produce a sound barrier in the path followed by the particles. In our opinion, no positive effect can be achieved without using a special radiator which generates asymmetric sound waves, as in Westervelt and Sieck's generator, but with the opposite phase shift in the harmonics (the force F_r mentioned by the author is insignificant, and is cancelled, as is shown in §6, by the force $F_{\eta + \varphi}$ directed toward the sound source).

Askloff's idea [313] for sonic filtration of fogs is based on a completely different physical principle. The drop collector filter that he constructed is shown schematically in Fig. 74. The gas, containing the fog droplets (or a mixture of droplets and dust), is fed to the bottom of the apparatus. After going through a preliminary separation from the large droplets in an internal cyclone, the gas passes to a porous packing which is irradiated from the top by a rod-jet whistle with a reflector behind it. Here, the sound produces intense filtration of the droplets out of the gas, so that it goes out of the top quite clean. In describing this method in [157], Boucher sets forth the essence of sonic filtration in the following way: "It was noticed long ago that when high intensity sound is irradiated onto a metal screen, the screen acts like an acoustic grating, which transmits and reflects the sound waves over a large area. By varying λ/D (the ratio of the wave length of the sound to the mean diameter of the openings in the screen), the sound may be intensified and concentrated in any space, or the radiated sound may be transmitted through a large solid angle. Here, any opening may be regarded as a point source of sound. Interference of the sound waves may also occur.

When a high powered generator is being used, a screen transmits a large amount of acoustic energy. For example, an ultrasonic gas-jet whistle (power 80 W), at a distance of 0.3 m or more from a filter packing 5.4 cm thick can degas the surface layer of water-mains water, located 0.3 m below the opening. The radiation pressure is so great that the force fields going through the openings can deflect suspended aerosol particles toward the fibers, or drive them away from the packing." And further: "When working with a liquid aerosol, a high-intensity sound field repels some particles and attracts others (orthokinetic coagulation), and breaks up the liquid film covering the metal wires of the screen."

It seems to us that the principal role in this sonic filtration process is not played by radiation pressure, but by the irregularity of the immediate sound field, which produces gas vortices, and particularly transverse movement, in the boundary layer of the filtering elements of the packing, thus making the aerosol particles precipitate on the packing by turbulent diffusion and inertial effects.

Asklöff states in [313] that when filtering a fine hydrocarbon fog through a network packing 100 mm thick at a rate of 3 m/sec, it is possible by sonic means (f = 8 kcps, J = 0.05 W/cm^2) to reduce the residual droplet concentration approximately from 10 mg/m^3 to 0.5 mg/m^3 of gas, i.e., by a factor of 20.

This is the factor by which one worker was able to reduce the residual particle concentration with sonic filtration of the radioactive uranium trioxide aerosol formed in evaporating of 0.5% uranium nitrate solution, with subsequent drying of the droplets. The capacity of the filter was 6000 m^3 of radioactive gas per hour, and the pressure drop was 25 - 50 mm of water (for a packing 900 mm thick). Here, the energy used in irradiation (f = 10 kcps, J = 0.1 W/cm^2), and in pumping the gas was only 0.4 kWh per 1000 m^3 of gas (in other cases, the energy gets as high as 1.2 kWh [157]).

Sonic filtration of aerosols deserves serious attention, since it provides the best purification of industrial gases (in particular the ventilating air of various factories) with a high filtration rate.

There is obvious interest in using sound waves to clean the collected dust out of sleeve filters. In the first idea, described in Ebboud's patent [135], the sound generator is mounted in the filter in such a way as to irradiate the cloth in a group of filter sleeves from the clean side. It turned out however [157] that irradiating the dirty side of the cloth by the method shown in Fig. 75 is a better and cheaper way of cleaning the filters.

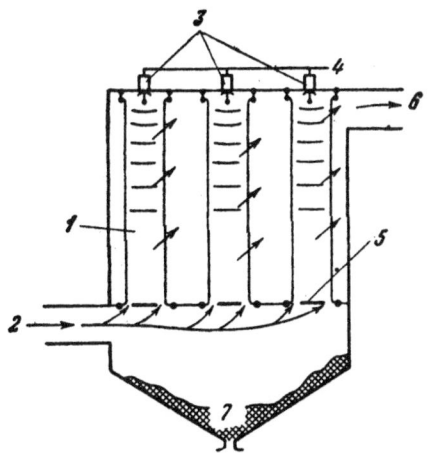

Fig. 75. Sonic-inertial sleeve filter (as proposed by Abboud). 1) Sleeve filter; 2) gas laden dust input; 3) sound radiator; 4) compressed air line (to the radiators); 5) resonating plates 6) clean air output; 7) precipitated dust.

In our opinion, the shaking effect of the sound is due to the fact that the resonating plates inside each of the sleeves sets up a standing wave, so that an appreciable periodic pressure change occurs at the nodes in the vibration, which forces the cloth to vibrate (if the frequency is not too high).*

A few words in conclusion on P. N. Kubanskii's idea for speeding up the precipitation of aerosol particles by means of longitudinal partitions, mounted inside the coagulation chamber. The idea is based on the fallacious conclusion of [48, 49] that the vortex-like acoustic streaming between the nodes and loops in a standing wave in some way favors coagulation of aerosol particles. Actually, acoustic streaming has very little coagulating effect, since the stream is not moving very fast when it changes direction, and as a result, the small particles are not dropped into the "dead" zones formed at the wall at the point where the two adjacent vortices come together at each

---

* Another type of sound-equipped sleeve filter has recently been patented [327].

node (see §7). The only things that can get into these zones are already coagulated groups of small particles (like the lycopodium particles in the experiments [48], where the radius was greater than 10μ).

This fact has also been noted by Brandt, Freund, and Hiedemann [167], who pointed out that local precipitation of aerosol particles at the nodes is a secondary effect of irradiation, which follows coagulation of the particles.

Note in addition to everything that has been said that according to Rayleigh's equation (1.25), the rate of the acoustic streaming in the direction of the wall drops off linearly with decrease in spacing between the walls. For this reason, putting in additional partitions does not increase the amount of precipitation at the nodes even for particles that are already coagulated.

APPENDIX

§ I. Evaporation and Growth by Condensation of Drops in Sound Irradiated Fogs

When fogs are treated with sound, in addition to accelerating coagulation and precipitation of the particles, we see that the phase transitions characteristic of the systems are also going faster. If the gas is not completely saturated with the vapor of the liquid, irradiating the fog speeds up evaporation of the drops in the system. If, however, the gas is supersaturated with the vapor of the liquid, and is sufficiently so, the irradiation, on the other hand, speeds up the growth of the drops by condensation which occurs in this case (as long as the drops are not too small).*

There are some definite conditions under which the above processes are more important than coagulation and precipitation of the droplets, and become the principal effect, so that sound waves may be used as a means of speeding up dissipation of natural fogs, drying atomized solutions, separating hydrocarbon gases, etc.

Evaporation of drops, as we know, is made up of two elementary processes [16]: a) Removing molecules from the liquid surface to form a layer of saturated vapor, and b) molecules diffusing from the saturated layer into the surrounding medium.

With these ideas in mind, Maxwell gave the following equation for the rate of evaporation from the surface of a drop in a stationary medium [16, 123]:

$$J_f = 4\pi \, Dr \, (c_s - c_\infty),$$

(AI.1)

where D is the diffusion coefficient of the vapor [128], c_s is the concentration of the saturated vapor of the substance and c_∞ is the concentration of the vapor in the surrounding medium.

For the system of drops making up the fog, it may be assumed to a good approximation that each drop evaporates at the same velocity as if it were in a vessel with nonabsorbing walls, of a volume equal to the mean volume associated with one drop in the system. This theory gives the following expression for the evaporation rate of the drops in the fog [123]:

$$J_f \simeq 4\pi Drc_s \exp \left[- \frac{3rD}{(b-r)^3} t \right],$$

(AI.2)

where b is the radius of the vessel, and t is the time.

In a moving medium, the diffusion boundary layer is to some extent "blown-off," so that the evaporation rate of the drops is higher than in a stationary medium by the factor f_w, where f_w is the so-called wind factor:

$$f_w = 1 + \beta \, Sc^{1/3} Re^{1/2}.$$

(AI.3)

Here β is a constant equal to approximately 0.276, Sc is the Schmidt number, which is the ratio v/D, equal for water vapor in air under ordinary conditions to about 0.7, and Re is the Reynolds number, characteristic of the

---

* The experiments of V. V. Bazilevich and N. P. Tverskii [4,5], have shown that irradiation also helps to make the drops freeze in supercooled fogs, but we shall not stop to consider this phenomenon since it is of minor interest.

flow around the drops: Re = $2ru_{gp}/\nu$. In this case, the evaporation rate of the drops is given, if we set $K = \beta S^{1/3}$, by equation:

$$J_f = 4\pi r D(c_s - c_\infty)(1 + K\sqrt{Re}),\tag{AI.4}$$

which is called Fressling's equation.

It may be seen from this equation that the evaporation rate of drops in a stream increases relatively slowly with increase in Reynolds number. Further, the experiments of Kintzer and Hann [123] have shown that for Re < 1, i.e., for viscous flow around the drops, the evaporation rate does not depend at all on the relative velocity of the medium, and is thus independent of Re. This is due to the fact that the concentration and temperature fields around a drop in viscous flow are only slightly distorted by the motion of the medium. The circulation inside the drop, caused by friction between the drop and the gas, which tends to even out the temperature in the drop, likewise plays no great role at small Re number. Further, as the Reynolds number increases from Re = 1 to Re = 1.75, a rapid increase occurs in the evaporation rate by about double, after which the evaporation rate increases much more slowly (for Re = 3, f_w = 2.5, etc.).

If we start with the fact that motion of the medium begins to promote evaporation of the drops at Re_{cr} = 1, we arrive at the conclusion that no increase in the evaporation rate is observed until the following critical value of the relative velocity of the medium has been reached:

$$u_{cr} = \frac{\nu}{2r}.\tag{AI.5}$$

Thus we see that the critical velocity of the medium rises rapidly with increase in degree of dispersion of the drops, and is moreover, generally speaking, of impressive magnitude. Thus, for drops of radius r = 7.5 μ, the critical velocity is 100 cm/sec, while for drops with r = 1.5 μ, it is 500 cm/sec. Note for comparison that the rates of free fall of the same drops are only 0.66 and 0.026 cm/sec respectively.

A characteristic of sound vibrations is that they can be used to produce relatively high velocities in a gas relative to any extremely fine particles suspended in it. In the limiting case, which occurs at high frequencies such as to give μ_g = 1, the rate of flow around the drops becomes equal to the particle velocity in the gas.

The minimum radius that gives good flow around water drops in air ($\mu_g \approx 0.8$), vibrating at the highest frequency used in large industrial installations (3.5 - 4.0 kcps) is about r = 2 μ.

The theory shows [123] that if the drops are not too large, evaporation under nonsteady conditions may be regarded as a quasi-stationary process. Hence it may be concluded that the equations (AI.3) and (AI.4) given above continue to hold even when the medium is vibrating, as long as the amplitude of the vibrations is large in comparison with the radius of the drops: $A_g \gg r$.

The critical sound level at which the sound waves begin to speed up evaporation of drops in air is, from (AI.5) equal to

$$L_{tr} = 164 - 20 \log(\mu_g r_p) \text{ db}.\tag{AI.6}$$

At these sound levels, the gas is as a rule turbulent, so that the turbulent pulsations in the medium are flowing around the drops. Further, as found in §11, a peculiar type of acoustic streaming is set up around any particle suspended in a sound field, even for Re < 1, with the vortices on a scale comparable with the amplitude of the vibrations.

What effect do these phenomena have on evaporation of drops in a sound field?

It does not seem to us that either of these phenomena has any direct additional effect on evaporation of the drops, since the turbulent pulsations and the acoustic streaming occur as a rule at velocities much less than the critical velocity given by Eq. (AI.5). They only serve to remove vapor from around the drops.

R. S. Tyul'panov [118] made an attempt to determine approximately how the radii of the drops change during evaporation in a pulsating stream, using the following idealized scheme for the process. It was assumed that during the first half of a half-period of a vibration in the medium, the vapor builds up in the boundary layer of the drop, with only a limited amount of evaporation from the outer surface. But in the next half of the half-period of the vibration, part of the boundary layer is "blown-off," removing molecules of the vapor accumulated on the surface of the drop. These ideas gave the following expression for the radius of the drop:

$$ r = \sqrt{ 0.328 \frac{D}{f} + \left(r_0^2 - 0.328 \frac{D}{f} \right) e^{-\frac{fc_s}{\rho_p}t} } \tag{AI.7} $$

(r_0 is the initial radius of the drop). This formula, can, however only be used for very large drops.

As we know, during evaporation, the size of the drops decreases, and the rate of flow around the drops decreases simultaneously, with the result that there is also a decrease in the value of the Reynolds number. The result of this is that there is a gradual reduction in the evaporation rate of the drops, and, finally, when Re becomes < 1, the speeding-up effect stops completely. The occurrence of this state of affairs can not be held up except by the parallel process of drop coagulation, which, however, is not important unless the concentration by weight of the drops is quite large. It may be shown in this connection that irradiating coarsely disperse fogs should give a larger effect than irradiating more finely disperse fogs. This is not actually the case.

The total amount of moisture evaporated by all the drops, from (9.1) and (AI.4), is equal to:

$$ G = J_f n \cdot 10^6 = \frac{3kD}{\rho_p r^2} (c_s - c_\infty)(1 + K\sqrt{Re}) \frac{g}{m^3 \cdot sec}, \tag{AI.8} $$

where n is the count concentration and k is the concentration by weight of the drops.

By noting that the second factor in parentheses increases with increase in r much more slowly than $1/r^2$, it is not difficult to see that the more coarsely disperse the fog, the less the total amount of moisture evaporated (for the same concentration by weight of the drops, and, of course, for the condition that Re > 1, and $\mu_g \rightarrow 1$).

Recently, B. V. Deryagin and Yu. S. Kurgin gave a theoretical treatment of what effect periodic pressure oscillations in the saturated vapor in the absence of air have on the liquid-vapor phase equilibrium for a plane interface [303], and for droplets of radii r < l_m [303a].

The first use proposed for the speeding-up effect of sound on evaporation was in solving the problem of dissipating natural fogs.

We know from §18 that acoustic dissipation of fogs has a limited range of action, requires large amounts of energy, and has other disadvantages. In view of this, the idea came up of using sound in conjunction with thermal heating of the fog, and in this way solving the problem of dissipating fogs by evaporating the drops in the sound field. This was first mentioned in 1943 by Rodebush in a report covering tests on acoustic fog dissipation.

The new composite method of dissipating fogs, which has been extensively developed in recent years by Boucher [156, 316], received the name thermoacoustic method.

It has already turned out that the thermal method of fog dissipation requires large amounts of heat, due to the fact that heating the atmosphere sets up strong convection currents, so that the hotter air mass goes up and is replaced by the surrounding cooler air, which also contains fog droplets. The result is that a large amount of fuel is used up in not merely heating the air and evaporating the droplets where the fog is being dissipated, but in heating large masses of the surrounding air. Hence it follows that the droplets in the fog must be evaporated as rapidly as possible, to avoid drawing in large masses of cold air. This is just what what Boucher felt that irradiating the fog should do.

The first thermoacoustic fog dissipation experiments, made in Arcata (USA) in 1950 were quite encouraging. The air heater used was a J-33 turbojet engine with an afterburner ($3 \cdot 10^8$ BTU/h), while the sources were U2 and U3A-1 dynamic sirens developing about 5kW of acoustic power at 3.5 kcps.

The fog was dissipated to a distance of about 300 m at heights of from 90 to 150 m. From the results obtained, Downey and Smith calculated that ten J-47 turbojet engines in conjunction with sound would take 5 minutes to do the work done by a FIDO outfit (10^9 BTU/h), which is equivalent to the heat output of fifty J-47 machines. Thus, the heat required is only one fifth that used in the thermal method.

Here, great importance attaches to the fact that a large amount of acoustic energy is generated as a by-product of the turbojet engine itself. It is assumed that the J-47 engine radiates from 10 to 25 kW of acoustic power, the greater part of which is in a low-frequency range very good for the process, of the order of 0.3 - 0.6 kcps (for small engines—0.5 kcps). This gave Boucher the idea of doing away with the siren altogether, and generating the sound with the same jet nozzles used to heat the air. It was assumed that at least 1% of the energy in the jet was transformed into sound, and that by mounting a resonator in the path of the jet, this figure could be increased to 5 - 10%. In this case, the exhaust pipe would be similar to a Hartmann shock-jet whistle. Instead of jet nozzles designed in this way, the vortex whistles described by Greguss can also be used.

An even better method seems to be combining sound with radiant thermal heating of the fog. The thing is that the hot exhaust gases given off by the FIDO heating equipment, as well as by the jet engines, contain a large amount of water vapor, which increases the amount of water in the air in the fog, and this makes it more difficult for the fog droplets to evaporate (particularly in calm weather). In those cases where the heater is turned alternately on and off for reasons of economy, it sometimes happens that the amount of water vapor is greater than that initially present in the atmosphere. This is probably what happened, for example, in 1953 in Los Angeles with LAKS-FIDO equipment, which was not able to increase the visibility beyond 180 m (it is true that the heat output was not very large).

Using the infrared radiation from hot bodies to evaporate a fog, which is a quite good absorber for this type of energy, would eliminate such abnormal cases. It has been shown experimentally that in a distance of 90 m an atmospheric fog mixed with water vapor absorbs about 50% of the energy radiated by a black body at a temperature of from 300 to 1100° C. Everything that has been said, however, requires a careful check, since in working out the proposals, no attention was given to the critical velocity of flow around the drops which we pointed out above [Eq. (AI.5)].

Boucher also proposed combining sound with atomizing the hygroscopic and other chemical substances mentioned at the start of the section. This method of dissipating fogs which we shall from now on call the sonic-chemical method, is described in the magazine "Interavia" [152].

The purpose of the sound when hygroscopic materials are used is to speed up condensation of the water vapor on the condensation nuclei that have been introduced, as well as speeding up evaporation of the fog drops. A scheme for using this method on a take-off and landing strip is shown in Fig. 76. We see that in this method atomizers and sound sirens, all pointing vertically upward, alternate on both sides of the runway. The hygroscopic nuclei get into the sphere of action of the sound field by following the convection currents in the air. It is assumed that it is possible in this case to cut down the height to which the hygroscopic nuclei need to be blown, which formerly consumed enormous amounts of energy. Instead of hygroscopic substances, materials like silver iodide, etc. may also be blown into the fog by cold air.

According to the calculations of the Society for the Use of Ultrasonics (France) a runway 1000 m long only takes 30 atomizers and 30 static sirens on Boucher's system. The cost of such an installation is much less than that of FIDO. Each of the atomizers (including the nozzle and the fan) takes about 7 kW, which makes 210 kW altogether. The air compressor for supplying the sirens takes about 250 kW. This effects impressive economies as compared with the FIDO thermal system of fog dissipation.

It is reported that the sonic-chemical method of fog dissipation, which Boucher has protected by appropriate patents, is being tried out in a number of foreign countries: in France (Society for the Use of Ultrasonics), in England ("Aerojet" Company, London), Sweden ("Aerojet Venturi AB," Växjö) and the USA ("Galton Industries," Metuchen, New Jersey).

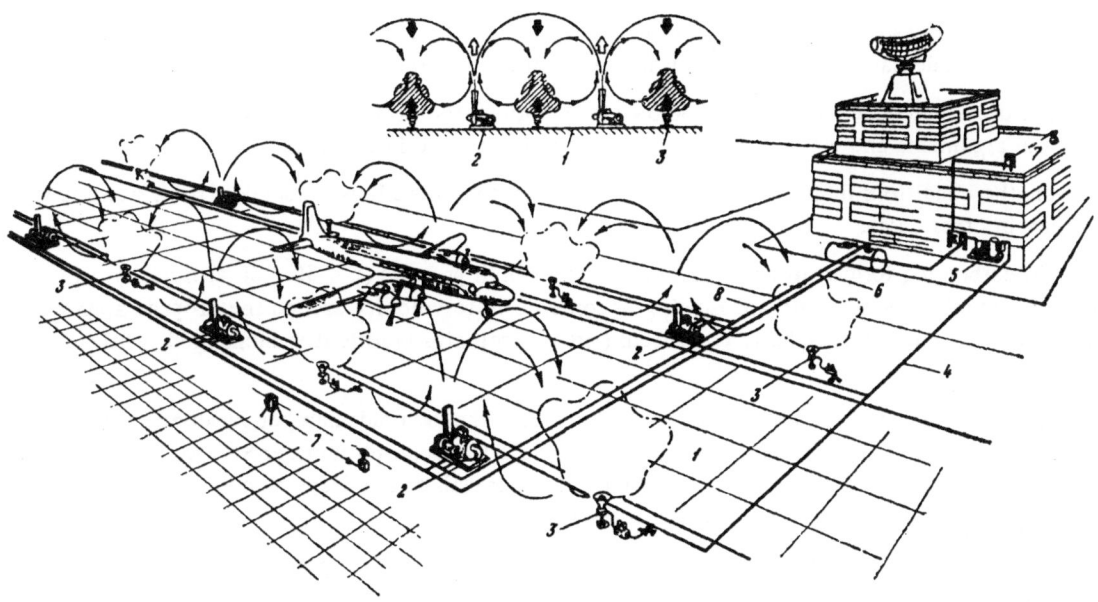

Fig. 76. Thermoacoustic method of dissipating airport fogs (according to Boucher). 1) Runway; 2) thermoatomizer; 3) sound siren; 4) compressed air line; 5) compressor; 6) electric power line; 7) visibility meter; 8) fuel line.

In addition to natural fogs, there are a number of industrial aerosols, in the production use of which it becomes necessary to speed up evaporation of liquid from the surface of the disperse phase. This is the case in spray drying of the viscous solutions used in making soap, dry milk and other materials, cooling hot gases with atomized water in scrubbers and other devices, combustion of atomized liquid fuel in internal combustion engines, liquid jet engines, and industrial furnaces, etc. Some of the above applications are formulated in patents [202, 207].

Two men at the Ultrasonic Corporation, USA, Horsley and Danser, as early as 1951 received a patent on sonic spray drying of wet materials [202], formulated in the following way:

1. A method of treating wet materials, consisting of squirting different sized particles of the wet material into a hot gas to form an aerosol, and irradiating the aerosol thus formed with high-intensity sound waves at a level of at least 150 db at a frequency of about 3.5 kcps, so that the sound waves not only promote evaporation of moisture but also form dry particle aggregates.

2. A method of treating wet materials consisting of squirting different size particles of the wet material into a stream of hot dry gas, generating in the stream sound waves at a frequency of about 3.5 kcps at a sound level of at least 150 db, for the purpose of giving the particles velocities different according to the dimensions of the particles, and then separating the material from the gas.

It is proposed to use this method for drying soap solutions and for other purposes, but no information as to its application has yet appeared in print. Evidently, the energy required in irradiating the drying chamber to get good results turned out to be too great for modest enterprises like soap factories. However, there are quite a few other industries in which sound-equipped spray drying could be successfully applied.

Let us now consider how sound speeds up growth by condensation of drops in a fog.

The first indication that vibrations could be used to speed up condensation was contained in an inaccessible paper by Karlström [Svensk Tandläk Tskr, 43:285 (1950)], who suggested trying the effect on producing the amalgams used in dentistry.

A large amount of practical interest attaches to the attempt that we made in cooperation with the people at the Kuban' Gas Industry on speeding up condensation and growth by coagulation of drops in separating natural gases. The sonic-inertial separators [79, 84, 80] designed for this purpose have already been described in §19. We shall accordingly only stop here to consider briefly what theoretical premises are involved in the effect of sound on growth by condensation of hydrocarbon fog drops in the separators.

Growth of drops by condensation, as we know [123], follows the same laws as evaporation. Hence it follows that all the arguments and equations given above remain in force in this case.

However, the conditions in gas separators are such as to give more hope of success from treating the fog with sound than in other cases.

The hydrocarbon fog formed in gas separators is under high pressure (p = 50 - 55 atm gage), which means that the Reynolds number for a gas stream flowing at some definite velocity around the drops is approximately a factor of p higher than under atmospheric conditions (since η remains practically unchanged, while ρ_g increases by a factor of p).

For a particle velocity of the order of u_{gp} = 100 cm/sec, the Reynolds number for condensate drops with radii r of from 1 to 100 μ lies in the range Re = 7 - 700, while the Schmidt number Sc stays within its usual limits. Accordingly, the wind factor, which shows how much growth of the drops by condensation is speeded up, is approximately in the range f_w = 2 - 10, which is very high.

Note in conclusion that all the arguments relating to the kinetics of drop evaporation in a sound field hold equally well for the heat exchange in both directions between the drops in the medium. In this case, for Re < 100, we have the following equation [123]:

$$Nu = 2(1 + \beta Pr^{1/3} Re^{1/2}), \tag{AI.9}$$

where Nu is the Nusselt number, $Q_f / 2\pi r \lambda_q (T_\infty - T_0)$, and Pr is the Prandtl number, ν / λ_q, which for air under ordinary conditions is equal to about 0.8 (Q_f is the amount of heat given off by a drop to the medium in unit time, λ_q is the coefficient of heat conduction of the medium, $T_\infty - T_0$ is the temperature difference between the body and the medium, and $\beta \approx 0.3$).

The papers [223, 289] are of interest in this connection.

II. Effect of Sound on Combustion and Degassing of Liquid Fuel Drops

It is well known that liquid fuel does not burn well unless it is atmoized, i.e., made into an aerosol. This is the same form in which crude petroleum is freed of dissolved hydrocarbon gases. Using sound on such aerodisperse systems greatly speeds up combusion or degassing, but the drops are so large that the sound has practically no coagulating effect. Combustion and degassing of liquid fuel drops have little in common from the physical or chemical standpoint, so that we shall consider them separately.

Combustion of liquid fuel droplets in a flame is, as we know, simply a matter of evaporation of individual drops and burnout of the resulting vapor at the drops and in the surrounding space, according to the laws governing combustion of a gaseous fuel.

We already know that sound vibrations speed up evaporation of the drops, and this provides a first explanation of why using sound gives better combustion. In addition, the vibrations seem to have an effect on the actual combustion of the vapor from the liquid fuel, in that they produce a large amount of turbulence in the gas. At any rate, the information given by Boucher in [157] on acoustic speed-up of solid jet fuel combustion leads to this conclusion.

Experimental studies of the effect of sound on combustion of atomized liquid fuel are exhausted at the present time by the work of Greguss [28, 196]. Here a study was made of the effect of sound waves on combustion of petroleum in a rotating furnace used for extracting malleable pig iron at a foundry and machine works in Budapest.

The failure of Tarnoczy and Somhegyi's experiments [276] on improving combustion of a gas flame by irradiating it externally with sound gave Greguss the idea of irradiating the fuel mixture from the inside. To

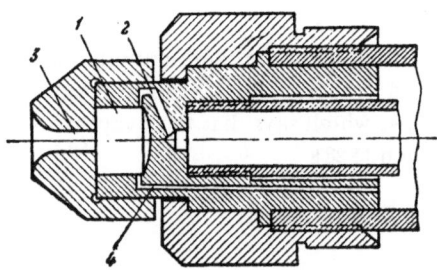

Fig. 77. Greguss' experiments on speeding up combustion of atomized liquid fuel in a furnace for extracting malleable pig iron. Design of vortex whistle nozzle (1. vortex chamber; 2. tangential air input; 3. output; 4. fuel line).

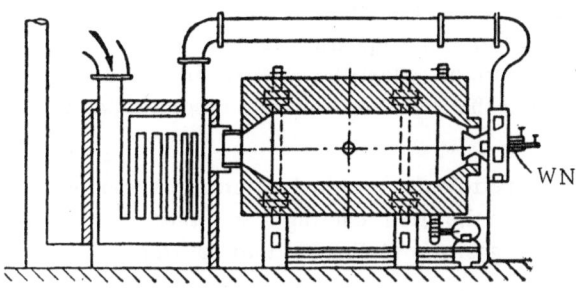

Fig. 78. Furnace with built in vortex whistle nozzle (WN).

this end, he constructed a special "acoustic burner" consisting of an ordinary vortex whistle, with the simple addition of a hole for letting in the liquid fuel (Fig. 77). Here, the sound vibrations are generated right in the fuel mixture, which keeps the sound waves from being reflected away from the edge of the flame (which was what happened in Tarnoczy and Somhegyi's experiments). Further, the flame tends to rotate, which exerts a stabilizing effect on the combustion process.

Figure 78 shows a whistle nozzle (WN) mounted in a furnace. The frequency generated by the whistle nozzle was 4 kcps, and the sound level got as high as 150 db. Greguss felt that the acoustic efficiency of the whistle was 10 - 15%.

When sound was used, it only took 40 - 50 min to reach the temperature required for melting, instead of an hour, and the fuel consumption was reduced 10%. Further, the metallurgist claimed that the casting produced afterward had a better structure, and was in better shape for heat treatment.

Greguss accounted for the improved combustion of atomized liquid fuel from the fact that using the whistle nozzle:

1) Gives better atomization of the liquid fuel,

2) Speeds up evaporation of the liquid fuel drops,

3) Increases the probability of collisions between the drops and molecules of liquid fuel and the oxidizing molecules, thus getting closer to the stoichiometric ratios,

4) Gives a more uniform temperature distribution around the rotating flame, and hence a more uniform diffusion coefficient, and

5) Makes the boundaries of the flame front more stable, giving more complete combustion of the fuel drops.

There are no quantitative equations for sonic combustion of atomized liquid fuel.

There is no doubt that sound waves speed up combustion of solid suspended fuel particles (see, for example, the new paper [329]).

It may be noted in conclusion that what has been presented above does not exhaust the possibilities of using sound waves to speed up combustion of atomized fuels.

In combustion of fuels, including atomized liquid fuel, interaction between the flame and the air not infrequently results in auto-oscillations. The primary cause is that combustion of fuels is of a pulsating nature. This type of combustion, which is called vibrational (less frequently pulsational), occurs in almost all heat and heat power installations, and in the majority of cases has a bad effect, since it interferes with normal combustion, makes noise, vibration, and sometimes even ruins furnaces and combustion chambers.

Nevertheless, this type of combustion goes at a high rate, and there are great advantages in using it to increase the calorific intensity of powdered coal furnaces, liquid fuel jet engines, and industrial furnaces, in which the fuel is burned in atomized form. However, the principles on which vibrational combustion is based have nothing to do with the fuel being in the aerosol state, so that it is beyond the range of this book to discuss the problem. Those interested may be referred to reviews [106] and [71], and the monograph by B. V. Raushenbakh, called "Vibrational Combustion."

The degassing effect that sound has on liquids suspended in a gas is based on the same principle as vacuum drying. Vacuum drying is based on the fact that the amount of liquid evaporated increases as the pressure in the surrounding medium is decreased. This follows from Daltaon's law, which says that the evaporation rate is related to the vapor pressure in the surrounding medium by the equation [128]:

$$J_p = kS \frac{p_s - p_\infty}{H}, \tag{II.1}$$

where p_s is the saturation vapor pressure at the temperature of the liquid, p_∞ is the vapor pressure in the surrounding space, H is the barometric pressure in the gas, S is the area of the evaporating surface, and k is a coefficient depending on how the medium flows over the surface.

When a sound wave passes through, no change is produced on the surface of the liquid drops at the instants at which compression takes place, since the medium is not completely saturated in the vapor from the liquid. However, when rarefaction occurs, and the pressure in the medium drops, there is more liberation (desorption) of gas from the liquid. Here the small amount of rarefaction produced at the surface of the drops is made up for by being repeated many times.

Important experimental confirmation of the degassing effect of sound on atomized liquids was obtained recently in extracting gas from petroleum at the Korobkov Oil Field in the Volgograd region. The gas is made up of light hydrocarbons which are dissolved in the petroleum in enormous quantities, and are liberated when the pressure is taken off the petroleum as it comes up the pipe from the well, and then in a special separator, called a trap.

In order to see what effect sound has on degassing atomized petroleum, a turbodynamic siren was mounted at the input to the trap. The petroleum-gas mixture was fed through the siren, causing it to rotate, thus generating sound, and the resulting atomized petroleum, together with the gas, was discharged into the trap.

It was found from the experiments that 13 - 32% more gas was released from the petroleum than when atomized in the usual way. It is not impossible though that some role was played in these experiments by the fact that the siren gave better atomization of the petroleum. If subsequent experiments confirm these results, sound equipped traps will find wide application in the petroleum gas industry. Of course, here, some more reliable nonrotating sound generator must be used instead of the turbodynamic siren, most likely a vortex whistle nozzle.

III. Behavior of Solid Precipitates in an Acoustic Field ("Acoustic Drying")

Materials that have passed from the suspended to the powdered state are not, generally speaking, aerodisperse systems (particularly if the pores are filled with moisture). However, if it is borne in mind that many powders and pastes are precipitation products of aerosols, and contain a coagulated disperse phase, it is of interest to consider how they behave in a sonic field.

The only reaction of dry powders to sound is that the layer is periodically "stirred up" in time with the static gas pressure hitting the surface, or that ridges are formed at the vibration nodes. This is observed not only in parallel irradiation of a powder layer as in a Kundt tube [218], but in perpendicular irradiation as well, where transverse vibration modes occur. The cause of the local accumulation of powder in both cases is the acoustic streaming which occurs between the nodes and the loops. The precipitated particles are carried into the nodal line from both sides, and the lightest particles are even pulled out of the layer, forming small dust clouds.

Wet powders are dried out by a sonic field, and that without any appreciable increase in temperature, which has given this acoustic type of drying its special name.

Let us consider the hypotheses in existence as to the mechanism of acoustic drying of materials. It is known that drying of wet porous materials consists of two stages: evaporation of liquid from the surface, and bringing the liquid to the surface from the inside pores.

Boucher[154, 155] assumes that the sound vibrations only affect the first stage, i.e., they increase the evapoartion rate of the liquid. Here he cites Dalton's law (AII.1), assuming that as the sound wave passes along the wet surface, no changes occur at the point of compression, but that the evaporation goes faster at the points of rarefaction, as is the case in degassing droplets, as described above. According to Boucher, the turbulence in the vibrating medium also helps the moisture to evaporate.

Greguss, while accepting the above mechanism for the initial stage of drying, nevertheless assumes from the results of experiments on drying materials containing small amounts of moisture, that the sound wave also helps to bring the moisture to the surface from the inside pores [197, 320].

It is known that the drying rate drops off as drying proceeds, because of the reduction in moisture conductivity of the material. The sound waves in the medium at the surface, according to Greguss, increase the moisture conductivity of the material because:

a) There is a reduction in viscosity of the liquid, which occurs, according to Altenberg's data, when liquids are treated with sound, and this accelerates diffusion of liquid from the pores,

b) Pulsations occur in the bubbles in the porous capillaries during the periodic change in pressure and temperature of the medium, and this helps to push the liquid out of the pores and capillaries, and

c) There is a radiation pressure in the pores and capillaries, directed out of the liquid into the gas, which moves the liquid columns to the outside.

That the drying is affected by increase in temperature in the surface capillaries, resulting from absorbing energy from the incident sound waves [see Eq. (1.18)], is denied by both investigators, and by all who have followed them, since they point to the fact that acoustic drying occurs "cold."

Yu. Ya. Borisov, from his first studies of the drying process made in collaboration with N. M. Gynkina [8, 9], concluded that the decisive factor in speeding up the drying is the acoustic streaming which occurs in a vibrating gas. The reason for this conclusion was the experimental fact that the sound begins to speed up the drying at about the same time that the dry powders start being stirred up at the nodal points in the standing wave, which, as we know, is due to the acoustic streaming between the nodes and the loops. However, neither this hypothesis nor the preceding ones have ever received any confirmation.

Special experiments made in the ultrasonic laboratory of the Acoustics Institute of the Academy of Sciences of the USSR, have shown that the fastest drying occurs at velocity loops in the vibrations, while the drying is not speeded up at the velocity nodes, where the acoustic streaming maintains a finite value.

Since the sound pressure is a minimum at the velocity loops (theoretically equal to zero), this means that acoustic drying of materials does not follow the principle of vacuum drying, as assumed by Boucher, but follows the principle of convection drying.

It has also been shown by experiment that the drying effect in a sonic field is approximately equivalent to the convection drying effect achieved by air flowing at a rate equal to the vibratory velocity. This fits in with the conclusions from spray drying in a sound field (see Appendix I), which is perfectly logical.

In the light of what has been presented, it is easy to understand the experimental fact that the acoustic drying rate is only slightly dependent on the frequency.

The first experiments on acoustic drying of materials were made in 1955 by Greguss, who used a dynamic siren at a frequency of 25 kcps, and got an almost ten-fold increase in the speed of drying raw cotton fiber.

Drying of powders has been investigated in detail by Boucher. Work was done on the following materials that are hard to dry: carboxylmethyl cellulose, titanium dioxide paste, and colloidal zirconium hydroxide, as well as silica gel, enzymes, and hormones.

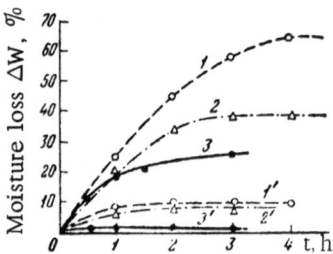

Fig. 79. Results of acoustic drying of some powdered materials (according to Boucher). 1) Colloidal zirconium hydroxide at f = 10 kcps; 2) carboxymethyl cellulose at f = 34 kcps; 3) titanium dioxide at f = 95 kcps; 1', 2', 3') the same materials with natural drying.

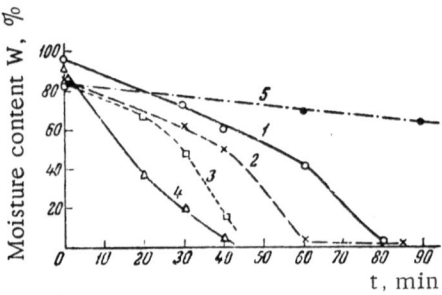

Fig. 80. Results of acoustic drying of ethyl cellulose from the experiments at the Acoustics Institute of the Academy of Sciences of the USSR: 1) for f = 6.7 kcps, L = 152 db, t = 20° C; 2) for f = 2.8 kcps, L = 152 db, t = 20° C; 3) for f = 2.8 kcps, L = 152, t = 32° C; 4) for f = 2.8 kcps, L = 156 db, t = 20° C; 5) no sound at t = 32° C.

The results of drying the first three materials are shown in Fig. 79, from which it may be seen that the sound speeded up the drying by a factor of 6 - 8.

Silica gel, containing 25% moisture initially, was completely dried out in 15 minutes at a sound level of 152 db and a frequency of 8 kcps. Only 10 - 15% of the moisture can be driven off in this length of time by the vacuum method, or by heating to 92° C in air.

Enzymes, which cannot be heated above 40° C, were dried out in 14 minutes, while the drying rate of heat sensitive hormones was increased by a factor of 3 - 4 over the vacuum method.

In addition to these materials, Boucher investigated drying a number of fibrous materials, such as blotting paper, asbestos sheets, etc. [154, 155, 157], but we cannot stop to discuss the results of these experiments here.

Some experiments were made at the Acoustics Institute of the Academy of Sciences of the USSR, on drying ethylcellulose [8]. This material was chosen for the first experiments for the reason that it is easily oxidized, and cannot be dried at high temperature, but takes several hours to dry at 80° C. Since ethylcellulose is highly disperse, the material was irradiated in a layer sprayed onto the bottom of a small tray.

Figure 80 shows the results obtained. It can be seen that at a sound level of 152 db the material dried out completely in 60 minutes, at normal temperature (20° C), and in 45 min at 32° C. Increasing the sound pressure by 3 db (which corresponds to doubling the sound energy density) speeded up the process by a factor of about one and a half.

The experimental information accumulated shows that the rate of acoustic drying is affected by: the initial moisture content, the way the moisture is bound to the material, the thickness and structure of the layer, whether or not the material is being agitated, and, of course, the sound intensity. There is a threshold sound level (140 - 145db), below which the drying is scarcely speeded up. It has been found that if the sound wave is propagated along the surface of the material that is being dried out, the drying only goes about half as fast as when the wave is incident normally. In our opinion, this is due to the fact that at normal incidence, the sound wave partially penetrates the layer of material, and flows to some extent around the elements in the layer (the distance between the elements is much greater than their dimensions, which can be seen, if only from the fact that the porosity of many materials is 80 - 85% or more). It has also been shown that the drying rate is only slightly dependent on the frequency. Nevertheless the process goes somewhat better at the lower frequencies (apparently because there is less sound absorption in the medium).

This runs counter to Boucher's original claim that drying only occurs at frequencies about 10 kcps, and that 9 kcps is the lower limit at which the drying is speeded up to any appreciable extent. He found out subsequently that lower frequencies also help the drying. The best were said to be 6 - 10 kcps [155].

From the data of the Acoustic Institute, Academy of Sciences, USSR, where studies were made on drying over a range of frequencies from 3 to 15 kcps, the results obtained at 2.8 kcps turned out to be better than at 6.7 kcps (see Fig. 80).

The most promising field of application of acoustic drying, which requires a fairly high amount of energy, is in drying easily oxidizable, low-melting, heat-sensitive, and explosive materials, for which other methods are counter-indicated, or give poor results in the final stage of drying. It is best not carry out acoustic drying of powdered materials in a stationary layer, but in drum dryers or as a suspension.

LITERATURE CITED

1. Acoustic coagulation of aerosols [Russian translation], Collection of translated papers, Moscow, Gos—khimizdat (1961).
2. V. I. Arabadzhi, Absorption of acoustic vibrations in moist air and fog, in collection: Meteorology and Hydrology, No. 3, Gidrometeoizdat (1947).
3. A. D. Bagrinovskii, Differential Equation of the Motion of a Dust Particle Suspended in Air Acted Upon by Standing Sound Waves, Transactions of the Mining Institute, Academy of Sciences, USSR, Vol. 2, Moscow, Academy of Sciences Press, USSR (1955).
4. V. V. Bazilevich Freezing of supercooled fog drops in an acoustic field, in collection: Investigation of Clouds, Precipitation, and Atmospheric Electricity, Leningrad, Gidrometeolizdat, pp. 120-123.
5. V. V. Bazilevich and N. P. Tverskoi, Freezing of supercooled water fog drops in an acoustic field, Zh. Tekhn. Fiz. 27,(8): 1826-1829 (1957).
6. L. Beranek, Acoustic Measurements [Russian translation], Moscow, IL (1952).
7. L. Bergman, Ultrasonics and Its Application to Science and Industry, Moscow, IL (1956).
8. Yu. Ya. Borisov, Speeding up drying processes in an acoustic field, in collection: Application of Ultrasonics in Chemical Engineering Process, TsINTI ÉP and P Press (1960).
9. Yu. Ya. Borisov and N. M. Gynkina, The problem of acoustic drying in a standing sound wave, Akust. Zh. 8 (1): 129-131 (1962).
10. L. M. Brekhovskikh, V. A. Krasil'nikov, and L. D. Rozenberg, Physical bases of the industrial use of ultrasonics, in collection: Application of Ultrasonics in Industry, MDNTP im F. É. Dzerzhinskogo, Moscow, Mashgiz (1959).
11. I. N. Bronshtein and K. A. Semendyaev, Handbook of Mathematics, Moscow, Gostekhizdat (1953).
12. L. I. Buravov and O. K. Éknadiosyants, The behavior of aerosol particles in an acoustic field, Akust. Zh. 7 (4): 492-493 (1961).
13. M. L. Varlamov, E. L. Krichevskaya, G. A. Manakin, L. M. Kozakova, and A. N. Gospodinov, Acoustic coagulation of a sulfuric acid fog, Zh. Prikl. Khim. 33 (1): 14-20 (1960).
14. M. L. Varlamov, E. L. Krichevskaya, G. A. Manakin, A. A. Énnan, L. M. Kozakova, and L. S. Zbrozhek, Investigation of acoustic coagulation of aerosols formed in chemical industries, in collection: Application of Ultra-Acoustics to the Study of Matter, No. 12, Moscow, MOPI Press (1960).
15. M. L. Varlamov, E. L. Krichevskaya, A. A. Énnan, L. M. Kozakova, and G. A Manakin, Acoustic coagulation of a fog containing fluorine compounds, Zh. Prikl. Khim. 34(1): 78-84 (1961).
16. Yu. I. Veitser and G.P. Luchinskii, Chemistry and Physics of Smoke Screens, Moscow-Leningrad, Oborongiz (1938).
17. V. A Veller, and K. P. Troitskii, Siren type ultrasonic generator, Russian patent 111446 (1956).
18. V. A. Veller and K. P. Troitskii, Ultrasonic and Sonic Siren Type Generators, in collection Ultrasonic Energy Sources, Moscow TsINTI ÉP and P Press (1960).
19. V. V. Vladimirskii, Theory of the Propagation of Sound in disperse systems, in the scientific collection of Moscow State University Studies "Fizika," No. 10, Book 2, Moscow State University Press (1939).
20. V. V. Vyal'tsev and V. G. Khorguani, High-powered low-frequency sound siren, Akust. Zh. 7(3): 377-378 (1961).
21. Wei Chun-tsue, Theory of attenuation of sound in a fog, due to evaporation and condensation, Uli Syuébao 9 (3): 149-169 (1953).
22. Wei Chun-tsue, Measurement of sound attenuation in foggy air of low sound frequencies, Uli Syuébao 10(3): 187-207 (1954).

23. S. B. Gateev, M. G. Lysikov, E. P. Mednikov, and K. P. Mynkin, Sonic-Inertial Trapping of Finely Dispersed Dust in the Exhaust Gases of a Bronze and Brass Factory, TsBTI Mossovnarkhoza Press (1960).

24. F. Geid and I. B. Slavik, Purifying the atmosphere of harmful contaminants by means of sound, Akust. Zh. 5 (2):243-244 (1959).

25. Z. A. Gol'dberg, The propagation of plain waves of finite amplitude, Akust. Zh. 3 (4):322-328 (1957).

26. S. V. Gorbachev, and A. B. Severnyi, The problem of the effect of sound waves on fog drops, Zh. Fiz. Khim. 7 (4):536-545 (1936).

27. L. P. Gor'kov, The forces acting on a small particle in an acoustic field in an ideal liquid, Dokl. Akad. Nauk SSSR 140 (1):88-91 (1961).

28. P. Greguss, Effect of sound on combustion processes, Akust. Zh. 8 (4):420-425 (1962).

29. Kh. Grigoryan, Equipment for precipitating dust-like particles, Russian patent 101433 (1953).

30. V. A. Gudemchuk, B. F. Podoshevnikov, and B. D. Tartakovskii, The problem of the role played by turbulence in acoustic coagulation of aerosols, Akust. Zh. 5 (2):246 (1959).

31. A. I. Gulyaev and V. M. Kuznetsov, Aerosol coagulation under the influence of periodic shock waves, Akust. Zh. 8 (4):473-475 (1962).

32. B. Danilin, Can man control the weather? Sound produces...rain, Krasnaya zvezda, No. 179, (July 31, 1960).

33. D. B. Dianov, L. G. Merkulov and V. I. Nikitenko, Precipitation of a zinc oxide aerosol in an acoustic field, Akust. Zh. 8 (1):60-66 (1962).

34. S. S. Dukhin, Theory of aerosol particle drift in a standing sound wave, Kolloidn. Zh. 22 (1):128-130 (1960).

35. V. V. Zolesskii, Ultrasonic siren, in collection: Ultrasonic and Electric Pulse Methods of Treating Metals, Rostov on the Don)(1961), pp. 210-229.

36. A. I. Ivanovskii, Theoretical and Experimental Study of Streams Produced by Sound, Moscow, Gidrometeoizdat (1959).

37. I. Inoue, Sonic agglomeration chamber, Kagaku Kogaku 18 (4):180-186 (1954).

38. I. Inoue, Modern sonic gas purification, Kagaku Kogé 6 (3):235-238 (1955).

39. É. Kamke, Handbook of Ordinary Differential Equations, Moscow, Fizmatgiz (1961).

40. I. N. Kanevskii, Constant forces set up in a sound field, Akust. Zh. 7 (1):3-17 (1961).

41. M. I. Karnovskii, Theory and design of sirens, Zh. Tekhn. Fiz. 15 (6):348-364 (1945).

42. M. I. Karnovskii, Design of sirens, Izv. Vuzov. Radiotekhn. (1):64-67 (1958).

43. V. A. Kireev, Course in Physical Chemistry, Moscow, Goskhimizdat (1955).

44. A. N. Kolmogorov, Local structure of the turbulence in an incompressible viscous liquid at very high Reynolds numbers, Dokl. Akad. Nauk SSSR 30 (4):299-303 (1941).

45. N. E. Kochin, I. A. Kibel' and N. V. Roze, Theoretical Hydromechanics, Part 2, Moscow-Leningrad, Gostekhizdat (1948).

46. V. A. Krasil'nikov, Sonic and Ultrasonic Waves, Moscow, Fizmatgiz (1960).

47. A. E. Crawford, Ultrasonic Engineering [Russian translation], Moscow, IL (1958).

48. P. N. Kubanskii, Coagulatin effect of acoustic streaming, Zh. Tekhn. Fiz. 24 (6):1049-1054 (1954).

49. P. N. Kubanskii, Trapping of the Material Carried by Smoke Gases from the Regenerative Boiler Assemblies of the TsBK by Means of Acoustic Vibrations, Transactions of the Leningrad Technological Institute, No. 4. Leningrad (1956).

50. P. N. Kubanskii, The problem of the effect of ultrasonics on combustion, Teploénerg. (1):14-18 (1962).

51. B. B. Kudryavtsev, Use of Ultra-Acoustic Methods in Physico-Chemical Research Practice, Moscow-Leningrad, Gostekhizdat (1952).

52. V. P. Kurkin, Static siren, Russian patent 132102 (1959).

53. V. P. Kurkin, Gas jet sound radiator of Hartmann type, Russian patent 140350 (1960).

54. V. P. Kurkin, Trapping highly disperse carbon black by means of acoustic coagulation, Kauchuk i Rezina (6):29-32 (1961).

55. V. P. Kurkin, High-efficiency sound radiator for acoustic coagulation of aerosols, Vestn. Tekhn.i Ékon. Inform (2):40-41 (1962).

56. V. P. Kurkin, Gas jet sound radiator with oblique shock wave, Akust. Zh. 8(4):438-441 (1962).

57. V. P. Kurkin, and B. F. Podoshevnikov, Acoustic coagulation of aerosols, in collection: Application of Ultrasonics in Chemical Engineering Processes, TsINTI ÉP and P Press (1960).

58. N. V. Lavrov and E. P. Mednikov The acoustic method of purifying dust-laden industrial gases. Gaz. Prom. (7):18-21 (1957).

59. N. V. Lavrov and E. P. Mednikov, Experience in the Scientific Classification of Dust and Drop Collecting Equipment, Transactions of the Institute of Mineral Fuels, Academy of Sciences USSR, Vol. 16, Moscow, Academy of Sciences Press, USSR (1961).

60. N. V. Lavrov, E. P. Mednikov, and A. I. Nikolaev, Acoustic purification of dust-laden gases and the outlook for application in underground gasification of coals, (USSR), (1):18-22 (1959).

61. G. Lamb, Hydrodynamics [Russian translation] Moscow-Leningrad, (1947)

62. L. D. Landau and E. M. Lifshits, Mechanics of Continuous Media, Moscow, Gostekhizdat (1954).

63. L. D. Landau and E. M. Lifshits, Mechanics, Moscow, Fizmatgiz (1958).

64. P. N. Lebedev, Experimental Study of the Ponderomotive Effect of Waves on Resonators, Selected Papers, Moscow-Leningrad, Gostekhizdat (1949).

65. N. Levenko, Filter for purifying gases of dust, Russian patent 98843, (1953).

66. L. M. Levin, Studies in the Physics of Coarsely Disperse Aerosols, Moscow, Academy of Sciences Press, USSR (1961).

67. V. G. Levich, Theory of coagulation of colloids in a turbulent liquid stream, Dokl. Akad, Nauk SSSR 99 (5):809-812 (1954).

68. V. G. Levich, Theory of coagulation and precipitation of aerosol particles in a turbulent gas stream, Dokl. Akad. Nauk 99 (6): 1041-1044 (1954).

69. V. G. Levich, Physico-Chemical Hydrodynamics, Moscow, Fizmatgiz (1959).

70. A. V. Lykov, Theory of Heat Conduction, Moscow, Gostekhizdat (1952).

71. M. S. Maslenikov, Pulsating combustion, Teploénerg. (3):74-78 (1961).

72. I. Mataushek, Ultrasonic Engineering, Moscow, Metallurgizdat (1962).

73. E. P. Mednikov, Sonic coagulation of aerosols and its application to cleaning dust-laden industrial gases, in particular heat-power engineering gases, Dissertation, Moscow Power Institute (1955).

74. E. P. Mednikov, Sonic coagulation of aerosols and its application to dust collection, in collection of Ultra-Acoustics to the Study of Matter, No. 3, Moscow, MOPI Press (1956).

75. E. P. Mednikov, Two designs of experimental sound sirens, Akust. Zh. 4 (1):59-63 (1958).

76. E. P. Mednikov, Theory of Acoustic and Electroacoustic coagulation of aerosols, in collection: Application of Ultra-Acoustics to the Study of Matter, No. 10, Moscow, MOPI Press (1960).

77. E. P. Mednikov, Method of acoustic coagulation of aerosols, Russian patent 149399 (1962).

78. E. P. Mednikov, Acoustic Coagulation of Aerosols as a Method of Speeding Up Purification of Fuel and Exhaust Gases, Transactions of the Institute of Mineral Fuels, Academy of Sciences, USSR, Vol. 16, Moscow, Academy of Sciences Press, USSR (1961).

79. E. P. Mednikov, Gas separator, Russian patent 141970 (1960).

80. E. P. Mednikov, Acoustic Method of Low-Temperature Separation of Natural Hydrocarbon Gases, Transactions of the Institute of Mineral Fuels, Vol. 18, Moscow, Academy of Sciences Press, USSR (1962).

81. E. P. Mednikov, Flow hysteresis around small obstacles in a sound field, Akust. Zh. 9 (3):383-384 (1963).

82. E. P. Mednikov, Self-centering of aerosol particles in a sound field, Akust. Zh. 9 (4) (1963).

83. E. P. Mednikov, The microstructure of acoustic turbulence, Zh. Prikl. Mekhan.i Tekhn.Fiz. (1963).

84. E. P. Mednikov, T. S. Alekseev, and A. M. Sirotin, Vertical self-heating sound equipped gas separator, Russian patent 144467 (1961).

85. E. P. Mednikov, A. I. Nikolaev, and V. Yu. Nikolaev, Experimental Acoustic Dust Collecting Equipment of the Institute of Mineral Fuels, Academy of Sciences, USSR, and the Results of the First Experimental Studies, Transactions of the Institute of Mineral Fuels, Academy of Sciences, USSR, Vol. 16, Moscow, Academy of Sciences Press, USSR (1961).

86. P. V. Mikhal'kov and T. P. Ivanov, Increasing the Efficiency of Gas Separation, Novosti Neft. Tekhn. Gasovoe Delo (4) (1961).

87. I. Miyagawa, K. Ito, S. Tsuda, and K. Ikeda, Precipitation of cyclohexaneoxime by ultrasonic coagulation, Kogyo Kagaku Zasshi 59 (11):1351-1353 (1956).

88. B. Maczewski-Rowinski, Results of Studies on Acoustic Coagulation of Aerosols. Collection of Scientific Papers of the Institutes of Industrial Safety, VTsSPS, No. 6:48-54 (1961).

89. V. I. Nikitenko and V. I. Turubarov, Equipment for precipitating zinc oxide aerosol particles in a low-frequency acoustic field, Akust. Zh. 8(3):370-372(1962).

90. V. I. Nikitenko and V. I. Turubarov, Precipitation of zinc oxide in a low-frequency acoustic field, Lakokrasochnye Materialy i ikh Primenenie (1):61-64 (1963).

91. N. N. Pisarevskii and T. V. Smyshlyaeva, Equipment for calibrating microphones at high sound pressure levels, in collection: Industrial Aerodynamics, No. 18, Moscow, Oborongiz (1960).

92. B. F. Podoshevnikov, Purifying industrial gases by means of acoustic vibrations in Poland, Vestn. Tekhn. i Ékon. Inform. Min. Khim. Prom. SSSR (4):32-40 (1958).

93. B. F. Podoshevnikov, Study of acoustic coagulation of a highly disperse aerosol, Vestn. Tekhn i Ekon. Inform. Kom. po Khim. pri SM SSSR (4):31-37 (1959).

94. B. F. Podoshevnikov, Study of Acoustic Coagulation of a Highly Disperse Aerosol, Dissertation, MIKhM - NIIOGAZ (1960).

95. B. F. Podoshevnikov, On the change in dispersion composition of a dioctylphthalate fog during coagulation in a sound field, in collection: Application of Ultra-Acoustics to the Study of Matter, No. 15, Moscow, MOPI Press (1961).

96. B. F. Podoshevnikov, Acoustic coagulation of aerosols as a function of the amount of sound Exposure, Zh. Prikl. Khimi. 34 (12):2664-2668 (1961).

97. B. F. Podoshevnikov and B. D. Tartakovskii, The attenuation of plane sound waves of finite amplitude in gases, Akust, Zh. 4 (4): 369-371 (1958).

98. B. F. Podoshevnikov and B. D. Tartakovskii, Method of designing a tower for sonic coagulation of aerosols with liquid disperse phase, Khim. Prom. (6):65-66 (1959).

99. B F. Podoshevnikov and B. D. Tartakovskii, Absorption of sound of finite amplitude in a coagulating aerosol, Zh. Prikl. Khim. 34 (11):2573-2574 (1961).

100. R. V. Pol', Mechanics, Acoustics, and the Study of Heat, Moscow, Gostekhizdat (1957).

101. S. V. Pshenai-Severin, Effect of hydrodynamic interaction of small cloud droplets on the rate of fall, Bull. Academ. Sci. USSR, Geophys. Ser. (8):1045-1051 (1957).

102. S. V. Pshenai-Severin, Hydrodynamic interaction between fog drops at small distances, Izv. Akad. Nauk SSSR, Geophys. Ser. (10):1254 (1958).

103. S. V. Pshenai-Severin, Approach of aerosol particles in a sound field under the action of Oseen hydrodynamic forces, Dokl. Akad. Nauk SSSR 125 (4):775-778 (1959).

104. S. V. Pshenai-Severin, Possible Effect of Hydrodynamic Interaction on the Coagulation of Cloud Drops, Transactions of the El'brus Mountain Climbing Expedition, Vol. 2 (5) "Physics of Clouds and Precipitation" Moscow, Academy of Sciences Press, USSR (1961).

105. S. N. Rzhevkin, Course of Lectures on the Theory of Sound, Moscow State University Press (1960).

106. O. G. Roginskii, Vibrational combustion, Akust. Zh. 7 (2): 131-154 (1961).

107. Rayleigh, Theory of Sound, Vols. 1, 2 [Russian translation], Moscow, Gostekhizdat (1955).

108. S. M. Rytov, V. V. Vladimirskii, and M. D. Galanin, Propagation of sound in disperse systems, Zh. Eksperim. i Teor. Fiz. 8 (5):614-621 (1938).

109. A. B. Severnyi, The ponderomotive effect set up between water drops in an acoustic field, Zh. Eksperim. i Teor. Fiz 6(7):705-717 (1936).

110. I. I. Slavin, Industrial Smoke and the Struggle with It, Moscow-Leningrad, Profizdat (1955).

111. N. A. Slezkin, Dynamics of a Viscous and Compressible Liquid, Moscow, Gostekhizdat (1955).

112. A. S. Smirnov and A. I. Shirkovskii, Production and Transportation of Gas, Moscow, Gostoptekhizdat (1957).

113. S. B. Stopskii, Spectrum Analyzers for Sonic and Infrasonic Frquencies in Acoustic Spectrometry, Moscow-Leningrad, Gosénergoizdat (1962).

114. S. P. Strelkov, Experience with vibration of a spherical pendulum in an air stream, Zh. Tekhn. Fiz. 9 (19):1763-1766 (1939).

115. N. P. Tverskoi, Effect of Frequency and Intensity of Acoustic Vibrations on the Rate of Dissipating a Water Fog, Transactions of the A. I. Voeikov Main Geophysical Observatory, No. 104 Leningrad, Gidrometeoizdat (1960).

116. V. I. Timoshenko, Investigation of the Interaction between Aerosol Particles in an Acoustic Field, Dissertation, Leningrad Engineering and Technological Institute, 1965; The Interaction between Aerosol Particles in Stokes Flow, Akust. Zh. 11 (1) (1965).

117. J. Tyndall, Sound, Gosizdat (1922).

118. R. S. Tyul'panov, Effect of pulsations in stream velocity on the evaporation of fuel drops, Inzh.-Fiz. Zh. 3 (5):119-123 (1960).

119. V. N. Uzhov, Purification of Industrial Exhaust Gases, Moscow, Goskhimizdat (1959).

120. Physics of the Formation of Precipitation, Collection of translations edited by B. V Deryagin and A. Kh. Khrgian, Moscow IL (1951).

121. N. A Fuks, Mechanics of Aerosols, Moscow, Academy of Sciences Press, USSR (1955).

122. N. A. Fuks, Advances in Aerosol Mechanics, Moscow, Academy of Sciences Press, USSR (1961).

123. N. A. Fuks, Evaporation and Growth of Drops in a Gas, Moscow, Academy of Sciences Press, USSR (1958).

124. V. V Furduev, Electroacoustics, Moscow-Leningrad, Gostekhizdat (1948).

125. A. A. Kharkevich, Autooscillations, Moscow, Gostekhizdat (1953).

126. S. A. Tsedilin and V. M. Tsetlin, Siren for acoustic coagulation of aerosols, Akust. Zh. 7(1):78-86 (1961).

127. V. M. Tsetlin, Acoustic Coagulation of Aerosols and Its Engineering Application, Moscow, TsIIN MTsM SSSR (1957).

128. Ya. Tsiborovskii, Chemical Engineering Processes, Leningrad, Goskhimizdat (1958).

129. N S. Shishkin, Clouds, Precipitation, and Atmospheric Electricity, Moscow, Gostekhizdat (1954).

130. R. Sh. Shkol'nikova, Coagulation of aerosols by sonic and ultrasonic vibrations, Byull. TsIIN MTsM SSSR (1):17-23 (1957).

131. R. Sh. Shkol'nikova and R. K. Orlova, The Possibility of Using Acoustic Vibrations to Purify Air of Dust in Underground Conditions, Transactions of the Scientific Research and Design Institute "Gipronikel'," No. 2, Leningrad (1958).

132. R. Sh. Shkol'nikova and R. K. Orlova, Experience with the use of acoustic vibrations of precipitate drilling dust, in collection: The Struggle with Silicosis, No. 3, Moscow, Academy of Sciences Press, USSR (1959).

133. A. A. Éikhenval'd, Large Amplitude Acoustic Waves. Selected Papers, Moscow, Gostekhizdat (1956); Usp. Fiz Nauk, 14 (5):552-585 (1934).

134. O. K Éknadiosyants, Use of ultrasonics in producing aerosols, in collection: Application of Ultrasonics to Chemical Engineering Processes, Moscow, TsINTI ÉP and P Press (1960).

135. H. I. Abboud, Apparatus for separating aerosols from gases, USA Patent N2769506 (1956).

136. B. Adamczyk and W. Staszewski, On the longitudinal attraction and repulsion of spheres in vibrating air, Acta Physiol. Polon. 15 (1):43-47 (1956).

137. C. H. Allen and J. Rudnick, A powerful high-frequency siren, J. Acoust. Soc. Am. 19 (5):857-865 (1947).

138. B. Altberg and M. Holtzmann, Über die Absorption des Schalles in trüben Medien, Phys. Z 26 (2):149-153 (1925).

139. E. V. Amy, Dispersing particles suspended in air, USA Patent N1980171 (1934).

140. E. N. da C. Andrade, On the circulations caused by the vibration of air in a tube, Proc. Roy. Soc. (London), A 134 (824):445-470 (1931).

141. E. N. da C. Andrade, On the groupings and general behavior of solid particles under the influence of air vibrations in tubes, Phil. Trans. Roy. Soc. London, Ser. A 230 (692):413-445 (1932).

141a. E. N. da C. Andrade, The coagulation of smoke by supersonic vibrations, Trans. Faraday Soc. 32 (184): 30-35 (1936).

142. E. N. da. C. Andrade and S. K. Lewer, New phenomena in a sounding dust tube, J Sci. Instr. 7 (2):53 (1930).

143. E. N. da C. Andrade and R. C. Parker, A standard source of sound and the measurement of minimum audibility, Proc. Roy. Soc. (London), A 159 (899):507-526 (1937).

144. J. M. Andres and U. Ingard, Acoustic streaming at high Reynolds numbers, J. Acoust. Soc. Am. 25 (5): 928-932 (1953).

144a. J. M. Andres and U. Ingard, Acoustic streaming at low Reynolds numbers, J. Acoustic. Soc. Am. 25 (5): 932-938 (1935).

145. A. Baczynski, W. Cieslak, Z. Garbarczyk, J. Horbaczewski, T. Janiczewski, M Kwiek, J. Maleski. B. Maczewski-Rowinski, K. Pluzanski, D. Rosiak, A. Skiodowski, L Taniewski. W. Twardowski. T. Wolff,

R. Wyrzykowski, Zajaczkowskii, (CIOP), Urzadzenie do koagulacji i stracania aerozoli z gazow, zwlaszcza przemyslowych przy uzyciu fal dzwiekowych lub ultradzwiekowych, Polish patent 38829 (1956).

146. V. B. Bjerkness, Vorlesungen über hydrodynamische Fernkräfte nach C A. Bjerkness Theorie, Leipzig (1900-1902); C. A. Bjerkness, Hydrodynamische Fernkräfte, Leipzig (1915).

147. R. M. G. Boucher, Procédé et appareil pour augmenter au moyen d'ondes soniques ou ultra-soniques les dimensions des particules suspendues dans un gaz, French patent 1052941 (1954).

148. R. M. G. Boucher, Production d'ultrasons par sifflets multiples, French patent 1056478 (1954).

149. R. M G. Boucher, Improvements in generators for sonic and ultrasonic vibrations, British Patent 752795 (1956).

150. R. M. G. Boucher, L'épuration acoustique des gas, Mines (6):497-517 (1956).

151. R. M. G. Boucher, La coagulation des aerosols industriels par ultrasons, Genie Chim. 77 (6):163-173 (1957); 78 (1):14-28 (1957).

152. The Boucher fog dispersal system, Interavia 12 (4):339-340 (1957).

153. R. M. G. Boucher, Industrial applications of airborne ultrasonics, Ultrasonic News 2 (4):8-13 (1958).

154. R. M. G. Boucher, Drying by airborne ultrasonics, Ultrasonic News 3(2):8-9, 14-16 (1959).

155. R. M. G. Boucher, Ultrasonics boosts heatless drying, Chem. Eng. 66 (19):151-154 (1959).

156. R. M. G. Boucher, Acoustic energy in fog dispersal techniques, Ultrasonic News 4 (1):11-19 (1960).

157. R. M. G. Boucher, Ultrasonics in processing, Chem. Eng. 68 (20):83-100 (1961).

158. R. M. G. Boucher and E. Brun, Research on the "multiwhistle" acoustic air-jet generator, Eng. Digest 17 (12): 511-514 (1956).

159. R. M. G. Boucher and A. L. Weiner, Effect of sound on aerosol scrubbing, Ultrasonic News 6 (2):14-18 (1962).

160. J. Boussinesq, Théorie analtique de la chaleur, Vol. 2, Paris (1903).

161. O. Brandt, Über das Verhalten von Schwebstoffen in schwingenden Gasen bei Schall- und Ultraschall-frequenzen, Kolloid-Z. 76 (3):272-278 (1936).

162. O. Brandt, Uber die Frequenzabhähgigkeit der Schallabsorption im Aerosoll, Kolloid-Z, 81 (1):2-6 (1937).

163. O. Brandt and H. Freund, Über die Aggregation von Aerosolen mittels Schallwellen, Z. Phys. 94 (5-6):348-355 (1935).

164. O. Brandt and H. Freund, Process and apparatus for separating suspended particles, British Patent 454050 (1936).

165. O. Brandt and H. Freund, Process and apparatus for separating suspended particles, British Patent 460795 (1937).

166. O. Brandt, H. Freund, and E. Hiedemann, Verfahren zum Ausscheiden von Schwebeteilchen aus Gasen oder Dampfen, German Patent 630452 (1936).

167. O. Brandt, H. Freund, and E.Hiedemann Zur Theorie der akustischen Koagulation, Kolloid-Z, 77 (1):103-115 (1936).

168. O Brandt, H Freund, and E Hiedemann, Schwebstoffe im Schallfeld Z. Phys. 104 (7-8):511-533 (1937).

169. O. Brandt, H. Freund, and E. Hiedemann, Vorrichtung zum Ausscheiden von Schwebeteilchen aus Gasen oder Dämpfen mittels Schallwellen, German Patent 680704 (1939).

170. O. Brandt, and E. Hiedemann, Über das Verhalten von Aerosolen im akustischen Feld, Kolloid-Z. 75 (2):129-135 (1936).

171. O. Brandt and E. Hiedemann, The aggregation of suspended particles in gases by sonic and suspersonic waves, Trans. Faraday Soc. 32 (184):1101-1110 (1936).

172. A. H. Brisse, Sonic agglomeration of fume in ferromanganese blast furnace gas, Ind. Heating 17 (11): 1966, 1970, 1972 (1950).

173. E Brun and R M. G. Boucher, Research on the acoustic air-jet generator, a new development, J. Acoust. Soc. Am 29(5):573-583 (1957).

174. M. Z. Carriere, Analyse ultramicroscopique des vibrations aerienes, J. Phys. Radium 10 (5):198-208 (1929).

175. H. M. Cassel and H. Schultz, A sonic method of determining particle size in aerosols, Air Pollution (1952).

176. H. W. St. Clair, Sonic Flocculator as a Fume Settler: Theory and Practice, U. S. Bureau of Mines, Rept. of Invest. N3400 (1938).

177. H. W. St. Clair, Sonic flocculator and method of flocculating smoke or the like, USA Patent 2215484 (1940).

178. H. W. St. Clair, An electromagnetic sound generator for producing intense high-frequency sound, Rev. Sc. Inst. 12 (5): 250-256 (1941).

179. H. W. St. Clair, Agglomeration of smoke, fog, or dust particles by sonic waves, Ind. Eng. Chem. 41 (11): 2434-2438 (1949).

180. H. W. St. Clair, Theory and basic principles of the sonic smoke flocculators, Air Pollution, (1952).

181. H. W. St. Clair, M. J. Spendlove, and E. V. Potter, Flocculation of Aerosols by Intense High-Frequency Sound, U. S. Bureau of Mines, Rept. of Invest. N4218 (1948).

182. S. R. Cook, On flutings in a sound wave and the forces due to a flux of a viscous fluid around spheres, Phil. Mag. 3 (17): 471-482 (1902).

183. H. W. Danser, Eliminate stack dusts and mists, Chem. Eng. 57 (5): 158-160 (1950).

184. H. W. Danser and E. P. Neumann, Industrial sonic agglomeration and collection systems, Ind. Eng. Chem. 41 (11): 2439-2442 (1949).

185. W. Dorr, Anziehende und abstossende Kräfte zwischen Kugeln im Schallfeld, Acustica 5 (3): 163-166 (1955).

186. C. R. Earle, Where will ultrasonics fit in the power field? Power Generation 52 (9): 86, 88, 132, 134, 136, (1948).

187. C. Eckart, Vortices and streams caused by sound waves, Phys. Rev. 73 (1): 68-76 (1948).

188. P. S. Epstein and R. R. Carhart, The absorption of sound in suspensions and emulsions, J. Acoust. Soc. Am. 25 (3): 553-565 (1953).

189. F. Fahnoe, A. E. Lindroos, and R. J. Abelson, Aerosol build-up techniques, Ind. Eng. Chem. 43 (6): 1336-1346 (1951).

190. V. Gavreau, Sifflets théorie de fonctionnement et rendement, Acustica 4: 555-562 (1954).

191. K. Gehlhoff. Über die Aufnahme von Schallkurven ohne Membran, Z. Phys. 3 (5): 330-336 (1920).

192. General Aniline and Film Corporation, Production of carbonyl metal powders of small size, USA Patent 2695925 (1953).

192a. General Discussion, Trans. Faraday Soc. 32 (184): 1119-1125 (1936).

193. J. R. Gies, Anwendung des Ultraschalls auf die Reinigung von Industriegasen, Z. Ver. Deut. Ing. Bieh. Verfahrenstechn. (6): 177 (1938).

194. S. Goldstein, The steady flow of viscous fluid past a fixed spherical obstacle at small Reynolds number, Proc. Roy. Soc. (London), 123 (791): 225-235 (1929).

195. S. W. Gorbatschew and A. B. Severny, Zur Frage der Bewegung eines schweren Tropfens im akustischen Felde, Kolloid-Z. 73 (2): 146-154 (1935).

196. P. Greguss, Influencing combustion processes by sound, Ultrasonic News 3 (4): 10-11, 17 (1959).

197. P. Greguss, Drying by airborne ultrasonics, Ultrasonics News 5 (3): 7-11 (1961).

198. F. T. Gucker and G. J. Doyle, The amplitude of vibration of aerosol droplets in a sonic field, J. Phys. Chem. 60 (7): 989-996 (1956).

199. J. Hartmann, On a new method for the generation of sound waves, Phys. Rev. 20 (6): 719-727 (1922).

200. E. Hiedemann, Grundlagen und Ergebnisse der Ultraschallforschung, Berlin (1939).

201. J. Holtsmark, J. Johnsen, T. Sikkeland, and S. Skavlem, Boundary layer flow near a cylindrical obstacle in an oscillating incompressible fluid, J. Acoust. Soc. Am. 26 (1): 26-39 (1954).

202. C. B. Horsley and H. W. Danser, Sonic spray drying, USA Patent 2576297 (1951).

203. C. B. Horsley and G. C. Seavey, Process of agglomerating aerosols, USA Patent 2535679 (1950).

204. J. Y. Houghton and T. H. Brown, Smoke and fume separating, USA Patent 2216779 (1940).

205. T. F. Hueter and R. H. Bolt, Sonics, New York, John Wiley & Sons, Inc., (1955).

206. R. Jahn, Neue Erkenntnisse auf dem Gebiete der Schallentstaubung, Radex Rundschau (7): 625-631 (1955); Eng. Digest 17 (1): 21 (1956).

207. T. D. Joeck, Method for atomizing by supersonic sound vibrations, USA Patent 2532554 (1950).

208. R. C. Jones, A fifty horsepower siren, J. Acoust. Soc. Am. 18 (2): 371-387 (1946).

209. L. F. Kastner and S. H. Shih, Critical Reynolds number for steady and pulsating flow, Engineering 172 (4470): 389-391 (1951).

210. M. Kawamura, The agglomeration of aerosol by sound waves, J. Acoust. Soc. Japan 17 (2): 123-133 (1961).

211. G. Kidoo, Sonic agglomeration—a new solution, Chem. Eng. 58 (5): 154-156 (1951).

212. L. V. King, On the acoustic radiation pressure on spheres, Proc. Roy. Soc. (London), A 147 (861): 212-240 (1934).

213. V. O. Knudsen, J. V. Wilson, and N. S. Anderson, The attenuation of audible sound in fog and smoke, J. Acoust. Soc. Am. 20 (6): 849-857 (1958).

214. W. König, I. Hydrodynamisch-akustische Untersuchungen, Ann. Phys. und Chem. 42 (3): 353-370 (1891).

215. W. König, Hydrodynamisch-akustische Untersuchungen. Über die Kräfte zwischen zwei Kugeln in einer schwingenden Flüssigkeit und über die Entstehung der Kundtschen Staubfiguren, Ann. Phys. 42 (4): 549-563 (1891).

216. J. Krebs and R. C. Binder, Use of ultrasonic coagulator with a cyclone separator, Combustion 23 (12): 45-47 (1952).

217. W. Kroll, Fliesserscheinigungen an Haufwerken in schwingenden Gefässen, Chem.-Ing.-Tech. 27(1): 33-38 (1955).

218. A. Kundt, Über eine neue Art Akustischer Staubfiguren und über eine Anwendung derselben zur Bestimmung der Schallgeschwindigkeit in festen Körpern und Gasen, Ann. Phys. und Chem. 127 (4): 497-523 (1866).

219. M. Kwiek, Zagadnienie przeplywu bocznego oraz turbulencji wiazki fal plaskich. Prace Komis, Mat.-Przyrodn. Poznan. Towarz Przyjacio. Nauk 8 (1): 95-111 (1957).

220. T. J. Laidler and E. G. Richardson, The absorption of supersonics in smokes, J. Acoust. Soc. Am. 9 (3): 217-223 (1938).

221. M. Le Landais, Research on the stem-jet acoustic whistle, Ultrasonic News 4 (4): 7-9 (1960).

222. C. A. Lane, Acoustical streaming in the vicinity of a sphere J. Acoust. Soc. Am 27 (6): 1082-1086 (1955).

223. R. Lemlich, Vibration and pulsation boost heat transfer, Chem. Eng. 68 (10): 171-174, 176 (1961).

224. R. Levavasseur, High power generators of sounds and ultrasounds, USA Patent 2755767 (1956).

225. R. Levavasseur, Perfectionnements relatifs aux generateurs de sons et d'ultra-sons de grande puissance, French Patent 1184551 (1959).

226. E. P. Lewis and L. P. Farris, A new method of determining the amplitude of sound waves in air, Phys. Rev. 6 (6): 491-493 (1915).

227. B. Maczewski-Rowinski, Syrena ultradzwiekowa Centralnego Instytutu Ochrony Pracy i dotychczasowe wyniki prac badawczych nad stracaniem aerosoli metoda akustyczna, Biuletyn PAN No. 6 Urzadzenia odpylajace Warszawa (1956).

228. B. Maczewski-Rowinski, Precipitation of dust from industrial waste gases by means of the C. I. W. P. siren Proc of the Second Conf. on Ultrasonics, PWN, Warsaw (1957).

229. B. Maczewski-Rowinski, Syrena ultradzwiekowa CIOP Prace, Centralnego Inst. Ochrony Pracy 7 (20): 1-22 (1957).

230. G. Maidanik, Acoustical radiation pressure due to incident plane progressive waves on spherical objects, J. Acoust. Soc. Am. 29 (6): 738-742 (1957).

231. B. Matula, Zagadnienie koagulacji dymow generatorem aerodynamicznym, Prace Komis. Mat.-Przyrodn. Poznan Towarz. Przyjacio. Nauk 8 (1): 21-39 (1957).

232. B. Matula, Koagulacja zaniesin pouretrznych ulepszonym generatorem aerodynamicznym, Dissertation PNR (1957).

233. M. Medwin, An acoustic streaming experiment in gases, J. Acoust. Soc. Am. 26 (3): 332-341 (1954).

234. E. Meyer, and R. W. Karmann, Die Schwingung der Luftteilchen in der Nähe einer schallabsorbierenden Wand, Acustica 1 (3): 130-136 (1951).

235. I. Mickelson, Theory of vortex whistel, J. Acoust. Soc. Am. 27 (5): 930-931 (1955).

236. W. R. Mickelson and L. V. Baldwin, Aerodynamic mixing in high-intensity standing-wave sound field, J. Acoust. Soc. Am. 29 (1): 46-49 (1957).

237. R. D. Morse, Sonic energy in granular solid fluidization, 47 (6): 1170-1175 (1955).

238. W. Müller, Industrierauchbeseitigung durch Ultrabeschallung, Energietechnik, 4 (10): 431-432 (1954).

239. E. P. Neumann and J. L. Norton, Application of sonic energy to commercial aerosol collection problems, Chem. Eng. Progr., Symp. Ser. 1, 47 (1): 4-10 (1951).

240. E. P. Neumann, C. R. Soderberg, and A. A. Fowle, Design, application, performance, and limitations of sonic type flocculators and collectors, Air Pollution, (1952).

241. M. Nord, Sonic Precipitation of Smoke, Fumes, and Dust Particles, Chem. Eng. 57 (10): 116-119 (1950).

242. M. H. Ollivier, Resherches sur la capillarité, Ann. Chim. et Phys., sér. 8, 10: 229-321 (1907).

243. C. W. Oseen, Über die Stokes'sche Formel und über eine verwandte Aufgabe in der Hydrodynamik, Arkiv Mat. Astron. Och. Fys. 6 (9) (1910).

244. C. W. Oseen, Neuere Methoden und Ergebnisse in der Hydrodynamik, Leipzig (1927).

245. K. L. Oswatitsch, Die Dispersion und Absorption des Schalles in Wolken, Phys. Z. 42 (21-22): 365-378(1941).

246. Y. Oyama, I. Inoue, Y. Sawahata, and M. Okada, On the sonic agglomeration and collection system, J. Sci. Res. Inst. (Tokyo) 48 (1369-1375): 260-271 (1954).

247. Y. Oyama, M. Okada, Y. Sawahata, and I. Inoue, Design note on siren-type sound generator, J. Sci. Res. Inst. (Tokyo) 50 (1415-1420): 37-42 (1956).

248. M. J. Palme, Le dépoussiérage par ultrasons, in collection: Journée du dépoussiérage des fumées et gaz industriels, Paris (1954).

248a. R. C. Parker, Experiments on coagulation by supersonic vibrations, Trans. Faraday Soc. 32 (184): 1115-1119 (1936).

249. H. S. Patterson and W. Cawood, Phenomena in a sounding tube, Nature 127 (3209): 667 (1931).

250. T. Pearcey and G. W. Hill, A theoretical estimate of the collection efficiencies of small droplets, Quart. J. Roy. Meteorol. Soc. 83 (355): 77-92 (1957).

251. T. Pearcey and B. McHugh, Calculation of viscous flow around spheres at low Reynolds numbers, Phil. Mag. 46 (378): 783-784 (1955).

252. L. Pimonow, Une sirène ultrasonore de grande puissance, Ann. Télécommun. 6 (1): 23-26 (1951).

253. L. Pimonow, Un nouveau modele amélioré de sirène ultrasonore, Ann. Télécommun. 6 (11): 337-341 (1951).

254. R. W. Porter, High-intensity sound waves now harnessed for industry, Chem. Eng. 55 (3): 100-101, 115 (1948).

255. W. P. Raney, J. C. Corelli, and P. J. Westervelt, Acoustic streaming in the vicinity of a cylinder, J. Acoust. Soc. Am. 26 (6): 1006-1014 (1954).

256. C. N. Richardson, Ammonia synthesis, USA Patent 2500008 (1950).

257. E. G. Richardson, Behavior of aerosols in acoustical and turbulence fields, Acustica 2 (4): 141-147 (1952).

258. J. Rudnick, Measurements of the acoustic radiation pressure on a sphere in a standing-wave field, J. Acoust. Soc. Am 23 (5): 633-634 (1951).

259. Y. Sawahata, I. Inoue, and Y. Oyama, On the sonic agglomeration and collection system. A plant on industrial scale, J. Sci. Res. Inst. (Tokyo) 49 (1376-1390): 39-45 (1955).

260. E. Schaufler, Einrichtung zur Erzeugung von Schall-oder Ultraschallschwingungen in einem Beschallungs-raum mit flüssigem oder gasförmigen Medium, German Federal Republic Patent 965799 (1957).

261. H. Schlichting, Berechnung ebener periodischer Grenzschichtströmungen, Phys. Z. 33 (8): 327-335 (1932).

262. H. Schnitzler, Anwendung von Schall-und Ultraschall bei der Gasreinigung, Arch. Eisenhuttenw. 24 (5-6): 199-202 (1953).

263. R. A. Scott, An investigation of the performance of the Rayleigh disk, Proc. Roy. Soc. (London), A 183 (944): 296-316 (1945).

264. G. C. Seavey and C. B. Horsley, Process of agglomerating and recovering aerosol particles, USA Patent 2535700 (1950).

265. C. J. T. Sewell, The extinction of sound in a viscous atmosphere by small obstacles of cylindrical and spherical form, Phil. Trans. Roy. Soc. London, Ser. A 210 (465): 239-270 (1910).

266. D. Sinclair, Stability of Aerosols and Behavior of Aerosol Particles. (Coagulation by Sonic and Super-sonic Vibrations) Handbook on Aerosols, Washington, (1950).

267. L. J. Sivian, High-frequency absorption in air and other gases, J. Acoust. Soc. Am. 19 (5): 914-916 (1947).

268. R. B. Smith, Pyrolic conversion of hydrocarbons, USA Patent 2517139 (1950).

269. C. R. Soderberg, Industrial applications of sonic energy, Iron Steel Eng. 29 (2): 87-95 (1952).

270. Sound waves form uniform drops in spray nozzle, Chem. Eng. 68 (18): 84, 86 (1961).

271. W. Staszewski, On the mutual influence of spheres in vibrating air, Acta Phys. Polon. 13 (3): 209-224 (1954).

272. C. A. Stokes, Sonic agglomeration of carbon black aerosol, Chem. Eng. Progr. 46 (8): 423-432 (1950).

273. C. A. Stokes and J. E. Vivian, Application of sonic energy in the process industries, Chem. Eng. Progr., Symp. Ser 1, 47 (1): 11-21 (1951).

274. O. Taraba and C. E. Brzica, Odprasovani plunuv intensivnim akustickem poli, Strojirenstvi 8 (2): 83-88 (1958).

275. T. Tarnoczy and P. Greguss, Szallo cementpor visszanyerese akusztikus uton Magy. Techn. (5): 21-25 (1951).

276. T. Tarnoczy and K. Somhegyi, Égési folyamatok befolyasolasa akusztikus energiaval, Fiz. Szemle, 3: 1-6 (Feb. 1953).

277. G. R. Tatum, The effects of high-intensity sound on smokes and other aerosols, J. Acoust. Soc. Am. 8 (3): 210 (1937).

278. Tchen Chan-mou Mean Value and Correlation Problems Connected with the Motion of Small Particles Suspended in a Turbulent Fluid, The Hague (1947).

279. G. Thomas, Die hydrodynamischen Wirkungen einer schwingenden Luftmasse auf zwei Kugeln, Ann. Phys. 42 (16);1079-1098 (1913).

280. S. Tomotika and T. Aoi, The steady flow of viscous fluid past a sphere and circular cylinder at small Reynolds numbers, 3 (2): 140-161 (1950).

281. S. Vajda, Open hearth dust control, Iron Steel Engr. 29 (7): 111-120 (1952).

282. B. Vonnegut, A vortex whistle, J. Acoust. Soc. Am 26 (1): 18-20 (1954).

283. M. Wagenschein, Experimentelle Untersuchung über das Mitschwingen einer Kugel in einer schwingenden Flussigkeits-oder Gasmasse Ann. Phys. 65 (13): 461-480 (1921).

284. G. D. West, Circulations occurring in acoustic phenomena, Proc. Phys. Soc.(London), B 64 (378): 483-487 (1951).

285. P. J. Westervelt, The mean pressure and velocity in a plane acoustic wave in a gas, J. Acoust. Soc. Am. 22 (3): 319-327 (1950).

286. P. J. Westervelt, The theory of steady forces caused by sound waves, J. Acoust. Soc. Am. 23 (3): 312-315 (1951).

287. P. J. Westervelt, The theory of steady rotational flow generated by a sound field, J. Acoust. Soc. Am. 25 (1): 60-67 (1953).

288. P. J. Westervelt, Acoustic radiation pressure, J. Acoust. Soc. Am. 29 (1): 26-29 (1957).

289. P. J. Westervelt, Effect of sound waves on heat transfer, J. Acoust. Soc. Am. 32 (3): 337-338 (1960).

290. P. J. Westervelt and P. W. Sieck, Acoustic separatory methods and apparatus, USA Patent 2766881 (1956).

291. S. Y. White, Inaudible sound—a new tool for air cleaning, Heat and Ventilat. 45 (9): 59-64 (1948).

292. A. Willner, Staubabscheidung mit Hilfe von Schall und Ultraschallschwingungen, Bergbautechnik (4): 201-209 (1955).

293. S. Woloszyn, Proba odpylania gazow hutniczych przy zastosowaniu techniki ultradzwiekowej, Prace Inst. Hutniczych 13 (1): 1-12 (1961).

294. R. W. Wood and A. L. Loomis, The physical and biological effects of high-frequency sound waves of great intensity, Phil. Mag. 4 (22): 417-436 (1927).

295. R. Wyrzykowski, Sonic agglomeration of aerosols, Proc. of the Second Conf. on Ultrasonics, PWN, Warsaw (1957).

296. R. Wyrzykowski, Dzwiekowa aglomeracja Zesz. nauk, Politechn. lodzkiej (20): 91-109 (1958).

297. J. W. Zink and L. P. Delsasso, Attenuation and dispersion of sound by solid particles suspended in a gas, J. Acoust. Soc. Am. 30 (8): 765-771 (1958).

298. A. A. Anan'eva, Cermaic Sound Receivers, Moscow, Academy of Sciences Press, USSR (1963).

299. M. L. Varlamov, G. A. Manakin, and K. K. Belenavichus, The problem of calculating the energy coefficients of gas-jet sound generators, Nauchn. Zap. Odessk. Politekhn. Inst. Vol. 37 (1962).

300. M. L. Varlamov, A. A. Énnan, R. A. Georgalin, E. L. Krichevskaya, G. A. Manakin, and L. M. Kozakova, Study of the dispersion composition of a water fog before and after acoustic coagulation, in collection: Application of Ultra-Acoustics to the Study of Matter, Vol. 17, MOPI Press (1963), pp. 133-143.

301. M. L. Varlamov and K. K. Belenavichus, Study of acoustic coagulation of a sulfuric acid aerosol, Zh. Prikl. Khim. 36 (4): 697-703 (1963).

302. V. A. Veller, and B. I. Stepanov, Ultrasonic sirens driven by an electric motor, Akust. Zh. 9 (3): 291-295 (1963).

303. B. V. Deryagin and Yu. S. Kurgin, Effect of periodic pressure oscillations on phase equilibrium. I. Liquid—vapor, plane interface, Kolloidn. Zh. 26 (1): 28-35 (1964).

303a. Yu. S. Kurgin and B. V. Deryagin, Effect of periodic pressure oscillations on phase equilibrium. II. Liquid—vapor—drop phase equilibrium, experimental applications, Kolloidn. Zh. 26 (2): 215-223 (1964).

304. V. P. Kurkin, Study of Acoustic Coagulation of Highly Disperse Carbon Black, Dissertation, MIKhM-NIIOGAZ (1963).

305. E. P. Mednikov, The problem of the approach of aerosol particles in a sound field under the influence of Oseen hydrodynamic forces, Akust. Zh. 10 (4) (1964).

306. B. Maczewski-Rowinski, Some experiments on acoustic coagulation of aerosols in Poland, in collection: Application of Ultra-Acoustics to the Study of Matter, No. 17, MOPI Press (1963), pp. 75-82.

307. T. Motohiko and F. Kiehiko, Application of ultrasonics in chemical industry. Separation of aerosols by the use of ultrasonics, Chem. Eng. (Tokyo), 8(2):127-133 (1963).

308. K. P. Mynkin, Industrial sonic drop collecting equipment,in collection: Application of Ultrasonics in Engineering Processes, Moscow, GOSINTI (1963).

309. B. F. Podoshevnikov, The problem of the mechanism of coagulation of aerosols in sonic coagulation towers, in collection: Application of Ultra-Acoustics to the Study of Matter, Vol. 17, MOPI Press, (1963), pp. 55-65.

310. R. Sh. Shol'nikova, Acoustic coagulation of aerosols in dust collecting engineering, in collection: The Struggle with Silicosis, Vol. 5, Academy of Sciences Press, USSR (1962).

311. R. Sh. Shkol'nikova, Air jet generators of acoustic vibrations for coagulating aerosols, Akust. Zh. 9 (3): 368-375 (1963).

312. A. A. Énnan, Study of the Acoustic Method of Purifying Gases Containing Fluorine Compounds, as Applied to Super Phosphate Production ,Dissertation, Odessa Polytechnic Institute (1964).

313. S. H. Asklöff, Ultrasonic demister, USA Patent 3026966 (1962).

314. H. Bayha [Siemens-Schuckertwerke A. G.] Verfahren zum Aneinanderlagern feinzerteilter Flüssigkeitsteilchen und feinzerteilter fester Stoffteilchen, German Federal Republic Patent 941607 (1956).

315. R. M. G. Boucher, Contribution a l'étude des ultrasons aériens: production et applications, Paris (1958).

316. R. M. G. Boucher, Akustische Energie als Mittel zur Nebelbeseitigung, Zbl. Biol. Aerosolforsch. 10 (1): 39-62 (1961).

317. J. N. Cole, R. G. Powell, H. L. Oestreicher, and H. E. Gierke, Acoustic siren for generating wide-band noise, J. Acoust Soc. Am. 35 (2):173-191 (1963).

318. T. F. Embleton, Mutual interaction between two spheres in a plane sound field, J. Acoust. Soc. Am. 34 (2):1714-1720 (1962).

319. P. Greguss, Kritikai megjegyzesek az ultrahangok vegyipari alkalmazhatosagarol, Magy. Kem. Lapja,17 (2):494-505 (1962).

320. P. Greguss, The mechanism and possible applications of drying by ultrasonic irradiation, Ultrasonics 1: 83-86 (April-June 1963).

321. A. E. Hamielec and A. I. Johnson, Viscous flow around fluid spheres at intermediate Reynolds numbers, Canad. J. Chem. Eng. 40 (2):41-45 (1962).

322. S. A. Hoenig, Acceleration of dust particles by shock waves, J. Appl. Phys. 28 (10):1218-1219 (1957).

323. B. Maczewski-Rowinski, Nowe urzadzenia do akustycznego stracania aerozoli, Ochrona Pracy 17 (10): 1-3 (1962).

324. B. Maczewski-Rowinski and B. L. Lesniak, Nowa statyczna syrena akustyczna CIOP, Prace Central Inst. Ochrony Pracy 13 (38): 33-56 (1963).

325. B. Maczewski-Rowinski and J. Zajaczkowski, Badania nad akustyczna koagulacja aerozoli i osiagniete wyniki, Biuletyn No. 66, Nowoczesne metody odpylania, PAN, Warsaw (1963).

326. S. L. Soo. Effect of transport processes on attenuation and dispersion in aerosols, J. Acoust. Soc. Am. 32 (8): 943-946 (1960).

327. W. O. Vedder and W. F. Gibby, Sonic cleaning of dust filter, USA Patent 3053031 (1962).

328. A. D. Wasel, Force on and motion of a spherical obstacle in a spherical sound field, J. Acoust. Soc. Am. 35 (8):1296 (1963).

329. F. A. Williams, Response of a burning solid to small amplitude pressure oscillations, J. Appl. Phys. 33 (2):3153-3166 (1962).

330. R. Wyrzykowski, Kryteria porownawcze i podstawy obliczenia urzadzeno odpylajacych 3. Odpylacze akustycne, Zeszyty Nauk.Politech. Wroclaw., Mechanika (80) (1963).

ABBREVIATIONS OF THE NAMES OF SOME ORGANIZATIONS

GNB	State Scientific Library, USSR
GOSINTI	State Scientific Research Institute of Scientific and Engineering Information
IGI	Institute of Mineral Fuels
MDNTP	Moscow House of Scientific and Engineering Propaganda
MIKhM	Moscow Institute of Chemical Machine Construction
MOPI	N. K. Krupskaya Moscow Regional Pedagogical Institute
NIIOGAZ	State Scientific Research Institute of Sanitary and Industrial Purification of Gases
NIITÉKhIM	Scientific Research Institute of Engineering Economic Studies
TsBTI	Central Bureau of Engineering Information
TsIIN MTsM	Central Information Institute of the Ministry of Light Metallurgy, USSR
TsINTI ÉP and P	Central Institute of Scientific and Engineering Information of the Electrical Engineering Industry and Instrument Construction
TsITÉIN MUP	Central Institute of Engineering Economics Information, Ministry of the Coal Industry, USSR
TsPTB	Central Polytechnic Library, USSR
CIOP, CJWP	Central Institute of Industrial Safety, Polish Peoples Republic
VNITI	All-Union Scientific Research Diesel Transport Institute
NIITM	Scientific Research Institute of Mechanical Engineering
LÉTI	V. I. Ul'yanov –Lenin Leningrad Electrical Engineering Institute